ELEMENTARY
DIFFERENTIAL EQUATIONS

ELEMENTARY DIFFERENTIAL EQUATIONS

LYMAN M. KELLS, Ph.D.

Professor of Mathematics

U.S. Naval Academy

FOURTH EDITION

McGRAW-HILL BOOK COMPANY, Inc.

New York   Toronto   London

1954

ELEMENTARY DIFFERENTIAL EQUATIONS

Library of Congress Catalog Card Number: 53-7120

VIII

THE MAPLE PRESS COMPANY, YORK, PA.

PREFACE

Differential equations furnish extremely powerful tools for analyzing functional relations. So numerous and far-reaching are their applications that the practical side rivals in importance purely theoretical considerations. In this book theory and applications go hand in hand.

This combination procedure in learning differential equations is ideal for integration of mathematical power, for understanding, and for assimilation. First the student expresses laws in mathematical symbols, thus giving them meaning and life; then he solves the resulting equations and in so doing continually reviews all the elementary mathematical processes and functions; finally by interpreting his results, he explores the implications of the laws, thus deducing basic and very illuminating knowledge.

An outstanding feature of this text is simplicity. The subject is divided into small natural compartments, each of which is easily mastered. Simple statements and proofs are followed by illustrative examples and carefully interspersed problems. The student becomes familiar with necessary basic ideas while solving elemental, but comprehensive, problems which require thought but little pencil work. Later problems are longer and more difficult. All are screened for suitability.

The purpose of this revision is to obtain maximum returns for time spent. Most of the discussions have been perfected and expanded. More emphasis on theory together with increased intuitive and imaginative appeal have been attempted. This applies particularly to the subjects, substitutions, operators, existence theorems, solutions by series, and the method of separation of variables in partial differential equations. Nearly all the lists of problems have been revised for quicker comprehension and better assimilation, and a considerable number of new and up-to-date applications have been added.

It is a pleasure to express my appreciation of the kindness of the many users who have sent in corrections and suggestions. Captain F. J. Foley has taken an interested and encouraging attitude. I am particularly indebted to Professor John Tyler of the U.S. Naval Academy, Professor R. H. Wilson, Jr., of the University of Louisville, and Professor C. B. Lindquist of the University of Minnesota for help on this revision.

Lyman M. Kells

CONTENTS

vii

CHAPTER IV

APPLICATIONS INVOLVING DIFFERENTIAL EQUATIONS OF THE FIRST ORDER

CHAPTER V

FIRST-ORDER EQUATIONS OF DEGREE HIGHER THAN THE FIRST

CHAPTER VI

LINEAR DIFFERENTIAL EQUATIONS WITH CONSTANT COEFFICIENTS

CHAPTER VII

APPLICATIONS OF LINEAR EQUATIONS WITH CONSTANT COEFFICIENTS

CHAPTER VIII

MISCELLANEOUS DIFFERENTIAL EQUATIONS OF ORDER HIGHER THAN THE FIRST

CHAPTER IX

APPLICATIONS

CHAPTER X

DIFFERENTIAL EQUATIONS IN MORE THAN TWO VARIABLES. EXISTENCE THEOREMS

CHAPTER XI

SOLUTION BY SERIES AND BY METHODS INVOLVING SUCCESSIVE APPROXIMATIONS

CHAPTER XII

PARTIAL DIFFERENTIAL EQUATIONS OF THE FIRST ORDER

CHAPTER XIII

PARTIAL DIFFERENTIAL EQUATIONS OF ORDER HIGHER THAN THE FIRST

CHAPTER XIV

APPLICATIONS OF PARTIAL DIFFERENTIAL EQUATIONS

CHAPTER I

DEFINITIONS AND ELEMENTARY PROBLEMS

1. General remarks

Differential equations furnish a very powerful tool for solving many practical problems of engineering and science generally, as well as a wide range of purely mathematical problems. While this book treats of the most important types of differential equations and gives strong emphasis to the outstanding applications to problems of a physical nature, it also takes up many interesting applications to geometry.

The applications to engineering, physics, and science generally are of the greatest importance. A law is conceived and set forth as a system of differential equations; the solution of these equations tells a rather complete story of the states and motions to be expected of the materials obeying that law. For example, we assume the law, suggested by experiment, that radium disintegrates at a rate proportional to the amount present and express this in mathematical symbols by the equation

$$\frac{dQ}{dt} = kQ.$$

By solving this equation for a 100-gram lump and using facts found from experiment, the equation

$$Q = 100e^{-0.041t}$$

is easily derived. This tells approximately the amount of radium to be expected in the lump t centuries from now.

Newton conceived the law of gravitation and then solved the corresponding system of differential equations to show that the earth moves about the sun approximately in an ellipse with the sun at one focus. He made a long step forward in the development of celestial mechanics. About 1865, Maxwell conceived a relation between an electric current and the corresponding magnetic field, expressed the relation as a system of partial differential equations, solved them, and from the result predicted the waves of radio. Differential equations have played a

1

prominent role in the development of the theories of radio, radar, television, and electricity generally. Similar remarks apply to nearly every great branch of science. The many applications in this book will show the great power of differential equations and give methods of using it.

2. Differential equation. Order. Degree

The student has already met differential equations of an elementary type in his study of the calculus. Thus,

$$\frac{dy}{dx} = x^2 + 3 \tag{1}$$

is a differential equation. In general, **a differential equation** *is an equation containing differentials or derivatives.* If the equation contains total differentials, total derivatives, or both, but does not contain partial derivatives, it is called an **ordinary differential equation;** if it contains partial derivatives, it is called a **partial differential equation.** Thus,

$$x^2 \frac{d^2y}{dx^2} + 2x \frac{dy}{dx} + y = x^2 + 2, \tag{2}$$

$$\left(\frac{d^3y}{dx^3}\right)^2 + 2 \frac{d^2y}{dx^2} \frac{dy}{dx} + x^2 \left(\frac{dy}{dx}\right)^3 = 0, \tag{3}$$

$$\left[1 + \left(\frac{dy}{dx}\right)^2\right]^{\frac{3}{2}} = k \frac{d^2y}{dx^2}, \tag{4}$$

$$(x + y^2 - 3y)\,dx + (x^2 + 3x + y)\,dy = 0 \tag{5}$$

are ordinary differential equations, whereas

$$\frac{\partial z}{\partial x} = y, \tag{6}$$

$$\frac{\partial^2 u}{\partial x^2} + \frac{\partial^2 u}{\partial y^2} + \frac{\partial^2 u}{\partial z^2} = 0 \tag{7}$$

are partial differential equations.

The **order** *of a differential equation is the order of the highest-ordered derivative involved in its expression.* Referring to the differential equations numbered (1) to (5), equations (1) and (5) are of the first order, (2) and (4) are of the second order, and (3) is of the third order.

The **degree** of an ordinary differential equation is the algebraic degree of its highest-ordered derivative.

Consider, for example,

$$\sqrt[3]{\left(\frac{d^2y}{dx^2}\right)^2} = \sqrt{1 + \left(\frac{dy}{dx}\right)^2}. \tag{8}$$

Here the highest-ordered derivative is d^2y/dx^2, and the order of the equation is 2.   Equating the sixth powers of the members of (8), obtain

$$\left(\frac{d^2y}{dx^2}\right)^4 = \left[1 + \left(\frac{dy}{dx}\right)^2\right]^3. \tag{9}$$

Here 4, the degree in d^2y/dx^2, is the degree of equation (8).   Equations (1), (2), (5), and (6) are of the first degree; (3) and (4) are of the second. Equation (4) is of the second degree; for d^2y/dx^2 appears to the second degree in the equation resulting from clearing (4) of the radical represented by the 2 in the exponent $\frac{3}{2}$.

EXERCISES

State the order and the degree of each of the following differential equations:

1. $\dfrac{dy}{dx} = 3y$ **2.** $\dfrac{d^2y}{dx^2} = 3\dfrac{dy}{dx} + y$

3. $\left(\dfrac{dy}{dx}\right)^2 = 3xy$ **4.** $\left(\dfrac{d^2y}{dx^2}\right)^2 = \left(\dfrac{dy}{dx}\right)^3 + xy$

5. $\dfrac{d^2y}{dx^2} = \sqrt{1 + \left(\dfrac{dy}{dx}\right)^4}$ **6.** $\sqrt{\dfrac{d^3y}{dx^3}} = \dfrac{dy}{dx}$

7. $\left(\dfrac{dy}{dx}\right)^3 - 4xy\dfrac{dy}{dx} = x^4\left(\dfrac{dy}{dx}\right)^2$ **8.** $(x + y^2)\, dx^2 + 2xy\, dx\, dy - dy^2 = 0$

9. $\sqrt{\dfrac{dy}{dx}} = 6\sqrt[3]{\dfrac{d^2y}{dx^2}}$ **10.** $\dfrac{d^2y}{dx^2} = k\left[1 + \left(\dfrac{dy}{dx}\right)^2\right]^{\frac{3}{2}}$

3. Solution of a differential equation

A solution of an ordinary differential equation *in x and y is a relation between x and y which satisfies the differential equation.*

If the solution has the form

$$y = f(x), \tag{10}$$

then the result of substituting $f(x)$ for y in the given equation is an identity.   In this case $f(x)$ is called an **integral,** or a **primitive,** of the given differential equation.   An equation

$$F(x,y) = 0 \tag{11}$$

is a solution of a differential equation if all the functions $f_1(x)$, $f_2(x)$, . . . , $f_n(x)$ obtainable by solving (11) for y in terms of x are integrals (or primitives) of the differential equation.   To show that an equation in the form (11) is a solution of a differential equation, the method of

Example 2 below is generally used instead of the method of finding primitive functions.

Example 1.   Prove that $y = Ae^x + Be^{-2x} + x^2 + x$, A and B constants, is a solution of $(d^2y/dx^2) + (dy/dx) - 2y = 3 - 2x^2$.

Proof.   From $y = Ae^x + Be^{-2x} + x^2 + x$, we obtain

$$\frac{dy}{dx} = Ae^x - 2Be^{-2x} + 2x + 1, \qquad \frac{d^2y}{dx^2} = Ae^x + 4Be^{-2x} + 2.$$

Substituting these values in the differential equation, we get the identity

$$Ae^x + 4Be^{-2x} + 2 + Ae^x - 2Be^{-2x} + 2x + 1 - 2Ae^x - 2Be^{-2x}$$
$$- 2x^2 - 2x = 3 - 2x^2.$$

Example 2.*   Prove that $\log y + (x/y) = c$ is a solution of $(y - x)\, dy + y\, dx = 0$.

Proof.   The given differential equation may be written

$$(y - x)\frac{dy}{dx} + y = 0. \tag{a}$$

Using the regular process of differentiating an implicit function, we obtain from $\log y + (x/y) = c$

$$\frac{1}{y}\frac{dy}{dx} - \frac{x}{y^2}\frac{dy}{dx} + \frac{1}{y} = 0$$

or, solving for dy/dx,

$$\frac{dy}{dx} = \frac{-y}{y - x}. \tag{b}$$

Substituting in (a) the value of dy/dx from (b), we obtain

$$(y - x)\left(\frac{-y}{y - x}\right) + y = -y + y = 0.$$

EXERCISES

Prove that each equation is a solution of the differential equation written opposite it:

1. $y = x^2 + c$ $\dfrac{dy}{dx} = 2x$

2. $y = x^2 + cx$ $x\dfrac{dy}{dx} = x^2 + y$

* The symbol $\log x$, with no base specified, indicates throughout this text a natural logarithm, that is, a logarithm to the base $e = 2.7183$ approximately. Also the letter e will often be used, without explanation, to represent this base of natural logarithms.

3. $y = c$ $\qquad\qquad\qquad\qquad$ $\dfrac{dy}{dx} = 0$

4. $cy = x^2$ $\qquad\qquad\qquad\qquad$ $x\dfrac{dy}{dx} = 2y$

5. $4xy = x^4 + c$ $\qquad\qquad\qquad$ $x\dfrac{dy}{dx} + y = x^3$

6. $y = x^3 + Ax + B$ $\qquad\qquad$ $\dfrac{d^2y}{dx^2} = 6x$

7. $y = A\sin x + B\cos x$ $\qquad$ $\dfrac{d^2y}{dx^2} + y = 0$

8. $y = A\sin 5x + B\cos 5x$ $\qquad$ $\dfrac{d^2y}{dx^2} + 25y = 0$

9. $x^2 + y^2 = c$ $\qquad\qquad\qquad$ $x\,dx + y\,dy = 0$

10. $y = (x + c)e^{-x}$ $\qquad\qquad$ $\dfrac{dy}{dx} + y = e^{-x}$

11. $y = c_1\sin 3x + c_2\cos 3x + 9x^2 - 2$ $\qquad$ $\dfrac{d^2y}{dx^2} + 9y = 81x^2$

12. $y = c^2 + cx^{-1}$ $\qquad\qquad$ $y + x\dfrac{dy}{dx} = x^4\left(\dfrac{dy}{dx}\right)^2$

13. $y = c_1e^{2x} + c_2e^{-4x} + 2xe^{2x}$ $\qquad$ $\dfrac{d^2y}{dx^2} + 2\dfrac{dy}{dx} - 8y = 12e^{2x}$

14. $y = c(x - c)^2$ $\qquad\qquad$ $\left(\dfrac{dy}{dx}\right)^3 - 4xy\dfrac{dy}{dx} + 8y^2 = 0$

15. $x^2 + y^2 = cx$ $\qquad\qquad$ $2xy\dfrac{dy}{dx} = y^2 - x^2$

16. $y^2 = cx^2 - 2x$ $\qquad\qquad$ $xy\dfrac{dy}{dx} = x + y^2$

17. $y^{-3} = x^3(3e^x + c)$ $\qquad\qquad$ $x\dfrac{dy}{dx} + y + x^4y^4e^x = 0$

18. $x^2 + y^2 = x^2y^2 + c$ $\qquad$ $(x - y^2x)\,dx + (1 - x^2)y\,dy = 0$

10. $\cos y = 1 - ce^{-\sin x}$ $\qquad$ $\sin y\dfrac{dy}{dx} + \sin x\cos y = \sin x$

20. $\sin^{-1}\dfrac{y}{x} = c - x,\ -\dfrac{1}{2}\pi < x < \dfrac{1}{2}\pi$ $\qquad$ $x\dfrac{dy}{dx} - y + x\sqrt{x^2 - y^2} = 0$

21. $\log y = c_1e^x + c_2e^{-x}$ $\qquad$ $y\dfrac{d^2y}{dx^2} - \left(\dfrac{dy}{dx}\right)^2 = y^2\log y$

4. Finding differential equation from general solution

The main process to be considered is that of finding the solutions of given differential equations.   Generally these cannot be found in finite form; consequently much of our work will deal with important special cases.   However, generally applicable methods by means of approximations and by infinite series will be considered in Chapter XI.

The reverse process, namely, that of finding a differential equation from its solutions, is comparatively simple and gives a clear picture of the relation between equation and solution.   This section deals with this reverse process.

A **particular solution** *of a differential equation is any relation satisfying it.* *The* **general solution,** or **complete solution,** *of a differential equation defines all, or nearly all, the solutions of the equation.* For the ordinary differential equations considered in this book, the general solutions will contain a number of arbitrary constants equal to the number expressing the order of the equation. The student may observe that the relation held true for the equations and their solutions in §3, and he will see further justification for it in the procedures of this section.

To find the differential equation when the general solution is given, *differentiate the general solution, differentiate the derived equation, differentiate the second derived equation, etc., until the number of derived equations is equal to the number of independent arbitrary constants in the general solution; finally eliminate the constants from the general solution and the derived equations.*

A few examples will illustrate the process.

Example 1.   Find the differential equation whose general solution is $y = c \cos x$.

Solution.   For convenience we shall use primes to indicate derivatives with respect to x.   From the given general solution, obtain

$$y = c \cos x, \qquad \frac{dy}{dx} = y' = -c \sin x. \tag{a}$$

Equate the values of c from the two equations in (a) to get

$$\frac{y}{\cos x} = \frac{-y'}{\sin x}, \qquad \text{or} \qquad \mathbf{y' \cos x + y \sin x = 0.}^* \tag{b}$$

Also, using determinants to eliminate c from (a), we obtain

$$\begin{vmatrix} y & \cos x \\ y' & -\sin x \end{vmatrix} = 0.$$

Example 2.   Find the differential equation whose general solution is $y = c_1 e^{2x} + c_2 e^{-x} + x$.

Solution.   The general solution and the first two derived equations are

$$y = c_1 e^{2x} + c_2 e^{-x} + x, \tag{a}$$

$$\frac{dy}{dx} = y' = 2c_1 e^{2x} - c_2 e^{-x} + 1, \tag{b}$$

$$\frac{d^2 y}{dx^2} = y'' = 4c_1 e^{2x} + c_2 e^{-x}. \tag{c}$$

Eliminating c_2 from (a) and (b) and then from (b) and (c), we get

$$y' + y = 3c_1 e^{2x} + x + 1, \qquad y'' + y' = 6c_1 e^{2x} + 1. \tag{d}$$

_____
* Throughout the text answers to examples appear in boldface type.

Multiplying the first equation of (d) by 2, subtracting the result from the second, and simplifying slightly, we get

$$\mathbf{y'' - y' - 2y = -2x - 1.}$$

Also by determinants we obtain from (a), (b), and (c):

$$\begin{vmatrix} y - x & e^{2x} & e^{-x} \\ y' - 1 & 2e^{2x} & -e^{-x} \\ y'' & 4e^{2x} & e^{-x} \end{vmatrix} = e^{2x}e^{-x} \begin{vmatrix} y - x & 1 & 1 \\ y' - 1 & 2 & -1 \\ y'' & 4 & 1 \end{vmatrix} = 0.$$

EXERCISES

1. $y = x^2 + c$
2. $y = cx^2$
3. $y = cx + 3$
4. $y = cx + c$
5. $y = ce^x$
6. $x^2 + y^2 = c$
7. $y = cx^2 + c_2$
8. $y = c_1x + c_2x^2$
9. $y = cx + c^2 - 2c$
10. $y = c_1 \sin 2x + c_2 \cos 2x$
11. $y = c_1e^x + c_2e^{2x}$
12. $y = c_1 \sin x + c_2 \cos x + x^2 - 2$
13. $y = c_1e^{2x} + c_2e^{3x} + x^2$
14. $y = e^x(c_1x + c_2)$
15. $y^2 = cx + c^2 + 3$
16. $y = x \sin (x + c)$
17. $(x - c)^2 + y^2 = 25$
18. $(x - c_1)^2 + (y - c_2)^2 = 25$

To find the differential equation of a system of curves, write an equation of the system in terms of x, y, and arbitrary constants, and then use the method of this section.

Find the differential equation of the systems of curves numbered 19 to 26:

19. All lines through the origin.
20. All circles with centers $(0,0)$.
21. All straight lines.

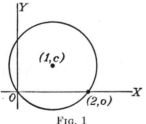

FIG. 1

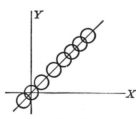

FIG. 2

★22.*All confocal conics defined by $x^2/(c + 2) + y^2/(c - 2) = 1$.

★23. All tangents to $x^2 = 4y$. Also prove that $x^2 = 4y$ is a solution of your answer. *Hint:* From $x^2 = 4y$ obtain $dy/dx = \frac{1}{2}x$. Hence the slope of the tangent through $(2c,c^2)$ is c.

★24. All normals to $y^2 = x$.

★25. All circles through points $(0,0)$ and $(2,0)$ (see Fig. 1).

26. All circles having radius 1 and centers on $y = x$ (see Fig. 2).

* A solid star ★ indicates a difficult problem or a complicated solution.

5. Geometric considerations

Any differential equation of the first order and the first degree may be written in the form

$$\frac{dy}{dx} = f(x,y). \tag{12}$$

From the form of (12) we conclude that it associates to each point (x_0,y_0) a line whose slope is $(dy/dx)_0 = f(x_0,y_0)$, or, in other words, it

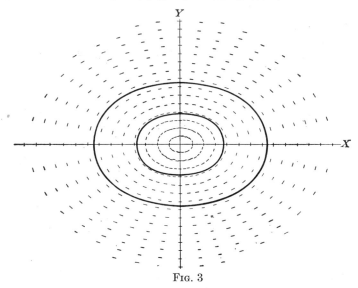

FIG. 3

associates to each point in the plane a direction. Any curve satisfying (12) must have at each of its points the slope given by (12); that is, the tangent line to the curve at any point on it has the direction associated with this point by (12).

Figure 3 represents some points with a line through each to represent the direction associated with the point by

$$\frac{dy}{dx} = \frac{-x}{2y}. \tag{13}$$

The ellipses shown represent solutions of (13). Observe that at each point on an ellipse the curve is tangent to the associated direction line.

The solution of equation (13) is

$$x^2 + 2y^2 = c. \tag{14}$$

Here the constant of integration may be any number; hence equation (14) represents a family of ellipses. Any point $P(x_0,y_0)$ in the plane, except $(0,0)$, will lie on the ellipse represented by equation (14) with $c = x_0^2 + 2y_0^2$, and through each point, except $(0,0)$, will pass one and only one of these ellipses. The two arbitrary constants in the solution $x^2 + 2y^2 = x_0^2 + 2y_0^2$ are really equivalent to only one, since all solutions could be obtained by taking $x_0 = 0$ and assigning values to y_0. The small ellipse is associated with the value $c = 1$ and the large one with $c = 2$.

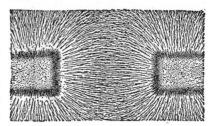

FIG. 4

Figure 4, showing the distribution of iron filings under the influence of a magnet, exhibits the same type of relationship. The iron filings serve as direction lines, and their distribution is such that the curves to which they belong are suggested. A map indicating the directions of ocean currents and winds by means of barbed lines suggests the same situation.

The relation just discussed illustrates a case covered by the general theorem stated below, but not proved here.

THEOREM I. *For a differential equation*

$$\frac{dy}{dx} = f(x,y), \tag{12}$$

there exists a unique continuous function $y = \varphi(x)$ defined for all values of x in a certain region including x_0, satisfying the given differential equation, and taking on the value y_0 when $x = x_0$, provided that $f(x,y)$ and $\partial f/\partial y$ are continuous single-valued functions of x and y in the region $|x - x_0| \leqq a$, $|y - y_0| \leqq b$, where $a > 0$ and $b > 0$.

In Fig. 3, through each point (x_0,y_0), $y_0 \neq 0$, there passes a unique semiellipse, either

$$y = \tfrac{1}{2} \sqrt{2x_0^2 + 4y_0^2 - 2x^2}, \qquad \text{or} \qquad y = -\tfrac{1}{2} \sqrt{2x_0^2 + 4y_0^2 - 2x^2},$$

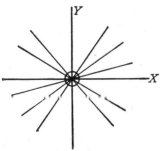

FIG. 5

which satisfies $dy/dx = -x/2y$. Observe that, in this case, the theorem says nothing about points on the X-axis, since the slope $-x/2y$ does not exist at such points; observe also that two semiellipses, not a unique one, pass through $(x_0,0)$.

The solution of $dy/dx = y/x$ is $y = cx$, and (see Fig. 5) it represents all lines through the origin. Observe that a unique line $y = (y_0/x_0)x$ passes through (x_0,y_0) if

$x_0 \neq 0$. The theorem says nothing about point $(0,0)$ since slope y/x is not defined there; and note that all the lines $y = cx$, not a unique one, pass through $(0,0)$.

EXERCISE

Show that $y = +(x + c)^{\frac{3}{2}}$ and $y = -(x + c)^{\frac{3}{2}}$ satisfy $\frac{2}{3} dy/dx = y^{\frac{1}{3}}$. Show that (x_0, y_0), $y_0 \neq 0$, lies on only one of the curves $y = (x - x_0 + y_0^{\frac{3}{2}})^{\frac{3}{2}}$, $y = -(x - x_0 + y_0^{\frac{3}{2}})^{\frac{3}{2}}$. Now both of the curves $y = (x - x_0)^{\frac{3}{2}}$ and $y = -(x - x_0)^{\frac{3}{2}}$ pass through $(x_0, 0)$. Why is this not contradictory to the general theorem?

6. Variables separable

To illustrate the type of problem which calls for the general solution of a given differential equation, we shall consider a type of the first order and first degree, which can easily be reduced to the form

$$\mathbf{f_1(x)\ dx + f_2(y)\ dy = 0,} \tag{15}$$

where $f_1(x)$ is a function of x alone and $f_2(y)$ is a function of y alone. This type is referred to as *variables separable*. Direct integration of equation (15) gives the general solution

$$\int f_1(x)\ dx + \int f_2(y)\ dy = c, \tag{16}$$

where c is an arbitrary constant. It is evident that equation (15) would result from differentiating equation (16), even if we should write any function of c instead of c. Hence, *we may use log c, $tan^{-1} c$, or any other function of c instead of c, in order to obtain the simplest form of a solution.*

Example 1. Find the equation of the curves for which

$$xy\ dy - \frac{1 + y^2}{1 + x^2}\ dx = 0. \tag{a}$$

Also find the solution of (a) having a graph containing point $(1, -3)$.

Solution. Division of (a) by $x(1 + y^2)$ gives

$$\frac{y\ dy}{1 + y^2} - \frac{dx}{x(1 + x^2)} = 0. \tag{b}$$

By integration we obtain from (b)

$$\int \frac{y\ dy}{1 + y^2} - \int \frac{dx}{x(1 + x^2)} = \text{constant,}$$

or

$$\frac{1}{2} \log (1 + y^2) - \frac{1}{2} \log \frac{x^2}{1 + x^2} = \frac{1}{2} \log c. \tag{c}$$

Canceling $\frac{1}{2}$ and using the laws of logarithms, we get

$$\log \frac{(1 + y^2)(1 + x^2)}{x^2} = \log c. \qquad (d)$$

Two numbers that have the same logarithm are equal. Hence

$$\frac{(1 + y^2)(1 + x^2)}{x^2} = c, \quad \text{or} \quad (1 + y^2)(1 + x^2) = cx^2. \qquad (e)$$

To find the equation of the curve through $(1, -3)$, substitute 1 for x and -3 for y in (e) to obtain $(1 + 9)(1 + 1) = c(1)^2$, or $c = 20$. Now replace c in (e) by 20 to obtain

$$(1 + y^2)(1 + x^2) = 20x^2.$$

Example 2. Find the general solution of $a[x(dy/dx) + 2y] = xy \, (dy/dx)$ and then find a particular solution in which $y = a$ when $x = 2a$.

Solution. Clearing of fractions and grouping the terms containing dx and those containing dy, we get

$$2ay \, dx + (ax - xy) \, dy = 0, \qquad (a)$$

or

$$2ay \, dx + x(a - y) \, dy = 0. \qquad (b)$$

Dividing through by xy and integrating, we obtain

$$2a \int \frac{dx}{x} + a \int \frac{dy}{y} - \int dy = \text{constant},$$

or

$$2a \log x + a \log y - y = a \log c. \qquad (c)$$

Dividing by a, replacing $2 \log x$ by $\log x^2$, and combining the logarithmic terms, we get

$$\log \frac{x^2 y}{c} = \frac{y}{a}.$$

Remembering that $e^{\log N} = N$, we obtain

$$e^{\log x^2 y/c} = e^{y/a}, \quad \text{or} \quad x^2 y = c e^{y/a}. \qquad (d)$$

To find c so that $y = a$ when $x = 2a$, substitute $2a$ for x and a for y in (d), and solve for c to obtain

$$4a^3 = c e^{a/a}, \quad \text{or} \quad c = 4a^3 e^{-1}.$$

Substitute this value of c in (d) to obtain the required particular solution

$$x^2 y = 4a^3 e^{-1} e^{y/a}.$$

EXERCISES

Find the general solutions of the differential equations numbered 1 to 18:

1. $x\,dx - y\,dy = 0$ **2.** $x^2\,dx + y^2\,dy = 0$

3. $(x - 1)\,dx + 2(y + 1)\,dy = 0$ **4.** $x^2\,dy - y^2\,dx = 0$

5. $2x(1 + y^2)\,dx - y(1 + 2x^2)\,dy = 0$ **6.** $x\,dy - y\,dx = 0$

7. $3x\,dy + y\,dx = 0$ **8.** $\rho\,d\theta + \theta\,d\rho = 0$

9. $\dfrac{d\rho}{d\theta} = \rho$ **10.** $L\dfrac{di}{dt} + Ri = 0$, L and R constants

11. $y^2\,dx + y^2\,dy = dy$ **12.** $x\,dy + \sqrt{1 + y^2}\,dx = 0$

13. $\dfrac{ds}{dt} = 3t^2 + 2t - 5$ **14.** $e^x e^y\,dy - e^{-2y}\,dx = 0$

15. $x\,dy + y\,dx = x^2\,dy$ **16.** $\dfrac{dy}{dx} - y = y^2$

17. $a\dfrac{dy}{dx} + ay^2 = y - x\dfrac{dy}{dx}$ **18.** $\sqrt{1 - y^2}\,dx = \sqrt{1 - x^2}\,dy$

Find the particular solution of each differential equation satisfied by the indicated values of the variables:

19. $3x^2\,dx + 2y\,dy = 0$; $x = 2$ when $y = 3$

20. $x\,dx - y\,dy = 0$; $y = \pm 4$ when $x = 1$

21. $2x\,dy + y\,dx = 0$; $x = 3$ when $y = 1$

22. $xy\,dy - (1 + y^2)\,dx = 0$; $y = \pm 4$ when $x = 1$

23. $(x + 1)\,dy + (y - 1)\,dx = 0$; $y = 3$ when $x = 0$

24. $d\rho = \rho \cot \theta\,d\theta$; $\rho = 2$ when $\theta = \dfrac{\pi}{2}$

25. $(1 + x^2)\,dy = xy\,dx$; $x = 0$ when $y = 2$

26. $2x\,dy + dx = dy$; $x = 3$ when $y = 0$

27. $2y\,dx + x^2\,dy = -dx$; $y = \dfrac{7}{2}$ when $x = \dfrac{1}{\log 2}$

28. $4\,dy + y\,dx = x^2\,dy$; $x = 4$ when $y = -1$

29. $x^3\,dy + xy\,dx = x^2\,dy + 2y\,dx$; $y = e$ when $x = 2$, where e $(= 2.7183$ nearly) is the base of natural logarithms.

30. $3e^x \tan y\,dx + (1 + e^x)\sec^2 y\,dy = 0$; $y = \tfrac{1}{4}\pi$ when $x = \log 2$

CHAPTER II

APPLICATIONS

7. Geometric applications using rectangular coordinations

A great number of geometric problems can be solved by using the process of expressing a geometric relation in the form of a differential equation and solving it. Take, for example, the problem of finding the equation of the curve through $(3, -4)$ having at each point (x,y) on it a slope of $2y/x$. Since dy/dx represents the slope of the curve, we have

$$\frac{dy}{dx} = \frac{2y}{x}. \qquad (a)$$

Integrating equation (a), obtain

$$\log y = 2 \log x + \log c = \log cx^2; \qquad (b)$$

hence

$$y = cx^2. \qquad (c)$$

Since $(3, -4)$ lies on the curve, substitute 3 for x and -4 for y in (c) to obtain

$$-4 = 9c, \qquad \text{or} \qquad c = -\tfrac{4}{9}. \qquad (d)$$

Therefore the required equation is

$$y = -\tfrac{4}{9}x^2,$$
$$\text{or} \qquad 4x^2 + 9y = 0. \qquad (e)$$

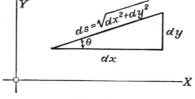

Fig. 1

Some important geometric relations are easily recalled by using figures. Thus from Fig. 1 read

$$ds = \sqrt{dx^2 + dy^2} = \sqrt{1 + \left(\frac{dy}{dx}\right)^2}\, dx = \sqrt{1 + \left(\frac{dx}{dy}\right)^2}\, dy, \qquad (1)$$

$$\tan \theta = \text{slope} = \frac{dy}{dx}, \qquad \sin \theta = \frac{dy}{ds}, \qquad \cos \theta = \frac{dx}{ds}, \text{ etc.} \qquad (2)$$

Example 1. Find the equation of a curve such that the part of the tangent line, at any point on the curve, between the tangent's inter-

13

section with the X-axis and the point of contact is bisected by the Y-axis.

Solution. To solve a problem of this kind, the student should *first draw a figure representing the curve with any point (x,y) on it and showing the essential relations involved in the problem; then try to find the value of the slope of the required curve or of some expression containing the slope, form an equation, and integrate it.*

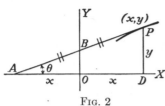

FIG. 2

Figure 2 relates to the problem under consideration. From it we see that $AO = OD = x$ and that the slope of the tangent at P is $y/2x$. Hence

$$\frac{dy}{dx} = \frac{y}{2x}.$$

The solution of this equation is

$$\mathbf{y^2 = cx}.$$

Example 2. *An* **orthogonal trajectory** *of a system of curves in a plane is a curve which intersects every member of the system at right angles and contains only points of orthogonal intersection with curves of the system.*

Find the equation of the orthogonal trajectories of the system of curves

$$y^2 = cx^3. \tag{a}$$

Also find the equation of the particular orthogonal trajectory through the point $(2,4)$

Solution. Differentiating (a) and solving the result for dy/dx, obtain

$$\frac{dy}{dx} = \frac{3x^2c}{2y}. \tag{b}$$

Replacing c in (b) by its value from (a), obtain

$$\frac{dy}{dx} = \frac{3x^2}{2y}\frac{y^2}{x^3} = \frac{3y}{2x} \tag{c}$$

Now, if a curve is to intersect a member of the system at right angles in (x,y), *this curve must have the negative reciprocal, namely, $-2x/3y$, as the slope of its tangent at (x,y).* Hence

$$\left(\frac{dy}{dx}\right)_{\text{orthog. traj.}} = -\frac{2x}{3y}. \tag{d}$$

The solution of (d) is

$$2x^2 + 3y^2 = c_1. \tag{e}$$

This represents a family of ellipses. To find c_1 for the particular curve through (2,4), substitute 2 for x and 4 for y in (e) and obtain $c_1 = 56$. Hence

$$2x^2 + 3y^2 = 56.$$

A brief consideration of Fig. 3 will serve to clarify essential relations.

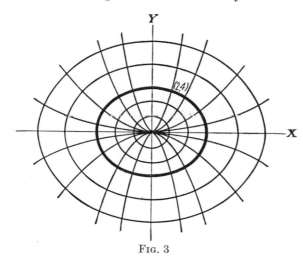

FIG. 3

EXERCISES

1. Find the equation of the system of curves and the equation of the particular curve that passes through point (3,4), if the slope of the tangent at any point (x,y) is

(a) $2x - 2$

(b) $\dfrac{1}{y}$

(c) $\dfrac{y}{x}$

(d) $\dfrac{9x}{16y}$

(e) $\dfrac{1 + x}{1 - y}$

(f) $\dfrac{y - 1}{1 + x}$

2. Prove that a curve having a constant slope is a straight line.

3. Find the orthogonal trajectories of the system of circles $x^2 + y^2 = c$. Sketch two of these circles and any two orthogonal trajectories.

Find the equations of the orthogonal trajectories of the systems of curves numbered 4 to 9:

4. The hyperbolas $y^2 = x^2 + c$.
5. The parabolas $y^2 = 2cx$.
6. The quintics $y = cx^5$.

7. The equilateral hyperbolas $xy = cx - 1$.

8. The probability curves $y = ce^{-x^2}$.

9. The cubics $y^2 = 4cx^3$.

10. In the solution of Example 2 the constant c in (b) was replaced by y^2/x^3 to obtain (c). Why was this necessary?

11. Find the most general kind of curve such that the normal at any point of it coincides in direction with the line connecting this point to the origin. Use Fig. 4.

12. The part of the normal to a curve, at any point (x,y) on the curve, between (x,y) and the point where the normal meets the X-axis is bisected by the Y-axis. Find the equation of the curve.

13. For a certain curve the point of contact of each tangent to it bisects the part of the tangent terminating on the coordinate axes. Find the equation of the curve.

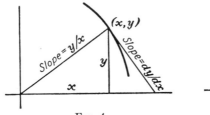

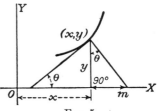

FIG. 4   FIG. 5

14. Find the equation of the curve so drawn that every point on it is equidistant from the origin and the intersection of the X-axis with the normal to the curve at the point.

15. The part of the X-axis between the normal to a certain curve at (x,y) and the ordinate of the point has constant length m (see Fig. 5). Find the equation of the curve.

16. A curve is so drawn that, for each point (x,y) on it, a circle cutting the curve orthogonally at (x,y) and passing through $(x,0)$ has a chord of constant length m lying along the X-axis. Find the equation of the curve.

17. The ordinate of any point on a curve, the tangent to the curve at the point, and the X-axis bound an area of constant magnitude. Find the equation of the curve.

18. The area bounded by a curve, the X-axis, a fixed ordinate, and a variable ordinate is proportional to the difference between the ordinates. Find the equation of the curve. *Hint:* $A = k(y - b)$, and $dA = k\,dy$; that is, $y\,dx = k\,dy$.

19. The area bounded by the X-axis, a curve, a fixed ordinate, and a variable ordinate is revolved about the X-axis. If the volume of the solid generated is proportional to the difference between the radii of its bases, find the equation of the curve.

20. Find the equation of a set of curves each of which crosses every member of the set $y = x^2 + c$ at an angle of 45 deg.

8. Geometric applications using polar coordinates

A basic formula for the equation of a curve in polar coordinates ρ and θ is

$$\tan \psi = \frac{\rho d\theta}{d\rho},\tag{3}$$

where, as indicated in Fig. 6, ψ represents the angle between the tangent to the curve at (ρ,θ) and the radius vector to (ρ,θ). This formula enables us to obtain the equations of many curves having interesting geometric properties.

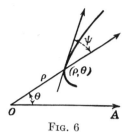

FIG. 6

Example. Find the equation of the orthogonal trajectories of the circles $\rho = c\cos\theta$.

Solution. If ψ_c represents the angle ψ of formula (3) for the given curve at a point and ψ_0 that for a perpendicular curve through the same point, then

$$\psi_0 = \psi_c \pm 90°,$$

$$\tan \psi_0 = -\cot \psi_c = -\frac{1}{\tan \psi_c}.\tag{4}$$

From (3), for circles $\rho = c\cos\theta$,

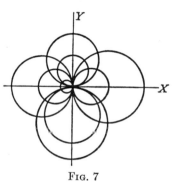

FIG. 7

$$\tan \psi_c = \frac{\rho\, d\theta}{d\rho} = \frac{\rho}{d\rho/d\theta} = \frac{c\cos\theta}{-c\sin\theta}.$$

Therefore, from (4), $\tan\psi_0 = \sin\theta/\cos\theta$. Hence, using (3) for the orthogonal trajectory, obtain

$$\left(\frac{\rho\, d\theta}{d\rho}\right)_{\text{orthog. trni.}} = \tan\theta.$$

The solution of this equation is

$$\log\rho = \log\sin\theta + \log c_1,$$

or　　　$$\rho = c_1 \sin\theta.*$$

Figure 7 represents the two systems of curves.

PROBLEMS

Find the equations of the orthogonal trajectories of the systems of curves defined by the equations numbered 1 to 9:

* The process employed in this solution may not give the desired answer, because an expression in ρ and θ may have several values at the same point. Thus

$$\rho(1 + 2\cos\theta)_{(1,\frac{1}{3}\pi)} = 1 + \sqrt{3}, \qquad \rho(1 + 2\cos\theta)_{(-1,\frac{7}{3}\pi)} = -1 + \sqrt{3}.$$

Some limitations of the process are illustrated in exercises 13 and 14. The process is valid for the exercises numbered 1 to 9.

1. $\rho = c \sin \theta$ **2.** $\rho = c \sin^2 \theta$ **3.** $\rho = c(\sin \theta + \cos \theta)$

4. $\rho = c \sin^n \theta$ **5.** $\rho = \dfrac{c}{1 - \cos \theta}$ **6.** $\rho = c(1 + \sin \theta)$, $\rho \neq 0$

7. $\rho = c(1 - \cos \theta)$, $\rho \neq 0$ **8.** $\rho = c \sin 2\theta$, $\rho \neq 0$ **9.** $\rho^2 = c \sin 2\theta$, $\rho \neq 0$

10. Find the equation of the curve through point $(\rho = a, \theta = 0)$ and cutting all lines through the pole at a constant angle α. *Hint:* $\tan \psi = \tan \alpha$.

11. Find the equation of the curve for which the angle between the radius vector to any point on it and the tangent to it at this same point is equal to (a) the vectorial angle of the point, (b) one-third of the angle between the tangent line and the polar axis. *Hint to (b):* Use $\psi = \frac{1}{3}(\psi + \theta)$ and $180° - \psi = \frac{1}{3}(\psi + \theta)$.

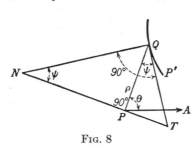

FIG. 8

12. A perpendicular at the pole P to the radius vector of any point Q on a certain curve meets the tangent at Q in point T and the normal at Q in point N (see Fig. 8). Find the equation of the curve (a) if $PN = a$, a constant, (b) if $PT = a$.

★**13.** Apply the process of the example of this section to $\rho = c\theta$ to obtain $\rho = Ae^{-\frac{1}{2}\theta^2}$ as the equation of possible orthogonal trajectories. Now show that for all integers k the curves $\rho = [\rho_1/(\theta_1 + k2\pi)]\theta$ pass through point (ρ_1, θ_1) with corresponding $\tan \psi_k = (\theta_1 + k2\pi)$. Hence conclude that no curve through (ρ_1, θ_1) can be perpendicular at (ρ_1, θ_1) to all the curves of $\rho = c\theta$ through (ρ_1, θ_1). Show that $\rho = c\theta$ and $\rho = Ae^{-\frac{1}{2}\theta^2}$ are mutually orthogonal systems provided that $0 < \theta \leq \pi$.

★**14.** Apply the process of the example of this section to the system

$$\rho = \frac{c}{1 + 2 \cos \theta} \qquad (a)$$

to obtain as the equation of possible orthogonal trajectories

$$\rho^2 = \frac{b}{\sin \theta(1 - \cos \theta)}. \qquad (b)$$

Show that, if $c = 2(\sqrt{3} - 1)$ and $b = 1/(2 + \sqrt{3})$, then point $P(-2, \frac{7}{6}\pi)$ lies on (a) and the same point $P(2, \frac{1}{6}\pi)$ lies on (b); now prove that the special curves (a) and (b) just considered do not intersect orthogonally at $(2, \frac{1}{6}\pi)$. What do you conclude?

9. Use of limits

In many cases it is convenient to use limits instead of determining the constant of integration and other constants. Integrating the differential equation

$$f_1(x)\, dx + f_2(y)\, dy = 0, \qquad (5)$$

we obtain

$$F_1(x) + F_2(y) = c, \qquad (6)$$

where $F_1(x)$ and $F_2(y)$ are got by integrating $f_1(x)\, dx$ and $f_2(y)\, dy$, respectively. Suppose then that (a,b) is a pair of values satisfying (6) for some value of c. Then

$$F_1(a) + F_2(b) = c. \tag{7}$$

Subtracting (7) from (6), obtain

$$F_1(x) - F_1(a) + F_2(y) - F_2(b) = 0,$$

or

$$\int_a^x f_1(x)\, dx + \int_b^y f_2(y)\, dy = 0.$$

It appears then that in solving $f_1(x)\, dx + f_2(y)\, dy = 0$, *we may write*

$$\int_a^x f_1(x)\, dx + \int_b^y f_2(y)\, dy = 0, \qquad \int_a^l f_1(x)\, dx + \int_b^m f_2(y)\, dy = 0, \tag{8}$$

where (a,b), (l,m), (x,y) represent corresponding pairs of values.

The use of limits will be illustrated in the examples of §§11 and 12.

10. Physical applications

Most situations in nature are so complicated that they cannot be dealt with exactly by mathematics. The regular procedure is to apply mathematics to an ideal situation having only important features of the actual one. The results are approximations having a practical importance which depends upon the closeness of approximation as verified by reasoning and experiment. Consider, for example, the procedure for the flight of a projectile. The forces of gravity and air resistance acting upon a large projectile rotating while moving forward are very complicated. If we assume that gravity is a constant vertical force and neglect both air resistance and rotary motion, a simple solution is easily obtained; it is practically worthless. If, as a better approximation, we assume that air resistance is proportional to velocity and acts opposite to the direction of motion, and if we get a good factor of proportionality based on experiment, the solution will give a better approximation to the actual motion and may be useful for some purposes. Finally, if a group of mathematicians, physicists, and technicians are supplied with powerful computing machines and a proving ground permitting extensive experimentation, they can get results accurate enough for any practical purpose. They would investigate all forces involved, devise a theory, and then apply methods in the development of which differential equations would play a prominent role.

In this treatment the laws obtained by observation, experimentation, and reasoning are given. The student is required to express them in mathematical symbols, solve the resulting differential equations, and interpret the solutions.

11. Compound-interest-law problems

Quantities which vary at a rate proportional to their size are said to obey the *compound-interest law* or the *snowball law*. Instances of such quantities are frequent in science.

The following example has reference to such a quantity:

Example. Radium decomposes at a rate proportional to the amount present.* If of 100 mg. set aside now there will be left 96 mg. 100 years hence, find how much will be left t centuries from the time when the radium was set aside, how long a time will elapse before one-tenth of the radium has disappeared, and the amount left after 30.3 centuries.

Solution. Let q be the number of milligrams of radium left after t centuries. Then, since dq/dt is the rate of increase,

$$\frac{dq}{dt} = kq, \qquad \text{or} \qquad \frac{dq}{q} = k\,dt. \tag{a}$$

We have as pairs of corresponding values

$$\begin{array}{c|c|c|c|c} q & 100 & 96 & 90 & Q \\ \hline t & 0 & 1 & T & 30.3 \end{array}. \tag{b}$$

From (a) and (b) obtain

$$\int_{100}^{q} \frac{dq}{q} = k \int_{0}^{t} dt, \qquad \int_{100}^{96} \frac{dq}{q} = k \int_{0}^{1} dt,$$
$$\int_{100}^{90} \frac{dq}{q} = k \int_{0}^{T} dt, \qquad \int_{100}^{Q} \frac{dq}{q} = k \int_{0}^{30.3} dt. \tag{c}$$

From the first equation of (c) obtain

$$\log q - \log 100 = kt, \qquad \text{or} \qquad q = 100e^{kt}. \tag{d}$$

Since $q = 96$ when $t = 1$, obtain from (d),

$$96 = 100e^{k}. \tag{e}$$

Replacing e^{k} in (d) by its value from (e), obtain

$$\mathbf{Q = 100(0.96)^{t}.} \tag{f}$$

---

* Radium does not disintegrate continuously as here indicated; very small particles radiate so that decrease of quantity takes place atom by atom, that is, discontinuously. However, the results obtained by the method of the example are reliable when fairly large amounts of radium are considered. If the method were applied to a single atom of radium, the result would be absurd.

Now using the Keuffel and Esser log-log duplex slide rule (any log-log slide rule may be used),

Set index of scale C opposite 0.96 on scale LL01.

Opposite 0.9 on LL02 read 2.58 ($= T$) on C.

Opposite 303 on C read 0.290 ($= Q/100$) on LL03.

Hence $T = $ **2.58 centuries**, $Q = $ **29.0 mg**.

Instead of using the slide rule we could solve the last three equations of (c), after supplying the logarithms, to obtain

$$k = -0.041, \qquad T = 2.58, \qquad Q = 29.0.$$

PROBLEMS

1. Assume that a body cools according to Newton's law $d\theta/dt = -k\theta$, where t is the time and θ is the difference between the temperature of the body and that of the surrounding air. Find the temperature at time t of a boiler of water cooling in air at 0°C. if the water was initially boiling at 100°C. and the temperature dropped 10° during the first 20 min. Also find the time for the temperature of the water to drop from 90°C. to 80°C., and the temperature of the water after 90 min.

2. Replace 0°C. for the temperature of the air in problem 1 by 20°C. and solve the resulting problem.

3. When an amount A of money is invested at r per cent compounded continuously, $dA/dt = \frac{1}{100}rA$. Find the amount of one dollar invested at 6 per cent compounded continuously at the end of (a) 1 year, (b) 10 years.

4. What time is required for an amount of money compounded continuously at 6 per cent to (a) double itself, (b) triple itself?

5. A man has a certain sum of money drawing interest at the rate of 6 per cent per year compounded continuously. Assuming that he draws out the money continuously at the rate of $10 per day ($3650 per year) and exhausts the sum in 20 years, find the original sum. *Hint.* If A is the amount of money at time t years, then $\Delta A = (0.06A - 3650 + \epsilon)\,\Delta t$, where $\epsilon \to 0$ when $\Delta t \to 0$.

6. When a simple electric circuit containing inductance and resistance but no condensers is cut off, the rate of decrease of current is proportional to the current. If the initial current is 30 amperes, and it dies down to 11 amperes in 0.01 sec., find the current in terms of the time.

7. If at time t sec. q coulombs is the charge of electricity on a condenser of capacity C farads discharging through a resistance of R ohms, the equation

$$\frac{dq}{dt} + \frac{1}{RC} q = 0$$

applies. If $R = 100$ ohms, $C = 3 \times 10^{-4}$ farad, and initially $q = 0.5$ coulomb, in what time will the condenser lose half its initial charge?

8. Assume that the rate of change of air pressure with altitude (distance above the earth) is proportional to the air pressure.* If the air pressure on the ground

* The rate of change of pressure depends on air pressure, temperature of the air, and other conditions. Hence a formula neglecting all conditions except air pressure will give only rough approximations.

is 14.7 lb./in.², and if at an altitude of 10,000 ft. it is 10.1 lb./in.², find air pressure in terms of altitude, and find the air pressure at an altitude of 15,000 ft.

12. Acceleration. Velocity. Distance

If a particle of mass m moves in a straight line with acceleration a, under the influence of several applied forces whose resultant is F, then, in accordance with Newton's laws of motion, we have

$$F = ma, \tag{9}$$

where F, m, and a must be expressed in corresponding units. The set of units which we shall use in most problems is force in *pounds*, mass in *slugs* (one slug $= g$ lb. $= 32.2$ lb. nearly), distance in *feet*, and time in *seconds*. Velocity will then be represented in feet per second and acceleration in feet per second per second. Using the notation t, s, v, and a for time, distance, velocity, and acceleration, respectively, we have from calculus

$$v = \frac{ds}{dt}, \qquad a = \frac{dv}{dt} = \frac{v\, dv}{ds}. \tag{10}$$

We may then write our equation of motion in the form

$$\mathbf{F(lb.)} = \frac{\mathbf{w(lb.)}}{\mathbf{32.2}} \frac{\mathbf{dv}}{\mathbf{dt}} = \frac{\mathbf{w}}{\mathbf{32.2}} \frac{\mathbf{v\, dv}}{\mathbf{ds}}. \tag{11}$$

Example. A coasting party weighing 1000 lb. coasts down a 5-deg. incline. The component of gravitational force parallel to the direction of motion is 87.2 lb. If the force of friction opposing the motion is 40 lb. and the air resistance in pounds is

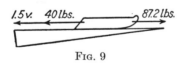

FIG. 9

numerically equal to 1.5 times the speed in feet per second,* find an expression for the speed after t sec. from rest, the speed after 10 sec. from rest, and the limiting speed.

Solution. If downhill is chosen as the positive direction, we see from Fig. 9 that $F = 87.2 - 40 - 1.5v$. Therefore, the equation of motion is

$$47.2 - 1.5v = \frac{1000}{32.2} \frac{dv}{dt}. \tag{a}$$

---

* The problem of finding the resistance of a fluid on a body moving through it is very complicated. It depends on speed, shape of the body, and properties of the fluid. Any such simple expression as 1.5v can represent it reasonably well for only a short period of time in most cases.

The initial conditions may be written

$$\frac{v \quad \mid \quad 0 \quad \mid \quad v_{10}}{t \quad \mid \quad 0 \quad \mid \quad 10}. \tag{b}$$

Separating the variables in (a) and integrating, we obtain

$$\int_0^{v_{10}} \frac{-1.5\,dv}{47.2 - 1.5v} = -\int_0^{10} 0.0483\,dt,$$

$$\int_0^v \frac{-1.5\,dv}{47.2 - 1.5v} = -0.0483 \int_0^t dt. \tag{c}$$

From the first part of (c)

$$[\log (47.2 - 1.5v)]_0^{v_{10}} = \log \frac{47.2 - 1.5v_{10}}{47.2} = -0.483.$$

Then

$$\frac{47.2 - 1.5v_{10}}{47.2} = e^{-0.483} = 0.617, \qquad \text{and} \qquad v_{10} = \mathbf{12.1 \ ft./sec.} \quad (d)$$

From the second part of (c)

$$\log \frac{47.2 - 1.5v}{47.2} = -0.0483t, \qquad \text{or} \qquad \frac{47.2 - 1.5v}{47.2} = e^{-0.0483t}. \tag{e}$$

Solving (e) for v, we obtain

$$v = \mathbf{31.5(1 - e^{-0.0483t})}. \tag{f}$$

From (f) it appears that, as t increases without limit, $e^{-0.0483t}$ approaches zero as a limit and v approaches **31.5 ft./sec.**

This last result could have been found from the fact that, as v approaches a limiting value, the rate of change of v, or dv/dt, approaches zero. Hence, from equation (a), $47.2 - 1.5v$ approaches zero, and v approaches 31.5 ft./sec.

PROBLEMS

1. A body moves in a straight line with a constant acceleration a of 10 ft./sec.^{2}. If velocity $v = 5$ ft./sec. when $t = 2$, show that $v = 10t - 15$.

2. Using the equation $a = v\,dv/ds$ for rectilinear motion, prove that, if a is constant, $v^2 = v_0^2 + 2as$, where $v = v_0$ when $s = 0$. Also prove that, if a is constant and $v = v_0$ when $t = 0$, then $v = v_0 + at$.

3. If distance is expressed in feet and time in seconds, then a and $-0.3v^2$ for a certain rectilinear motion are expressed by the same number; that is, $a = -0.3v^2$.*

* This equation appears to be incorrect dimensionally; for, if L represents distance and T time, a has dimensions LT^{-2} and v^2 the dimensions L^2T^{-2}. To obtain balance, we assign to the constant 0.3 the dimension of L^{-1}. In general, we shall assume that the constants in our equations are such that the equations are dimensionally correct.

If $v = 20$ ft./sec. when $t = 0$, find v in terms of t and find v when $t = 10$ sec. Also using $s = 0$ when $v = 20$ ft./sec. and $v\,dv/ds$ for a, find v in terms of s.

4. A boat with its load weighs 400 lb. (see Fig. 10). If the force exerted upon the boat by the motor in the direction of motion is equivalent to a constant force of 15 lb., if the resistance (in pounds) to motion is equal numerically to twice the speed (in feet per second), that is, is $2v$ lb., and if the boat starts from rest, find the speed (*a*) after t sec.; (*b*) after 10 sec.; (*c*) when $t = \infty$, that is, the limiting speed.

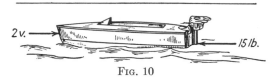

Fig. 10

5. Work problem 4 under the assumption that the boat was being towed at 15 mi./hr. (22 ft./sec.), and that at the time $t = 0$ the towing line was suddenly severed and the motor started.

6. Work problem 4 under the assumption that the boat is a scow so built that the resistance in pounds is four times the velocity in feet per second.

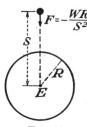

Fig. 11

7. A freighter of 30,000 tons displacement (1 ton $= 2000$ lb.) starts from rest. Assuming that the resistance in pounds to motion is $6000v$, where v is the speed in feet per second, and that the force exerted on the ship by the propellers is 120,000 lb., find (*a*) the speed at any time; (*b*) the limiting speed; (*c*) the time taken to speed up to nine-tenths of the limiting speed.

8. Figure 11 represents a uniform ball E having the weight and radius of the earth pulling a w-lb. body toward it with a force inversely proportional to the square of the distance s from the center of E. By applying Newton's law of motion, we obtain the equation

$$\frac{w}{32.2}\,a = \frac{w}{32.2}\,\frac{v\,dv}{ds} = -\frac{wR^2}{s^2},$$

where $R = 4000 \times 5280$ ft., s is in feet, and t in seconds. Find the velocity attained by the body in falling from rest at a distance of $4R$ from the center of E to its surface. What velocity would correspond to a fall from an infinite distance?

9. A ship of w tons displacement is moved by a constant propeller force of p lb., its limiting speed being m ft./sec. If resistance to motion is proportional to the nth power of the speed, express in the form of a definite integral the time for the speed to change from $\frac{1}{2}m$ ft./sec. to $\frac{3}{4}m$ ft./sec.

10. A force that increases uniformly at the rate of 6 lb./sec. from a value of 0 lb. when $t = 0$ acts on a 32.2-lb. body initially at rest. Find v in terms of t, then replace v by ds/dt and again integrate to find s in terms of t.

★**11.** A 64.4-lb. weight on a spring attached to a ceiling moves

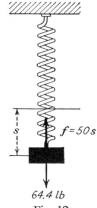

$f = 50s$

64.4 lb

Fig. 12

up and down under the action of its weight and a restoring force $f = 50s$ lb. (see Fig. 12), where s is the number of feet the spring is stretched. Using the equation $F = ma$, show that $2a = 64.4 - 50s$. If velocity $v = 0$ when $s = 0$, show that v in feet per second is given by $v = \pm \sqrt{64.4s - 25s^2}$. Replace v in the equation by ds/dt and show that $s = 1.288 + 1.288 \sin (\pm 5t + \frac{3}{2}\pi) = 1.288(1 - \cos 5t)$, provided $s = 0$ when $t = 0$. Show that s varies from 0 to 2.576 ft. and back to zero again periodically, the period being $\frac{2}{5}\pi$ sec.

13. Other rate problems

The idea of rate is basic in a great variety of problems, but only one more type will be illustrated at this point.

Example. A tank contains initially 100 gal. of brine holding 150 lb. of dissolved salt in solution. Salt water containing 1 lb. of salt per gallon enters the tank at the rate of 2 gal./min., and the brine flows out at the same rate. If the mixture is kept uniform by stirring, find the amount of salt in the tank at the end of 1 hr.

Solution. If Q represents the amount of salt in the tank at the end of t min., we have

$$\frac{dQ}{dt} = \text{rate of gain} - \text{rate of loss.}$$

Evidently the rate of gain is 2 lb./min., and as each gallon of brine in the tank contains $Q/100$ lb. of salt, the rate of loss is $2Q/100$ lb./min. Hence the equation is

$$\frac{dQ}{dt} = 2 - \frac{2Q}{100}, \quad \text{or} \quad \frac{dQ}{Q - 100} = \frac{-2\,dt}{100}.$$

Corresponding values of Q and t are

$$\begin{array}{c|c|c} Q & 150 & Q_{60} \\ \hline t & 0 & 60 \end{array}.$$

Hence

$$\int_{150}^{Q_{60}} \frac{dQ}{Q - 100} = -0.02 \int_0^{60} dt.$$

From this we obtain

$$\log \frac{Q_{60} - 100}{150 - 100} = -(0.02)(60) = -1.2.$$

Hence

$$\frac{Q_{60} - 100}{50} = e^{-1.2} = 0.3012, \text{ and } \mathbf{Q_{60} = 115.1 \text{ lb.}}$$

PROBLEMS

1. Into a 100-gal. tank initially filled with fresh water flow 2 gal./min. of salt water containing 2 lb. of salt per gallon. The solution, kept uniform by stirring, flows out at the same rate. (*a*) How many pounds of salt will there be in the tank at the end of 1 hr. 40 min.? (*b*) What is the upper limit for the number of pounds of salt in the tank if the process keeps up indefinitely? (*c*) How much time will elapse while the quantity of salt in the tank is changing from 100 lb. to 150 lb.?

2. A 100-gal. tank initially filled with fresh water has a mixture of salt and insoluble material in its bottom. If the salt dissolves at a rate per minute equal to one-third of the difference between the concentration (number of pounds of salt per gallon) of the brine and the concentration of a saturated solution (3 lb./gal.), and if the concentration is kept uniform by stirring, find the number of pounds of salt dissolved in 1 hr.

3. A mass of inert material containing 15 lb. of salt in its pores is agitated with 10 gal. of water initially fresh. The salt dissolves at a rate which varies jointly as the number of pounds of undissolved salt and the difference between the concentration of the solution and that of a saturated solution (3 lb. of salt per gallon). If 9 lb. are dissolved in 10 min., when will 90 per cent be dissolved?

4. The differential equation expressing the generalized compound-interest law is

$$\frac{dy}{dx} = ay + b.$$

Show that its solution is $y = ce^{ax} - (b/a)$.

To apply this solution for solving problem 1, what values for a and b should you use?

5. Apply the solution of problem 4 to solve the following problem: Air containing 20 per cent oxygen passes slowly into a 2-gal. flask initially filled with pure oxygen, and the mixture of air and oxygen, assumed uniform, passes out at the same rate. How much oxygen will the flask contain after 5 gal. of air have passed into it?

14. Miscellaneous applications

A wide variety of interesting mathematical and physical problems can be solved by the use of the methods we have been considering.

MISCELLANEOUS PROBLEMS

Solve each of the differential equations numbered 1 to 4 subject to the initial conditions.

1. $\dfrac{dQ}{dt} = 3 - 0.02Q$; $Q = 50$ when $t = 0$

2. $\dfrac{dv}{dt} + 5v = 100$; $v = 15$ when $t = \log 2$

3. $L\dfrac{di}{dt} + Ri = E$; where L, R, and E are constants and $i = 0$ when $t = 0$.

4. $(4y^2 + 4)\, dx = 5x\, dy + 8y\, dx$; $y = 2$ when $x = e^2$

5. When a gas expands without gain or loss of heat, the rate of change of pressure with volume varies directly as the pressure and inversely as the volume. Find the law connecting pressure and volume in this case.

6. Find the equation of the curve for which the area bounded by the tangent, the normal, and the Y-axis is proportional to the slope.

Find the equations of the curves having the properties numbered 7 to 11:

7. Angle between the radius vector and tangent equals the angle between the radius vector and initial line. *Hint:* Use $\psi = \theta$ and $\psi = 180° - \theta$; therefore, $\tan \psi = \pm \tan \theta$.

8. Perpendicular from the pole to a tangent is constant.

9. Tangent is equally inclined to the radius vector and to the initial line. *Hint:* $\theta = 180° - 2\psi$, or $\psi = 90° - \frac{1}{2}\theta$.

10. Radius vector is equally inclined to the normal and to the initial line.

11. Area bounded by the radius vector, the tangent, and the initial line is proportional to ρ^2. *Hint:* To find the intercept of the tangent on the initial line, apply the law of sines to the triangle bounded by the tangent, the radius vector, and the initial line.

12. A man and a parachute are falling (see Fig. 13) with a speed of 173 ft./sec. when the parachute opens, and the speed is reduced so as to approach the limiting value of 15 ft./sec. by air-resistance proportional to the square of the speed. Show that

$$t = \frac{15}{g}\left(\coth^{-1}\frac{v}{15} - \coth^{-1}\frac{173}{15}\right).$$

By Newton's law $F = ma$,

$$W - kv^2 = \frac{W}{g}\frac{dv}{dt}$$

Fig. 13

Hint: When the speed is close to the limiting speed, the velocity is almost constant and the acceleration nearly zero. Hence $w - k15^2 = 0$.

13. Assuming that a man weighing w lb. falls from rest, that the resistance of the air is proportional to his speed v, and that his limiting speed is 173 ft./sec., find an expression for his speed at any time and find his speed at the end of the eleventh second.

14. Heat is flowing through a wall at each point of which the temperature remains constant, although the temperatures at different points may be different. When the wall receives or loses no heat except through its faces, and its faces are kept at constant temperature, the following equation is satisfied:

$$-kA\frac{dT}{dx} = Q, \tag{I}$$

where k is a constant found by experiment, A is the area of the face of the wall, x is the distance from one of its faces, T represents temperature, and Q is a constant quantity of heat flowing through the wall per unit of time. When c.g.s. (centimeter-gram-second) units are used, Q will be expressed in calories per second.

(*a*) Integrate equation (I) assuming A constant, and use your answer to find the number of calories of heat per day passing through the wall of an icehouse having an area of 10^7 cm.², a thickness of 30.5 cm., an inside temperature of 0°C., an outside temperature of 21.1°C., and a conductivity $k = 0.00023$.

(b) Find the heat lost per hour through 1 m² of furnace wall, if this wall is 45.7 cm. thick, if k for its masonry is 0.0024, and if the faces of the wall are at 1000°C. and 120°C., respectively.

★15. Equation (I) of problem 14 applies to a protected cylindrical hot-water or steam pipe under the conditions of problem 14, if x represents the distance from the axis of the pipe and A the lateral area of a cylinder of radius x and length equal to the length of the pipe considered, that is, if $A = 2\pi x l$.

Two steam pipes of 20 cm. diameter, protected with coverings 10 cm. thick of concrete ($k = 0.0022$) and magnesia ($k = 0.00017$), respectively, are run underneath the soil. If the outer surfaces are at 30°C. and the pipes themselves are at 160°C., compute the losses per hour per meter length of pipe in the two cases. Also find the heat lost per hour per meter length of pipe from one of those pipes, if it is protected with a covering 5 cm. thick of magnesia and, over this, a covering of concrete 5 cm. thick.

16. When water is forced by its own weight to issue from an open tank through a small orifice h units below the surface of the water, the rate of flow is given by

$$\frac{dv}{dt} = -0.6b \sqrt{2gh} = -a\frac{dh}{dt}, \tag{II}$$

where v represents volume of water in the tank, b the area of the orifice, a the area of the cross section of the tank at water level, t the time, and g the acceleration of gravity. A consistent set of units is h in feet, a and b in square feet, v in cubic feet, t in seconds, and $g = 32.2$ ft./sec.².

Use equation (II) to find the time to empty a cylindrical tank 2 ft. in diameter and 3 ft. high, through a hole 2 in. in diameter in the bottom of the tank. The tank is initially full of water and its axis is (a) vertical; (b) horizontal.

★17. Use equation (II) of problem 16, properly modified, to find the time required to fill a cubical tank whose edge is 3 ft., if there is a round hole 1 in. in diameter in the bottom of the tank and if water is poured into the tank at the rate of π ft.³/min.

★18. A cubical tank of edge 4 ft. is full of water which runs out a vertical slit $\frac{1}{8}$ in. wide and extending from the top to the bottom of the tank. If the quantity of water per second issuing from a small part of the slit of area a situated at distance x from the surface of the water is $0.6a \sqrt{2gx}$, find the time for the surface of the water to fall 3 ft. *Hint:* First, find the number of cubic feet per minute of water issuing from the slit when the water is h ft. deep.

CHAPTER III

DIFFERENTIAL EQUATIONS OF THE FIRST ORDER AND THE FIRST DEGREE

15. Simple substitutions

Many problems may be reduced to the case of *variables separable* by simple substitutions. Thus, to solve

$$(x + y - 3)\, dx + (x + y + 4)\, dy = 0, \qquad (a)$$

let us try the substitution

$$z = x + y. \qquad (b)$$

Then

$$dz = dx + dy. \qquad (c)$$

The next step is to eliminate either y or x from (a) by using (b) and (c). From (b), $y = z - x$; and from (c), $dy = dz - dx$. Substituting these values in (a), we obtain

$$(z - 3)\, dx + (z + 4)(dz - dx) = 0,$$

or

$$-7\, dx + (z + 4)\, dz = 0.$$

Here the variables are separated, and, solving, we find

$$14x - z^2 - 8z = -c.$$

Replacing z by its equal $x + y$, we find

$$14x - (x + y)^2 - 8(x + y) = -c,$$

or

$$\mathbf{x^2 + 2xy + y^2 - 6x + 8y = c.}$$

If the form of an equation indicates that two expressions play a prominent role, it may be well to introduce two new variables. Thus, in considering the equation

$$x(x + y)(dx + dy) = \frac{y}{x}\,(x\, dy - y\, dx), \qquad (d)$$

29

we note that $x + y$ and y/x stand out.   This suggests the substitution

$$z = x + y, \qquad w = \frac{y}{x}. \tag{e}$$

Taking differentials of equations (e), and also solving (e) for x in terms of z and w, obtain

$$dz = dx + dy, \qquad dw = \frac{x\,dy - y\,dx}{x^2}, \qquad x = \frac{z}{1 + w}. \tag{f}$$

Substituting from (e) and (f) in (d), obtain

$$zx\,dz = x^2 w\,dw,$$

and from this

$$z\,dz = \frac{zw\,dw}{1 + w}. \tag{g}$$

The solution of (g) is

$$z = w - \log(1 + w) + c. \tag{h}$$

Replacing w and z in (h) by their values from (e), obtain

$$\mathbf{x + y = \frac{y}{x} - \log\left(1 + \frac{y}{x}\right) + c.} \tag{i}$$

To solve a differential equation by substitution: (a) *write the substitution equations; (b) differentiate the substitution equations; (c) eliminate all but two of the unknowns from the given differential equation and the results of (a) and (b); (d) solve the result from (c); (e) replace the new variables in terms of the old in the result of (d).*

No general rule for finding effective substitution equations can be given; however the form of the differential equation may be suggestive. Any outstanding expression may be made the basis of a substitution. Occasionally substitutions effective for certain types will be given.

EXERCISES

Solve the following differential equations and determine the constants of integration when initial conditions are given:

1. $2(x - y)\,dx + dy = 0$; let $z = x - y$
2. $2\,dx + (2x + 3y)\,dy = 0$
3. $(x + y)\,dx + (x + y - 2)\,dy = 0$; let $z = x + y$
4. $(2x + y + 6)\,dx + (2x + y)\,dy = 0$
5. $(x - 2y + 5)\,dx - [2(x - 2y) + 9]\,dy = 0$
6. $(2x + y + 9)\,dx + (2x + y + 6)\,dy = 0$
7. $(2x + y)^2\,dx - 2\,dy = 0$

8. $16\,dx - (4x - y)^2\,dy = 0$

9. $xy(x\,dy + y\,dx) = 6y^3\,dy$; let $z = xy$; when $y = 1$, $x = \pm 2$

10. $x^2(x\,dx + y\,dy) = (x^2 + y^2)^2\,dx$; let $z = x^2 + y^2$; when $x = 1$, $y = \pm 2$

11. $(st + 1)t\,ds + (2st - 1)s\,dt = 0$; let $z = st$

12. $(x^2 + y^2)\,dx + 2xy\,dy = 0$; let $y = vx$; when $x = 2$, $y = \pm 1$

13. $(x^3 + y^3)\,dx + 3xy^2\,dy = 0$; let $y = vx$; when $x = 1$, $y = 1$

★14. $(2x + y)\,dx + (x - 2y)\,dy = 0$; let $y = vx$

15. $(5x - y)\,dx + (y - x)\,dy = 0$; let $y = vx$

16. $3\theta\dfrac{d\rho}{d\theta} + 3\rho = \rho^4\theta^4 e^\theta$; let $z = \rho\theta$

★17. $x\dfrac{dy}{dx} + 3y = 8x^5$; let $z = x^3 y$; when $x = 1$, $y = 3$

18. $2(x + y)(dx + dy) + (6x - 2y)(3\,dx - dy) = 0$; let $z = x + y$, $w = 3x - y$

19. $dx + dy = (x + y)\left(1 + \dfrac{y}{x}\right)^2 (x\,dy - y\,dx)$; let $z = x + y$, $w = \dfrac{y}{x}$

20. $(x^2 + y^2)(x\,dy + y\,dx) - xy(x\,dx + y\,dy) = 0$; let $z = x^2 + y^2$, $w = xy$

16. Homogeneous equations

A **homogeneous expression** of the nth degree in x and y is an expression such that, if x and y are replaced by tx and ty, the result will be the original expression multiplied by t^n, or, analytically expressed,

$$\mathbf{f(tx,ty) = t^n f(x,y).} \tag{1}$$

Thus, $x^2 + y^2$ is homogeneous in x and y, for $(tx)^2 + (ty)^2 = t^2(x^2 + y^2)$. In fact, *any polynomial all terms of which are of the same degree in x and y is homogeneous.* It appears also that such an expression as $\sqrt{x^2 + y^2} + y\tan^{-1}(y^2/x^2)$ is homogeneous, since

$$\sqrt{(tx)^2 + (ty)^2} + ty\tan^{-1}\frac{(ty)^2}{(tx)^2} = t\left(\sqrt{x^2 + y^2} + y\tan^{-1}\frac{y^2}{x^2}\right).$$

A useful relation is obtained by letting $t = 1/x$ in the definition expressed by (1). This gives for a homogeneous expression of the nth degree

$$\frac{1}{x^n}f(x,y) = f\left(\frac{x}{x}, \frac{y}{x}\right) = \varphi\left(\frac{y}{x}\right),$$

or

$$f(x,y) = x^n f\left(1, \frac{y}{x}\right) = x^n\varphi\left(\frac{y}{x}\right). \tag{2}$$

A differential equation

$$M\,dx + N\,dy = 0 \tag{3}$$

is homogeneous in x and y if M and N are homogeneous functions of the same degree in x and y.

Either of the substitutions, $y = vx$, or $x = vy$, will reduce any homogeneous differential equation of the first order and first degree to the type of variables separable. To prove this for the substitution $y = vx$, let n be the degree of the homogeneous differential equation and write in accordance with (2),

$$M \, dx + N \, dy = x^n \varphi_1 \left(\frac{y}{x} \right) dx + x^n \varphi_2 \left(\frac{y}{x} \right) dy = 0. \qquad (4)$$

Make the substitution

$$y = vx, \qquad dy = v \, dx + x \, dv \qquad (5)$$

in (4) and obtain

$$x^n \varphi_1(v) \, dx + x^n \varphi_2(v)(v \, dx + x \, dv) = 0. \qquad (6)$$

Dividing (6) by x^n and collecting the terms involving dx and those involving dv, we have

$$[\varphi_1(v) + v\varphi_2(v)] \, dx + x\varphi_2(v) \, dv = 0,$$

or

$$\frac{dx}{x} + \frac{\varphi_2(v) \, dv}{\varphi_1(v) + v\varphi_2(v)} = 0, \qquad (7)$$

and the variables are separated.

Example. Solve $(x^2 + y^2) \, dx - 2xy \, dy = 0$.

Solution. Since the equation is homogeneous, write

$$y = vx, \qquad dy = v \, dx + x \, dv.$$

Substituting these values for y and dy in the equation, we get

$$(x^2 + v^2x^2) \, dx - 2vx^2(v \, dx + x \, dv) = 0.$$

Collecting coefficients of dx and dv, we obtain

$$(x^2 + v^2x^2 - 2v^2x^2) \, dx - 2vx^3 \, dv = 0,$$

or

$$x^2(1 - v^2) \, dx - 2vx^3 \, dv = 0.$$

Division by $x^3(1 - v^2)$ gives

$$\frac{dx}{x} - \frac{2v \, dv}{1 - v^2} = 0.$$

Integrating this, we obtain

$$\log x + \log (1 - v^2) = \log c, \qquad \text{or} \qquad x(1 - v^2) = c.$$

Replacing v by its equal y/x, we have

$$x \left(1 - \frac{y^2}{x^2} \right) = c, \qquad \text{or} \qquad \mathbf{x^2 - y^2 = cx}.$$

EXERCISES

1. Show that each expression is homogeneous:

(a) $x^2 + 8xy - 10y^2$ (b) $x^3 + y^3 - 3x^2 y$

(c) $x^n + 3x^{n-k} y^k + y^n$ (d) $x^2 \sin \dfrac{y}{x} + y^2 \cos \dfrac{y}{x} + xy \log \dfrac{x+y}{x-y}$

Solve the following differential equations and determine constants of integration when initial conditions are given:

2. $(2x - y)\,dx - (2y + x)\,dy = 0$
3. $(3x + y)\,dx + x\,dy = 0$
4. $(4x + 3y)\,dx + (3x - 2y)\,dy = 0$
5. $(5x^2 - 7y^2)\,dx - 14xy\,dy = 0$
6. $(\theta + 2\rho)\,d\theta + (2\theta - 6\rho)\,d\rho = 0$
7. $xy^2\,dy - (x^3 + y^3)\,dx = 0$; $y = 0$ when $x = 1$
8. $(2xy + y^2)\,dx - 2x^2\,dy = 0$; $y = e$ when $x = e$
9. $(4xy + x^2)\,dy - 4y^2\,dx = 0$; $x = e$ when $y = e$
10. $2xy\,dx + (4y^2 - x^2)\,dy = 0$
11. $(x^2 + xy)\,dy + (y^2 - xy)\,dx = 0$
12. $y(x^2 + y^2)\,dx + (2x^3 - xy^2)\,dy = 0$
13. $(3x^2 y - 2xy^2)\,dx + (4x^2 y - 5x^3)\,dy = 0$
14. $y(x^2 + xy - 2y^2)\,dx + x(3y^2 - xy - x^2)\,dy = 0$
15. $(xy + 3y^2)\,dx + (3y^2 - x^2)\,dy = 0$
16. $x\,dy - y\,dx = \sqrt{x^2 + y^2}\,dx$
17. $x \cos \dfrac{y}{x} \dfrac{dy}{dx} = y \cos \dfrac{y}{x} - x$
18. $\left(x + y \cos \dfrac{y}{x}\right) dx - x \cos \dfrac{y}{x}\,dy = 0$

19. Show that a straight line through the origin intersects at a constant angle all integral curves of a homogeneous differential equation.
20. Find the orthogonal trajectories of the circles $x^2 + y^2 + 2cx = 0$.
21. Find the equation of all curves that cut the circles $x^2 + y^2 = r^2$ at an angle of 45 deg.
22. Show that an equation of the type $\varphi(y)\,dy + x^n \psi(x/y)(x\,dy - y\,dx) = 0$ can be transformed by the substitution $x = vy$ to one of the type *variables separable*.

17. Equations of the form $(ax + by + c)\,dx + (\alpha x + \beta y + \gamma)\,dy = 0$ omit

To solve this type of equation, make the substitution

$$x = x' + h,\ y = y' + k,\qquad dx = dx',\ dy = dy',\qquad (8)$$

to obtain

$$(ax' + by' + ah + bk + c)\,dx' + (\alpha x' + \beta y' + \alpha h + \beta k + \gamma)\,dy' = 0. \qquad (9)$$

If we now choose h and k so that

$$ah + bk + c = 0,\quad \alpha h + \beta k + \gamma = 0, \qquad (10)$$

the equation (9) in x' and y' becomes homogeneous. We then apply the method for solving homogeneous equations and replace, in the resulting solution, the new variables in terms of the old.

The method just described breaks down if $a/b = \alpha/\beta$. In this case the substitution $z = ax + by$, or $z = \alpha x + \beta y$, will give rise to an equation in which the variables are separable.

Example. Solve $(2x - 3y + 4)\,dx + (3x - 2y + 1)\,dy = 0$.

Solution. Substituting $x = x' + h$, $y = y' + k$ in the given equation, we obtain

$$(2x' - 3y' + 2h - 3k + 4)\,dx' + (3x' - 2y' + 3h - 2k + 1)\,dy' = 0. \tag{a}$$

Let $2h - 3k + 4 = 0$, and $3h - 2k + 1 = 0$. Then $h = 1$ and $k = 2$, and the equation (a) reduces to

$$(2x' - 3y')\,dx' + (3x' - 2y')\,dy' = 0. \tag{b}$$

Solving this homogeneous equation and simplifying, we get

$$(y' + x')^5 = c(y' - x'). \tag{c}$$

Since $x = x' + h = x' + 1$, $y = y' + k = y' + 2$, we have

$$x' = x - 1, \qquad y' = y - 2. \tag{d}$$

Substituting the values of x' and y' from (d) in (c), we obtain

$$\mathbf{(x + y - 3)^5 = c(y - x - 1).}$$

EXERCISES

Solve the following differential equations:

1. $(x - 2y + 5)\,dx + (2x - y + 4)\,dy = 0$
2. $(2x + 3y - 1)\,dx - 4(x + 1)\,dy = 0$
3. $(2x + 3y)\,dx + (y + 2)\,dy = 0$
4. $(2x + y)\,dx - (4x + 2y - 1)\,dy = 0$.   *Hint:* Let $z = 2x + y$
5. $(2x - y + 2)\,dx + (4x - 2y - 1)\,dy = 0$
6. $(4x + 3y - 4)\,dx + (3x - 7y - 3)\,dy = 0$
7. $(2x - 2y)\,dx + (y - 1)\,dy = 0$

18. Exact differential equation

The formula for the total differential of a function $f(x,y)$ is

$$df(x,y) = \frac{\partial f}{\partial x}\,dx + \frac{\partial f}{\partial y}\,dy. \tag{11}$$

Any expression that is exactly the total differential of some function of x and y is called an exact differential, and such an expression equated to *zero is an exact differential equation.*   For example, in accordance with (11),

$$d(x^2 + 8x^2y - 10y^3) = (2x + 16xy)\,dx + (8x^2 - 30y^2)\,dy$$

is an exact differential, and

$$(2x + 16xy)\,dx + (8x^2 - 30y^2)\,dy = 0$$

is an exact differential equation.

EXERCISES

1. Find the total differential of each expression:

(a) $x^3 - xy^2 - 4x^2y$ (b) $5 \log (xy) + 12$ (c) $x^4y^4 + \sin x$

2. Form an exact differential equation from each of the following expressions by equating its total differential to zero:

(a) $x^3y - y^2$ (b) $x^2 - y^2 - \log y^3$ (c) $ax^2 + bxy$

3. If M represents the coefficient of dx and N that of dy in each of the answers to exercise 2, show that $\partial M/\partial y = \partial N/\partial x$ in each case.

4. Each of the following expressions is an exact differential.   In each case find a function of x and y which has the given expression as its total derivative:

(a) $(2x + y)\,dx + (x - 2y)\,dy$
(b) $(2x + y)\,dx + (x - 3y^2 - 3)\,dy$
(c) $(3x^2 - 2xy)\,dx + (4y^3 - x^2 + 3)\,dy$
(d) $(2x + \tan y)\,dx + (x \sec^2 y - 3y^2)\,dy$

19. Condition that a differential be exact

From (11) it appears that an expression

$$M\,dx + N\,dy \tag{12}$$

is exact, if there exists a function $f(x,y)$ such that

$$M = \frac{\partial f}{\partial x}, \qquad N = \frac{\partial f}{\partial y}.* \tag{13}$$

From (13) we obtain

$$\frac{\partial M}{\partial y} = \frac{\partial^2 f}{\partial y\,\partial x}, \qquad \frac{\partial N}{\partial x} = \frac{\partial^2 f}{\partial x\,\partial y}.$$

---

* It is assumed that M, N, and their partial derivatives of the first and second orders are continuous.

Since $\dfrac{\partial^2 f}{\partial y\,\partial x} = \dfrac{\partial^2 f}{\partial x\,\partial y}$, it appears that

$$\frac{\partial M}{\partial y} = \frac{\partial N}{\partial x} \tag{14}$$

is a necessary condition that (12) *be an exact differential.*

Conversely, we shall show that, *if* (14) *holds, then* (12) *must be an exact differential*, by finding a function $f(x,y)$ whose differential is $M\,dx + N\,dy$, that is, a function f such that

$$\frac{\partial f}{\partial x} = M, \qquad \frac{\partial f}{\partial y} = N. \tag{15}$$

If the first equation of (15) holds,

$$f = \int^x M\,dx + \varphi(y), \tag{16}$$

where $\varphi(y)$ does not contain x and the superscript x means that y is to be held constant during the integration. Substituting the value of f from (16) in the second part of (15), we obtain

$$\frac{\partial f}{\partial y} = \frac{\partial}{\partial y} \int^x M\,dx + \frac{d\varphi}{dy} = N, \tag{17}$$

or

$$\frac{d\varphi}{dy} = N - \frac{\partial}{\partial y} \int^x M\,dx. \tag{18}$$

Since the partial derivative with respect to x of the right member of (18) is $(\partial N/\partial x) - (\partial M/\partial y)$, it is zero because of (14). Therefore the right member of (18) does not contain x. Hence we find, by integrating (18), that

$$\varphi = \int \left(N - \frac{\partial}{\partial y} \int^x M\,dx \right) dy. \tag{19}$$

Substituting φ from (19) in (16), we have

$$f(x,y) = \int^x M\,dx + \int \left(N - \frac{\partial}{\partial y} \int^x M\,dx \right) dy. \tag{20}$$

This value of f satisfies (15) provided (14) is true.

20. Solution of exact differential equations

From §19, it appears that an equation

$$M\,dx + N\,dy = 0 \tag{21}$$

is exact if

$$\frac{\partial M}{\partial y} = \frac{\partial N}{\partial x}, \tag{22}$$

and a general solution of (21) is

$$f(x,y) = \int^x M\, dx + \int \left(N - \frac{\partial}{\partial y} \int^x M\, dx \right) dy = c, \tag{23}$$

where the superscript x indicates that y is to be considered constant in the integration.

An exact differential equation can be solved by substituting for M and N in (23) their values from the given equation and carrying out the integrations. The second integral in (23) often consists of the sum of the integrals of those terms in N which do not contain x. This will always be true when M and N are polynomials. The following procedure is effective:

To integrate a differential equation $M\, dx + N\, dy = 0$ for which $\partial M/\partial y = \partial N/\partial x$, equate to a constant the sum of the integral of M with respect to x and the integrals of the terms in $N\, dy$ which do not contain x; if the derivative of the result does not give $M\, dx + N\, dy = 0$, use (23).

Example 1. Solve $(2x + y^{-1})\, dx + (y^{-1} - xy^{-2})\, dy = 0$.

Solution. Here $M = 2x + y^{-1}$, $N = y^{-1} - xy^{-2}$, and

$$\frac{\partial M}{\partial y} = -y^{-2}, \qquad \frac{\partial N}{\partial x} = -y^{-2},$$

that is, $\partial M/\partial y = \partial N/\partial x$, and the equation is exact. In accordance with the rule, the solution is

$$\int^x (2x + y^{-1})\, dx + \int y^{-1}\, dy = c,$$

or

$$x^2 + xy^{-1} + \log y = c. \tag{a}$$

From this we obtain by differentiation the original equation, and therefore (a) is the required solution.

Example 2. Solve $(3x^2 + 2y \sin 2x)\, dx + (2 \sin^2 x + 3y^2)\, dy = 0$.

Solution. Here $\partial M/\partial y = \partial N/\partial x = 2 \sin 2x$. Hence the equation is exact. The first part of the italicized statement does not yield a correct answer; hence use (23). Substituting M and N from the given equation in (23) and noting that $\int^x (3x^2 + 2y \sin 2x)\, dx = x^3 - y \cos 2x$, obtain

$$x^3 - y \cos 2x + \int \left[2 \sin^2 x + 3y^2 - \frac{\partial}{\partial y} (x^3 - y \cos 2x) \right] dy = c. \quad (a)$$

The integral in (a) gives $y^3 + y$. Substitute $y^3 + y$ for the integral in (a) to obtain

$$\mathbf{x^3 - y \cos 2x + y^3 + y = c.}$$

EXERCISES

Test the differential equations numbered 1 to 18 for exactness by using (14), and solve.

1. $(2x - y + 5) \, dx + (2y - x) \, dy = 0$
2. $(3x^2 + 3xy^2) \, dx + (3x^2y - 3y^2 + 2) \, dy = 0$
3. $(x^2 + y^2) \, dx + (2xy + 3y - 1) \, dy = 0$
4. $(a^2 - 2xy - y^2) \, dx - (x + y)^2 \, dy = 0$
5. $(2ax + by + g) \, dx + (2cy + bx + e) \, dy = 0$
6. $\rho^2 \sec 2\theta \tan 2\theta \, d\theta + \rho(\sec 2\theta + 2) \, d\rho = 0$
7. $(\sin 2\theta - 2\rho \cos 2\theta) \, d\rho + (2\rho \cos 2\theta + 2\rho^2 \sin 2\theta) \, d\theta = 0$
8. $\dfrac{1}{y} \, dx - \dfrac{x}{y^2} \, dy = 0$
9. $\dfrac{y \, dx - x \, dy}{x^2} = 0$
10. $\dfrac{my \, dx + nx \, dy}{xy} = 0$
11. $\dfrac{my \, dx - nx \, dy}{xy} = 0$
12. $(\tan y + x) \, dx + (x \sec^2 y - 3y) \, dy = 0$
13. $(\sec x \tan x - y) \, dx + (\sec y \tan y - x + 2) \, dy = 0$
14. $(2xy + y^2) \, dx + \dfrac{x^2y + 2xy^2 + 1}{y} \, dy = 0$
15. $\dfrac{x \, dy - y \, dx}{y^2} = x^3 \, dx$
16. $\dfrac{dx}{\sqrt{x^2 + y^2}} + \left(\dfrac{1}{y} - \dfrac{x}{y \sqrt{x^2 + y^2}} \right) dy = 0$
17. $\dfrac{y^2 - 2x^2}{xy^2 - x^3} \, dx + \dfrac{2y^2 - x^2}{y^3 - x^2y} \, dy = 0$
18. $\sin 2x \cos^2 y \, dx + \cos^2 x \sin 2y \, dy = 0$
19. Prove that the equation

$$[f(x) + \varphi(y)] \, dx + \left[x \frac{d\varphi(y)}{dy} + \psi(y) \right] dy = 0$$

is exact provided all derivatives involved are continuous.

21. Integrating factors

If, when a differential equation is multiplied through by an expression, the result is an exact differential equation, then the expression is said to be an **integrating factor** of the differential equation.

Integrating factors of many differential equations may be found by recognizing certain groups as differentials of known expressions. Since $d(y/x) = (x\,dy - y\,dx)/x^2$, it appears that $1/x^2$ is an integrating factor of

$$x\,dy - y\,dx + f(x)\,dx = 0,$$

and the solution is

$$\frac{y}{x} + \int \frac{f(x)}{x^2}\,dx = c.$$

Similarly $1/y^2$ is an integrating factor of

$$x\,dy - y\,dx + f(y)\,dy = 0,$$

and its solution is

$$-\frac{x}{y} + \int \frac{f(y)\,dy}{y^2} = c.$$

In fact, division of $x\,dy - y\,dx$ by x^2, y^2, $x^2 + y^2$, or $x^2 - y^2$ gives an exact differential, as may be seen by inspection or by applying test (14) of §19. Other simple exact differentials are $x\,dy + y\,dx = d(xy)$ and $x\,dx + y\,dy = d[(x^2 + y^2)/2]$. Hence the group $x\,dy - y\,dx$ suggests as integrating factors $\dfrac{1}{x^2}, \dfrac{1}{y^2}, \dfrac{1}{xy}, \dfrac{1}{x^2 \pm y^2}$, the group $x\,dy + y\,dx$ suggests some function of xy; and the group $x\,dx + y\,dy$ suggests a function of $x^2 + y^2$.

From time to time, integrating factors applying to special cases will be given.

It is worthy of note that the differential expressions here considered suggest substitutions; thus, $x\,dy - y\,dx$ suggests the substitution $z = y/x$, $x\,dx + y\,dy$ suggests $z = x^2 + y^2$, etc.

Example 1. Solve $x\,dy + y\,dx = x^2y\,dy$.

Solution. $1/x^2y^2$ is observed to be an integrating factor. Multiplying the equation through by this, we have

$$\frac{x\,dy + y\,dx}{(xy)^2} = \frac{x^2y\,dy}{x^2y^2}.$$

As this equation is exact, we can solve it as such, or we may write it

$$\frac{d(xy)}{(xy)^2} = \frac{dy}{y}.$$

Integrating this, we have

$$\frac{-1}{xy} = \log cy, \qquad \text{or} \qquad \textbf{xy log cy + 1 = 0.}$$

Example 2.   Solve $(x^2y + x)\, dy + (xy^2 - y)\, dx = 0.$

Solution.   This equation may be written

$$x\, dy - y\, dx + xy(x\, dy + y\, dx) = 0.$$

Hence $1/xy$ is an integrating factor, and the solution is

$$\textbf{log y} - \textbf{log x} + \textbf{xy} = \textbf{c}.$$

Example 3. Solve $y\, dx - x\, dy = x^3 \sqrt{x^2 - y^2}\, dx.$

Solution.   If we write this in the form

$$y\, dx - x\, dy = x^4 \sqrt{1 - \left(\frac{y}{x}\right)^2}\, dx,$$

it appears that $1 \div [x^2 \sqrt{1 - (y/x)^2}]$ is an integrating factor.   Multiplying by this, we get

$$\frac{(y\, dx - x\, dy)/x^2}{\sqrt{1 - (y/x)^2}} = \frac{-d(y/x)}{\sqrt{1 - (y/x)^2}} = x^2\, dx.$$

Therefore

$$-\sin^{-1}\frac{y}{x} = \frac{x^3}{3} - c, \qquad \text{or} \qquad \textbf{sin}^{-1}\frac{\textbf{y}}{\textbf{x}} = \textbf{c} - \frac{\textbf{x}^3}{3}.^*$$

EXERCISES

Solve each of the equations numbered 1 to 6 by using integrating factors:

1. $x\, dy + y\, dx = x^3 y\, dx$
2. $x\, dx + y\, dy = y^2(x^2 + y^2)\, dy$
3. $x\, dy - y\, dx = (xy)x^2\, dx$
4. $x\, dy - y\, dx = (x^2 - 3)\, dx$
5. $x\, dy - y\, dx = y^3(x^2 + y^2)\, dy$
6. $x\, dy + y\, dx = x^m y^n\, dx,\ m \neq n - 1$

7. Prove that x^2 is an integrating factor of $x(dy/dx) + 3y = x$ and solve.

8. Prove that x^{-4} is an integrating factor of $(x^3 + y^3)\, dx - xy^2\, dy = 0$ and solve.

9. Solve $x\, dy - y\, dx = x\, dx + y\, dy.$

10. Solve $x\, dy - y\, dx = (x^2 + y^2)^2(x\, dx + y\, dy).$

11. If the differential equation $M\, dx + N\, dy = 0$ is homogeneous, then

$$\frac{1}{xM + yN}$$

is an integrating factor.   Use this fact to solve the equations:

(a) $(y^2 - xy)\, dx + x^2\, dy = 0$ (b) $(x^3 - y^3)\, dx + xy^2\, dy = 0$
(c) $(x^2 - xy + y^2)\, dx + (x^2 - xy)\, dy = 0$

* Because of the fact that $\sqrt{1 - (y/x)^2}$ must be positive, any solution involving a value of c and ranges of values of x must satisfy the condition $\cos (c - \tfrac{1}{3}x^3) > 0.$

12. $d(x^m y^n) = mx^{m-1}y^n\, dx + nx^m y^{n-1}\, dy = x^{m-1}y^{n-1}(my\, dx + nx\, dy)$.   Hence an expression $nx\, dy + my\, dx$ occurring in a differential equation suggests the substitution $z = x^m y^n$.   For example, to solve equation (a) below, make the substitution $z = x^3 y^2$, and eliminate y (or x) to obtain an equation in z and x (or y) of the type variables separable.   Solve the following differential equations:

(a) $3y\, dx + 2x\, dy = xy\, dx$ (b) $3y\, dx + 2x\, dy = x^4 y^4\, dy$
(c) $5y\, dx + 3x\, dy = x^4 y^7\, dx$ (d) $3yx^2\, dx - 4x^3\, dy = 7y^{11}\, dy$

★13. Prove that x^k is an integrating factor of $M\, dx + N\, dy = 0$ when $(\partial M / \partial y) - (\partial N / \partial x) = Nk/x$.   Use this fact to solve:

(a) $(y^4 + x^3)\, dx + 8xy^3\, dy = 0$
(b) $(5x^3 + 3xy + 2y^2)\, dx + (x^2 + 2xy)\, dy = 0$

★14. Prove that $e^{-\int f(y)\, dy}$ is an integrating factor of $M\, dx + N\, dy = 0$ if $(\partial M / \partial y) - (\partial N / \partial x) = Mf(y)$.   Use this fact to solve:

(a) $x^2 y^2\, dx + (x^3 y + y + 3)\, dy = 0$
(b) $(x^2 y + y^3)\, dx - (x^3 + xy^2 + 2y)\, dy = 0$
(c) $x^2\, dx - (x^3 y^2 + 3y^2)\, dy = 0$

★15. Find an integrating factor of $M\, dx + N\, dy = 0$ if $(\partial M / \partial y) - (\partial N / \partial x) = Nf(x)$.   Then solve

$$(xy^2 + x^2 y^2 + 3)\, dx + x^2 y\, dy = 0.$$

16. It can be shown that every equation of the form

$$yf_1(xy)\, dx + xf_2(xy)\, dy = 0$$

has $1 \div xy[f_1(xy) - f_2(xy)]$ as an integrating factor.   Make use of this fact to solve

(a) $(1 + x^2 y^2)x\, dy + (x^2 y^2 - 1)y\, dx = 0$
(b) $x^3 y^4\, dx - (x^2 y - x^4 y^3)\, dy = 0$
(c) $y(xy + 2x^2 y^2)\, dx + x(xy - x^2 y^2)\, dy = 0$

★17. Prove the statement made in exercise 16 by test (14) of §19.

22. Linear differential equation

A differential equation of any order is said to be **linear** *when it is of the first degree in the dependent variable and its derivatives.*   It follows that a general type of linear differential equation of the *first order* is

$$\frac{dy}{dx} + Py = Q, \tag{24}$$

where P and Q are functions of x only.*

To find an integrating factor of (24), let us solve

$$\frac{dy}{dx} + Py = 0, \quad \text{or} \quad \frac{dy}{y} = -P\, dx. \tag{25}$$

* This equation is involved in many useful applications.

Here the variables are separated, and the solution is

$$y = ce^{-\int P\,dx}, \quad \text{or} \quad ye^{\int P\,dx} = c. \tag{26}$$

The differential of the left-hand member of (26) is $e^{\int P\,dx}(dy + Py\,dx)$. It appears then that, if (24) is multiplied by $e^{\int P\,dx}\,dx$, the left-hand member will be an exact differential and the right-hand member will contain x only. Hence, multiplying (24) by $e^{\int P\,dx}\,dx$, we obtain the exact equation

$$e^{\int P\,dx}(dy + Py\,dx) = Qe^{\int P\,dx}\,dx. \tag{27}$$

The solution of (27), and therefore of (24), is

$$ye^{\int P\,dx} = \int Qe^{\int P\,dx}\,dx + c. \tag{28}$$

Hence, to solve an equation having the form (24), *either substitute in form* (28), *or multiply by $e^{\int P\,dx}$ and integrate the result as an exact differential equation.*

Example 1. Solve $x(dy/dx) + 2y = x^3$.

Solution. Division by x gives

$$\frac{dy}{dx} + \frac{2}{x}y = x^2.$$

This has the form (24), and

$$Q = x^2, \quad P = \frac{2}{x}, \quad e^{\int P\,dx} = e^{2\int dx/x} = e^{\log x^2} = x^2.$$

Substituting these values in (28), we obtain

$$yx^2 = \int x^2 \cdot x^2\,dx + \frac{c}{5} = \frac{x^5}{5} + \frac{c}{5},$$

or

$$5yx^2 = x^5 + c.$$

Example 2. Solve $(dy/dx) + y\cot x = \csc x$.

Solution. Multiplying by the integrating factor $e^{\int P\,dx} = e^{\int \cot x\,dx} = e^{\log \sin x} = \sin x$, we obtain

$$\sin x \frac{dy}{dx} + y\cos x = 1.$$

Since this is exact, we write the answer by the method of §20,

$$y\sin x = x + c.$$

EXERCISES

Solve each of the following differential equations and, when initial conditions are indicated, find the particular solution satisfied by them:

1. $\dfrac{dy}{dx} + \dfrac{1}{x} y = x^3 - 3$

2. $\dfrac{dy}{dx} + \dfrac{2}{x} y = x^2 + 2$

3. $x\dfrac{dy}{dx} - 2y = x^2 + x; \ y = 1$ when $x = 1$

4. $\dfrac{dy}{dx} - y \tan x = 3e^{-\sin x}; \ y = 4$ when $x = 0$

5. $x^2\, dy - \sin 2x\, dx + 3xy\, dx = 0$

6. $\dfrac{dy}{dx} - my = ae^{nx}, \ m \neq n$

7. $\dfrac{dy}{dx} - my = ae^{mx}$

8. $\dfrac{dx}{dy} - \dfrac{4x}{y} = y^5; \ x = 4$ when $y = 1$

9. $dy(1 + 2x \cot y) = dx$

10. $t\, ds - (3t + 1)s\, dt = t^3 e^{3t}\, dt$

11. $\dfrac{dy}{dx} - xy = xe^{x^2}; \ y = 5$ when $x = 0$

12. $(x + 2y)\, dx + dy = 0; \ y = -1$ when $x = 0$

13. $(1 + x^2)\, dy - a\, dx = xy\, dx; \ y = 2a$ when $x = 0$

14. $x(1 - x^2)\, dy - ax^3\, dx = (2x^2 - 1)y\, dx$

15. $(\sin 2\theta - 2\rho \cos \theta)\, d\theta = 2\, d\rho$

16. $x^2\dfrac{dy}{dx} = x^2 + 2xy - y$

17. $(1 + x)\, dy = (xy + a)\, dx$

18. $f(x)\dfrac{dy}{dx} + f'(x)y = f'(x)$

19. $f(x)\dfrac{dy}{dx} + 3f'(x)y = [f(x)]^3 f'(x)$

23. Equations reducible to linear form

The equation

$$\frac{dy}{dx} + Py = Qy^n, \qquad (29)$$

where P and Q are functions of x only, is named *Bernoulli's equation*, after James Bernoulli, who studied it in 1695. To solve it,* we first divide by y^n and obtain

* Also the equation is readily solved by the method indicated in exercise 11 of this article.

$$y^{-n}\frac{dy}{dx} + Py^{1-n} = Q. \tag{30}$$

This form suggests the substitution

$$v = y^{1-n}, \qquad \frac{dv}{dx} = (1 - n)y^{-n}\frac{dy}{dx}. \tag{31}$$

Substituting from (31) in (30), we get

$$\frac{1}{1-n}\frac{dv}{dx} + Pv = Q, \tag{32}$$

a linear equation. *Hence, to solve an equation of type* (29), *make the substitution* (31) *and then proceed as in the case of the linear equation.*

Example. Solve $(dy/dx) - (2/x)y = y^4$.

Solution. Multiplying by $-3y^{-4}$, we get

$$-3y^{-4}\frac{dy}{dx} + \frac{6}{x}y^{-3} = -3.$$

Substituting $v = y^{-3}$, $dv/dx = -3y^{-4}\,dy/dx$, we obtain

$$\frac{dv}{dx} + \frac{6}{x}v = -3.$$

The solution of this equation by means of (28) is

$$ve^{6\,\log x} = vx^6 = \int -3x^6\,dx + c = -\tfrac{3}{7}x^7 + c.$$

Simplifying and replacing v by y^{-3}, we get

$$\mathbf{y}^{-3} = -\tfrac{3}{7}\mathbf{x} + \mathbf{cx}^{-6}.$$

EXERCISES

Solve each of the following differential equations and determine the constant of integration when initial conditions are given:

1. $2\dfrac{dy}{dx} - \dfrac{y}{x} = 5x^3y^3$

2. $3\dfrac{dy}{dx} + \dfrac{3}{x}y = 2x^4y^4$

3. $\dfrac{dy}{dx} + y = 12e^{2x}y^2$

4. $3\dfrac{dy}{dx} + \dfrac{1}{x+1}y = 3(x+1)y^{-2}$

5. $\dfrac{dy}{dx} - 4xy = 16xe^{3x^2}\sqrt{y}$

6. $\dfrac{dy}{dx} + y^2 = \dfrac{y}{x}$; $y = 1$ when $x = 1$

7. $x\dfrac{dy}{dx} + y = y^2 x \log x$; $y = 2$ when $x = 1$

8. $y - \cos x \dfrac{dy}{dx} = y^2 \cos x(1 - \sin x)$; $y = 2$ when $x = 0$

9. $\dfrac{dx}{dy} - xy = x^2 y^3$; $y = 0$ when $x = 1$

10. $(x + myx^3)\, dy = dx$

★11. Show that $y^{-n}e^{(1-n)\int P\,dx}$ is an integrating factor of (29). Use this fact to integrate the equations of exercises 1 to 5.

24. Simultaneous equations

Two differential equations in three variables often arise in applications. Only pairs of equations that can be solved by means of the theory already developed will be considered at this time. Two equations,

$$A_1\, dx + A_2\, dy + A_3\, dt = 0, \left.\vphantom{\begin{matrix}a\\b\end{matrix}}\right\}$$
$$B_1\, dx + B_2\, dy + B_3\, dt = 0, \tag{33}$$

where the A's and B's represent functions of x, y, and t, have solutions consisting of two relations of the form

$$f_1(x,y,t,c_1,c_2) = 0, \qquad f_2(x,y,t,c_1,c_2) = 0. \tag{34}$$

One relation is generally found by eliminating one of the variables from the given equations and solving the resulting equation in two unknowns by methods already considered. When one relation has been found, it may be used with the given differential equations to find others. Of course, if an equation contains all three variables but separated so that no term contains more than one variable or, more generally, if an equation is exact, it may be integrated directly to obtain one of the required equations. Thus from $2x\, dx + 2y\, dy + 2t\, dt = 0$, obtain $x^2 + y^2 + t^2 = c$.

Example 1. Solve

$$\dfrac{dx}{dt} + y = x, \qquad \dfrac{dy}{dt} = 3y. \tag{a}$$

Solution. Since there are only two variables in the second equation, we solve it to obtain

$$y = c_1 e^{3t}. \tag{b}$$

Substituting y from (b) in the first of (a), we obtain

$$\dfrac{dx}{dt} + c_1 e^{3t} = x. \tag{c}$$

Since (c) is a linear equation in two variables, we solve it by §22 to find

$$xe^{-t} = \frac{-c_1}{2} e^{2t} + c_2. \tag{d}$$

Rewriting equations (b) and (d) slightly simplified, we have

$$y = c_1 e^{3t}, \qquad x = -\tfrac{1}{2} c_1 e^{3t} + c_2 e^t.$$

Example 2. Solve

$$\frac{dx}{dt} + t \frac{dy}{dt} = 2t, \qquad t \frac{dx}{dt} - \frac{dy}{dt} = -x. \tag{a}$$

Solution. To eliminate y multiply the second equation of (a) by t and add the result to the first and obtain

$$(1 + t^2) \frac{dx}{dt} = -tx + 2t. \tag{b}$$

Equation (b) may be solved by separating the variables. The solution is

$$\log (x - 2) = \log c_1 (1 + t^2)^{-\frac{1}{2}}$$

or

$$x = 2 + c_1 (1 + t^2)^{-\frac{1}{2}}. \tag{c}$$

Substituting x from (c) in the first of (a), we get

$$-c_1 t (1 + t^2)^{-\frac{3}{2}} + t \frac{dy}{dt} = 2t. \tag{d}$$

Separating the variables in (d) and integrating, we find

$$y = 2t + \frac{c_1 t}{\sqrt{1 + t^2}} + c_2. \tag{e}$$

Equations (c) and (e) constitute the solution.

EXERCISES

1. $\dfrac{dx}{dt} - 2t = 0, \dfrac{dy}{dt} - x + t^2 = 0$

2. $\dfrac{dy}{dt} + y = e^{-t}, \dfrac{dx}{dt} + y = te^{-t}$

3. $\dfrac{dx}{dt} = 1000, \dfrac{dy}{dt} = 0.5 \dfrac{dx}{dt} - 16t$

4. $\dfrac{d\rho}{dt} + \rho = e^t, \dfrac{d\theta}{dt} = \rho$

5. $(t - 1) \dfrac{dx}{dt} + \dfrac{dy}{dt} = 6t^2, \dfrac{dx}{dt} - \dfrac{dy}{dt} = x$

6. $x\,dt + t\,dx = 2t\,dt,\ \dfrac{dx}{dt} + \dfrac{dy}{dt} = x - t$

7. $(x^2 + t^2)\,dt - xt\,dx = 0,\ t\dfrac{dy}{dt} = x^2 t + y$

8. $t\dfrac{dx}{dt} + \dfrac{dy}{dt} = 4(t^2 + 1)e^t,\ \dfrac{dx}{dt} - t\dfrac{dy}{dt} = 4(t^2 + 1)e^{2t}$

9. $\dfrac{d\rho}{\rho} = \dfrac{d\theta}{\rho + \theta + t} = \dfrac{dt}{t}$

10. $dx + ay\,dt = 0,\ dy - ax\,dt = 0$

25. Summary

In solving a differential equation of the form $M\,dx + N\,dy = 0$, the student will often find it helpful to proceed, until a method of solution is found, as follows:

I. Consider whether the equation comes under the case of

(*a*) Variables separable (§6).
(*b*) M and N homogeneous and of the same degree (§16).
(*c*) Linear equation (§22).
(*d*) Reducible to linear equation (§23).
(*e*) Exact differential equation (§20).
(*f*) M and N linear but not homogeneous (§17).

II. Search for an integrating factor (§21).

III. Make a substitution and consider the result under headings I and II (§15).

At present we have studied a few important special types of the differential equation having the form $M\,dx + N\,dy = 0$. It may be of interest to consider what remains to be done with this form. The result of multiplying this equation by $\mu(x,y)$ will be exact, provided $\partial(\mu M)/\partial y = \partial(\mu N)/\partial x$. In Chapter XII, §93, we shall learn how to solve this partial differential equation for μ in terms of x and y. Not only will this furnish a general method of attack, but also it will enable us to make up types of equations that are readily solvable. In Chapter XI, two of the many methods of approximating a particular solution of a differential equation are explained. Also, in Chapter XI the method of integration in infinite series is considered. This method may be applied to solve a great variety of differential equations.

EXERCISES

Solve each of the following differential equations and determine the constant of integration when initial conditions are given:

1. $x^2 \, dy + y^2 \, dx = x^2 y \, dy - xy^2 \, dx$

2. $(x^2 + 3) \dfrac{dy}{dx} + 2xy + 5x^2 = 0$

3. $(5x^2 + y^2) \, dx + 2x^2 \, dy = 0$

4. $(y + x)^2 \dfrac{dy}{dx} = 2(y + x)^2 - 3$

5. $\cos x \, dy + 3y \sin x \, dx - 2 \cos^2 x \, dx = 0$

6. $(xy^2 + y) \, dx - x \, dy = 0$

7. $(3x^2 + 2xy) \, dx + (x^2 + \cos y) \, dy = 0; \; y = \dfrac{\pi}{2}$ when $x = 0$

8. $y^2 + x^2 \dfrac{dy}{dx} = xy \dfrac{dy}{dx}; \; y = 1$ when $x = 1$

9. $y \, dx + x \, dy = xy(dx + dy)$

10. $x^2 \, dy^2 - y^4 \, dx^2 = 0$

11. $xy \left(\dfrac{dy}{dx} \right)^2 - (2x^2 + y^2) \dfrac{dy}{dx} + 2xy = 0.$ *Hint:* Solve for $\dfrac{dy}{dx}$

12. $2x^3 y \, dx + x^2 y^2 \, dy = y \, dx + x^2 \, dy; \; y = 1$ when $x = 1$

13. $(xy + 1)(x \, dy - y \, dx) = y^2(x \, dy + y \, dx); \; y = 2$ when $x = 1$

14. $y^2 \, dx + y \, dy = 2 \cos x \, dx; \; y = 0$ when $x = \dfrac{\pi}{2}$

15. $x \, dy = (xy^2 - 3y) \, dx; \; y = 2$ when $x = 2$

16. $(2x + 3y - 1) \, dx = (5 - 2x - 3y) \, dy$

17. $(x^2 y + y^3) \, dx - 2x^3 \, dy = 0; \; y = 3$ when $x = 2$

18. $(x^3 - x) \dfrac{dy}{dx} = (x^2 + 1)y + 12x(x^2 - 1)^3; \; y = 9$ when $x = 2$

19. $[6x(x + 2y) + a^2] \, dy + (12xy + 6y^2 + b^2) \, dx = 0$

20. $\left(\dfrac{1}{x} + \dfrac{2y}{x^2 - 1} \right) dx + \left(\log \dfrac{x - 1}{x + 1} + \dfrac{1}{y} \right) dy = 0$

21. $(x + y - 3) \, dx + (x + y + 5) \, dy = 0; \; y = 0$ when $x = 1$

22. $(5x + 4y + 4) \, dx + (4x + 3y + 1) \, dy = 0$

23. $4(x^2 - y)^3(2x \, dx - dy) = 3(x^2 - y^2)^{-\frac{1}{2}}(x \, dx - y \, dy)$

24. Using the principles of exercises 14 and 15 in §21, solve the following differential equations:

(a) $(2x - y) \, dx + (x^2 y - y^2 x - x) \, dy = 0$

(b) $(6xy + 6x^2 y + 2x) \, dx + 3x^2 \, dy = 0$

(c) $(2xy + 1) \, dx + x(x + xy + 1) \, dy = 0$

(d) $(6x^2 y + 2xy + 3y^2) \, dx + (x^2 + y) \, dy = 0$

25. $(x^2 - y^2)(x \, dy + y \, dx) = 2xy(x \, dy - y \, dx)$

26. $(4x - 3y)^2 \, dy = 2(4x - 3y) \, dy + 4 \, dx$

27. $\dfrac{dy}{dx} - xy = xy^2 - 2xy^3; \; y = 2$ when $x = 0$

28. $(3x^2 + 4y^2 - 5)x \, dx = (6 - 3x^2 - 4y^2)y \, dy;$ let $u = x^2, \; v = y^2$

29. $\cos x \dfrac{dy}{dx} + \sin x = 1 - y$

30. $2x^3 y^2 \, dx + 2x^2 y^3 \, dy = x \, dy + y \, dx; \; y = -1$ when $x = 1$

31. $(x - y^2) \, dx + 2xy \, dy = 0; \; y = -2$ when $x = 1$

32. $x(x + y) \, dx + y(y \, dx - x \, dy) = 0; \; y = 2$ when $x = 2$

33. $(x - 2y) \, dx + (2x - y - 3) \, dy = 0; \; y = -1$ when $x = -1$

34. $(y^2 + 4xy + 3x^2) \, dx + (x^2 - y^2) \, dy = 0$

35. $(\rho + \sin \theta \cos \theta) \, d\theta + (\theta - \rho^2) \, d\rho = 0$

36. $x^2(x + y)^2 \, (dx + dy) = m(x \, dy - y \, dx)$

37. $(x + y)^2 \, (x \, dy - y \, dx) + [y^2 - 2x^2(x + y)^2] \, (dx + dy) = 0$; let $v = x + y$, $w = \dfrac{y}{x}$

38. $2(x^2 + y^2 + x)(x \, dx + y \, dy) - xy \, dy + y^2 \, dx = 0$; let $z = x^2 + y^2$ and eliminate y

39. $(x^2 + y^2)(x \, dy + y \, dx) + 2xy(x - y)(dx - dy) = 0$

40. Prove that the substitution $z = xy$ may be used to transform the equation $\varphi(xy)y \, dx + \psi(xy)x \, dy = 0$ to the type of variables separable. Solve

    (a) $(x^2y^2 - 1)x \, dy + (x^2y^2 + xy - 2)y \, dx = 0$

    (b) $[xy \cos (xy) + n \sin (xy)]y \, dx + xy \cos (xy) \, x \, dy = 0$

41. Transform $\varphi(x^my^n)y \, dx + \psi(x^my^n)x \, dy = 0$ to the type variables separable by the substitution $z = x^my^n$. Solve $(2 + 4x^2 \sqrt{y})y \, dx + x^3 \sqrt{y} \, dy = 0$.

★42. The equation $(3xy^2 + 7x^3) \, dx + (4x^2y + 3 \sqrt{xy}) \, dy = 0$ has an integrating factor of the form x^k. Determine k and solve the equation.

★43. In the equation $(P + Rx^{k+1}) \, dy = (Q + Ryx^k) \, dx$, P, Q, and R are homogeneous functions of x and y, P and Q are of the same degree, and k is a constant. Transform the given equation to the type considered in §23 by the substitution $y = vx$. Solve

$$[x^2 + y^2 + (y + 2x)x^{-1}] \, dy = [2(x^2 + y^2) + (y + 2x)x^{-2}y] \, dx.$$

44. $\dfrac{dx}{dt} - 3x = e^{3t}, \; dx - dy + x \, dt = 0$

45. $dx - dy = dt, \; x \, dt + y \, dx = 0$

46. $x \, dy + y \, dx = 2t \, dt, \; (xy + t^2)(dx + dy) = 4t \, dt$

47. $\left(\dfrac{dx}{dt}\right)^2 + \left(\dfrac{dy}{dt}\right)^2 = 25, \; y \dfrac{dy}{dx} = 1$

CHAPTER IV

APPLICATIONS INVOLVING DIFFERENTIAL
EQUATIONS OF THE FIRST ORDER

26. Miscellaneous elementary applications

The solutions of the following problems involve various types of first-order differential equations. Inasmuch as no new knowledge or new methods are needed in finding and solving the appropriate differential equations, no introductory illustrative examples will be given.

PROBLEMS

1. A curve passing through $(3, -2)$ has a slope given by $(x^2 + y^2)/(y^3 - 2xy)$. Find the equation of the curve.

2. The radius vector, length ρ, of a moving point (ρ, θ) sweeps out an area proportional to ρ^n as θ changes from zero to any angle θ in the range $0 \leq \theta \leq 2\pi$. Find the equation of the path of the point.

3. Find the equation of the curve for which the intercept of the tangent on the X-axis is proportional to the second power of the radius vector for every point on the curve.

4. Find the equation of the curve for which the area bounded by the curve, any two ordinates, and the X-axis is equal to the average of these two ordinates multiplied by the distance between them.

5. The differential equation for the tension T in a chain hanging over a rough cylinder is given, under certain conditions, by

$$\frac{dT}{d\varphi} - \mu T = \rho a(\cos \varphi + \mu \sin \varphi),$$

where T and φ are the only variables. (a) Solve the given differential equation. (b) Show that $l(1 + \mu^2) = 2\mu a(1 + e^{\pi\mu})$, if $T = 0$ when $\varphi = 0$ and $T = \rho l$ when $\varphi = \pi$. (c) Show that $e^{\pi\mu/2}(1 - \mu^2) = 2\mu$, if $T = 0$ when $\varphi = \frac{1}{2}\pi$ and also $T = 0$ when $\varphi = \pi$.

6. A point (x,y) moves, relative to a set of rectangular axes, in such a way that the area of the triangle bounded by the normal at (x,y), the ordinate of (x,y), and the X-axis is proportional to the difference of the cubes of x and y. Show that

$$y^3 = 6ke^{-6kx}(\int x^3 e^{6kx} \, dx + c).$$

7. Find the equation of the curve for which the abscissa x of the point of contact of a tangent and the perpendicular from the origin to the tangent have equal lengths. *Hint:* The distance from $(0,0)$ to the tangent at (x,y) on the curve is

$$\frac{y - x\, dy/dx}{\sqrt{1 + (dy/dx)^2}}.$$

8. Suppose that amounts a and b, respectively, of two substances are involved in a chemical reaction in which the velocity of transformation dx/dt is proportional to the product $(a - x)(b - x)$ of the amounts remaining untransformed. Integrate on the suppositions that, when $t = 0$, $x = 0$ and $a \neq b$. Also find t in terms of x, if $a = 0.6$, $b = 0.4$, and if $x = 0.2$ when $t = 300$ sec.

9. Integrate the equation of problem 8 if $a = b$.

10. In the chemical process called fractional precipitation the equations

$$\frac{dx}{dt} = k_1(a - x)(c - z), \qquad \frac{dy}{dt} = k_2(b - y)(c - z)$$

apply. Given that $x = 0$ when $y = 0$, prove that

$$k_1 : k_2 = \log \frac{a}{a - x} : \log \frac{b}{b - x}.$$

11. A light situated at a point in a plane sends out beams in every direction. The beams in the plane meet a curve and are all reflected parallel to a fixed straight line in the plane. If the angle of incidence with the normal to the curve at the point of incidence is equal to the angle of reflection, find the equation of the curve. Solve by using polar coordinates and also by using rectangular coordinates (see Fig. 1). *Hint:* In Fig. 1, $\psi = 180° - \frac{1}{2}\theta$; also $\varphi = \frac{1}{2}\theta$ and $\tan \varphi = dy/dx$.

★12. Find the equation of the orthogonal trajectories (§8) of the system of circles $\rho = c \cos \theta + 6 \sin \theta$.

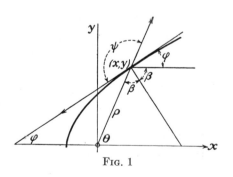

Fig. 1

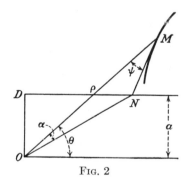

Fig. 2

13. Find the equation of the orthogonal trajectories (Example 2, §7) of all circles $x^2 + y^2 - 2my = 0$ tangent to the X-axis at the origin.

14. Given a point O and a straight line D, find a curve such that the portion of the tangent MN included between the point of contact M and the point of intersection N of the tangent and the line D subtends a constant angle at O (see Fig. 2). *Hint:* Use the law of sines to obtain

$$\frac{ON}{\sin \psi} = \frac{\rho}{\sin (\psi + \alpha)}.$$

Also $ON = a \csc (\theta - \alpha)$.

15. If in problem 14, the angle MON, instead of being constant, is equal to angle OMN, show that the differential equation of the curve is either $d\theta = 0$ or $(2a - \rho \sin \theta) \, d\rho + \rho^2 \cos \theta \, d\theta = 0$. Prove that $1/\rho^3$ is an integrating factor of this latter equation and find its solution.

16. One end of an inextensible string, of length l, is fastened to a weight which rests on a rough horizontal table. The other end is carried slowly along a straight line in the table. Find the path of the weight. Assume that the string is always tangent to the curve described by the weight.

27. Applications involving simultaneous equations

Let x, y, s, v, and t represent abscissa, ordinate, arc length, velocity, and time, respectively, for a point moving in a plane, and let dots denote derivatives with respect to the time. Then the quantities

$$v = \frac{ds}{dt} = \dot{s}, \qquad \dot{x} = \frac{dx}{dt}, \qquad \dot{y} = \frac{dy}{dt} \tag{1}$$

have the relations indicated in Fig. 3. From the triangle we read, for example,

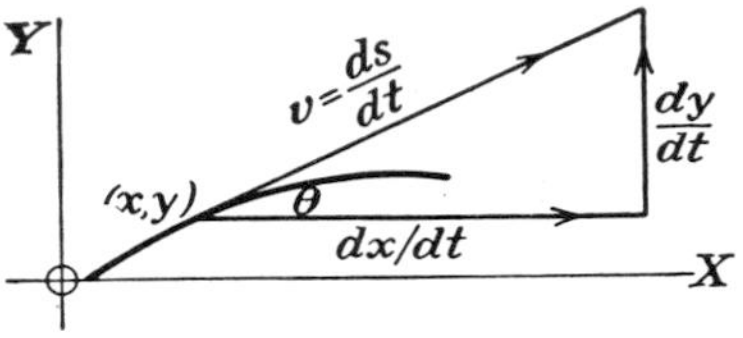

$$\frac{dy}{dx} = \tan \theta, \qquad \dot{x} = v \cos \theta,$$

$$\dot{y} = v \sin \theta, \tag{2}$$

FIG. 3

$$|v| = \sqrt{\dot{x}^2 + \dot{y}^2}. \tag{3}$$

$\dot{x}$ is called the component of velocity along the X-axis, and $\dot{y}$ the component along the Y-axis. A number of the problems in this article refer to plane motion.

Some problems will refer to substances in solution. In these a pertinent equation will often be obtained by using the expression

$$\begin{Bmatrix} \text{Rate of change of sub-} \\ \text{stance in a region} \end{Bmatrix} = \begin{Bmatrix} \text{rate of} \\ \text{entrance} \end{Bmatrix} - \begin{Bmatrix} \text{rate of} \\ \text{exit.} \end{Bmatrix} \tag{4}$$

Example 1. A particle moves on the curve $y = \frac{2}{3}x^{\frac{3}{2}}$ with a constant velocity of $\frac{2}{3}$ unit/sec. Find x and y in terms of t if $\dot{x}$ is positive and $x = 0$ when $t = 1$.

Solution. Two equations for the motion are

$$y = \frac{2}{3}x^{\frac{3}{2}}, \qquad \dot{x}^2 + \dot{y}^2 = \frac{4}{9}. \tag{a}$$

Differentiating the first equation of (a) with respect to t and substituting $\dot{y}$ thus obtained in the second equation, we get

$$\dot{y} = \sqrt{x}\,\dot{x}, \qquad \dot{x}^2 + x\dot{x}^2 = \tfrac{4}{9}. \tag{b}$$

From the second equation of (b), we get

$$(1 + x)^{\frac{1}{2}}\,dx = \tfrac{2}{3}dt, \qquad \tfrac{2}{3}(1 + x)^{\frac{3}{2}} = \tfrac{2}{3}t + c.$$

Since $x = 0$ when $t = 1$, $c = 0$. Hence

$$(1 + x)^{\frac{3}{2}} = t, \qquad \text{or} \qquad \mathbf{x = t^{\frac{2}{3}} - 1.}$$

Since $y = \tfrac{2}{3}x^{\frac{3}{2}}$ from (a), we have

$$\mathbf{x = t^{\frac{2}{3}} - 1,} \qquad \mathbf{y = \tfrac{2}{3}(t^{\frac{2}{3}} - 1)^{\frac{3}{2}}.}$$

Example 2. Initially tank I and tank II (see Fig. 4) each contain 100 gal. of brine, tank I having 200 lb. of salt and tank II 50 lb. of salt in solution. Brine runs at 2 gal./min. from tank I to tank II through one pipe and at 3 gal./min. from tank II to tank I through another pipe. The brine is kept well stirred. How much salt will the second tank contain at the end of 50 min.?

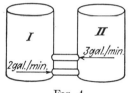

Fig. 4

Solution. Let Q_1 and Q_2 represent the respective amounts of salt in tanks I and II at time t. Then, using (4), we obtain

$$\dot{Q}_1 = \frac{3Q_2}{100 - t} - \frac{2Q_1}{100 + t}, \tag{a}$$

$$\dot{Q}_2 = \frac{2Q_1}{100 + t} - \frac{3Q_2}{100 - t}. \tag{b}$$

Addition of these equations gives

$$\dot{Q}_1 + \dot{Q}_2 = 0, \qquad \text{or} \qquad dQ_1 + dQ_2 = 0.$$

Hence $Q_1 + Q_2 = $ constant, and since $Q_1 + Q_2 = 250$ initially,

$$Q_1 + Q_2 = 250 \tag{c}$$

at all times. Substituting Q_1 from (c) in (b), we get

$$\frac{dQ_2}{dt} = \frac{500 - 2Q_2}{100 + t} - \frac{3Q_2}{100 - t} = \frac{-(500 + t)Q_2}{100^2 - t^2} + \frac{500}{100 + t}.$$

The general solution of this linear equation is

$$Q_2 = \frac{500}{(100 + t)^2}[100(100 - t) - (100 - t)^2 + c(100 - t)^3]. \tag{d}$$

Using the fact that $Q_2 = 50$ when $t = 0$, we get $c = 0.001$. Then replacing t by 50, we get $(Q_2)_{t=50} = \mathbf{58\frac{1}{3}\ lb.}$

PROBLEMS

1. A particle moves on parabola $y^2 = 4x$ with a velocity such that $\dot{x} = 2t + 2$ at all times. Find x and y in terms of t if the particle passes through $(4,4)$ at time $t = 1$ with positive y-component.

2. A particle moves on the catenary $y = \cosh x$ with a velocity of constant magnitude 2 ft./sec. It passes through $(0,1)$ at time $t = 0$. Show that $x = \pm \sinh^{-1}(2t)$, $y = \sqrt{1 + 4t^2}$.

3. A particle moves on curve $y = x^2 - \frac{1}{8}\log x$ with a velocity of constant magnitude 10. If it passes through $(1,1)$ with positive x-component of velocity at time $t = 0$, show that $8x^2 + \log x = 80t + 8$.

4. Under certain conditions the motion of a projectile is given approximately by the equations

$$\dot{x} + 0.032x = 1600, \qquad \dot{y} + 0.032y = 1600 - 32t.$$

If $x = 0$ and $y = 0$ when $t = 0$, find x and y in terms of t.

5. Brine from a first tank runs into a second tank at 2 gal./min., and brine from the second tank runs into the first at 1 gal./min. Initially there are 100 gal. of brine containing 200 lb. of salt in the first tank and 100 gal. of fresh water in the second tank. How much salt will the first tank contain after 50 min.? Assume that the brine in each tank is kept uniform by stirring.

6. Brine containing 2 lb. of salt per gallon runs into a first tank at 4 gal./min., brine from the first tank runs into a second tank at 3 gal./min., and brine runs out of the second tank at 2 gal./min. Initially the first tank contains 100 gal. of brine with 300 lb. of salt in solution and the second tank 100 gal. of fresh water. Assuming uniform concentration in each tank, find the quantity of salt in the second tank at the end of 50 min.

7. If the brine running from the second tank in problem 6 should run into the first tank instead of escaping, how much salt would the second tank contain after 50 min.?

8. Referred to a set of rectangular axes, the path of a moving particle is given by $x^2 - y^2 = 25$, and the components $\dot{x}$ and $\dot{y}$ of its velocity satisfy $\dot{x} + \dot{y} = 1$. Find the position of the particle at time t, if $x = 5$ when $t = 5$.

9. A point moves in a plane curve through $(1,1)$ so that its components $\dot{x}$ and $\dot{y}$ are given by

$$\dot{x} = -2x + 6y, \qquad \dot{y} = 2x + 2y.$$

Prove that it must move either on the line $x = y$ or on the line $x + 3y = 0$, and find x and y in terms of t for its motion on the line $x = y$. *Hint:* Divide the second equation by the first, member by member.

10. Differential equations of the type $(d^2s/dt^2) + a(ds/dt) + bs = 0$ are involved in the investigation of important vibratory motions. In the equation

$$\frac{d^2s}{dt^2} + 2\frac{ds}{dt} - 3s = 0,$$

make the substitution

$$\frac{ds}{dt} = v, \qquad \frac{d^2s}{dt^2} = \frac{dv}{dt} = \frac{ds}{dt}\frac{dv}{ds} = \frac{v\,dv}{ds},$$

and solve the result to obtain $(v + 3s)^3 (v - s) = c$.

28. Applications to the flow of electricity

We may think of electricity as a substance which flows through conductors such as wires. *One unit of electricity is the* **coulomb.** Just as we speak of gallons of water, we speak of coulombs of electricity. The rate of flow of electricity is called current. If I coulombs of electricity per second are passing a point in a conductor, the current is I amperes.

For the circuit indicated in Fig. 5 the following equations hold:

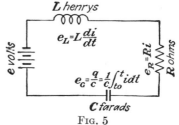

$$L\frac{di}{dt} + Ri + \frac{q}{C} = e, \qquad i = \frac{dq}{dt}, \quad (5)$$

FIG. 5

where e represents electromotive force, i represents current, q represents the charge, or quantity of electricity, on the condenser, and L, R, and C are constants. *Electromotive force e is analogous to force, inductance L to mass or inertia, resistance R to friction, and capacity C to the size of a storage tank.*

If there is no condenser in a circuit, the corresponding equation (5) does not contain the term q/C and no consideration of q enters the discussion.

A set of units in common use are *quantity* **q** *in coulombs, current* **i** *in amperes, electromotive force* **e** *in volts, inductance* **L** *in henrys, resistance* **R** *in ohms,* and *capacity* **C** *in farads.*

Example. Discuss the charging of a large condenser, or battery, in a circuit containing a constant electromotive force E, a resistance R, and no inductance.

Solution. Setting $L = 0$, and $i = dq/dt$ in the first of equations (5), obtain

$$R\frac{dq}{dt} + \frac{q}{C} = E. \qquad (a)$$

The initial condition may be taken as $q = 0$ when $t = 0$. The solution of (a) subject to this condition is

$$q = CE(1 - e^{-t/(RC)}). \qquad (b)$$

From the second equation of (5)

$$i = \frac{dq}{dt} = \frac{E}{R} e^{-t/(RC)}. \qquad (c)$$

The upper limit of the charge is found from (b) to be CE. When $t = RC$, $q = CE(1 - e^{-1}) = 0.632CE$, and when $t = 2RC$, $q = CE(1 - e^{-2}) = 0.865CE$. The initial current is E/R when $t = 0$, and it dies away as t increases.

EXERCISES

1. Discuss the *discharge of a condenser* through a resistance R by solving (5) with $L = 0$, $e = 0$, subject to initial conditions $q = q_0$ when $t = 0$, and by finding q when $t = \infty$, $t = CR$, and $t = 2CR$. Also find t when $q = 0.01q_0$.

2. Discuss the *decay of a current* of initial value I_0 in a circuit containing neither electromotive force nor condenser, after solving $L\, di/dt + Ri = 0$ and finding the value of i when $t = L/R$, $2L/R$, and ∞.

3. Discuss the growth of current of zero initial value in a circuit containing no condenser, a resistance R, an inductance L, and electromotive force (a) E, (b) $E \sin \omega t$.

4. By setting $L = 0$ and $e = E \sin \omega t$ in (5), show that the corresponding current i approaches $EC\omega/(1 + R^2C^2\omega^2)(\cos \omega t + RC\omega \sin \omega t)$ as t increases without bound.

5. By solving (5) for q and i in terms of t with $L = 0$, $R = 10$ ohms, $C = 250 \times 10^{-6}$ farad, and $e = 110 \sin 300t$, show that q rapidly approaches $11(4 \sin 300t - 3 \cos 300t)/2500$ and that i rapidly approaches $1.32(4 \cos 300t + 3 \sin 300t)$.

6. If there is no condenser in a circuit of the type shown in Fig. 5 and if $L = 0.1$ henry, $R = 10$ ohms, and $e = 100 \sin 200t$, show that the current i is given (nearly) by $i = 2 \sin 200t - 4 \cos 200t$ after a very short time.

7. Use equations (5) with $R = 0$ and $e = 0$ to find i and q for the discharge of a condenser through an inductance L. Assume as initial conditions $q = q_0$, $i = 0$, when $t = 0$. *Hint:* To solve $L(d^2q/dt^2) + (q/C) = 0$, first let

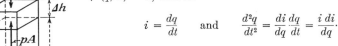

$$i = \frac{dq}{dt} \qquad \text{and} \qquad \frac{d^2q}{dt^2} = \frac{di}{dq}\frac{dq}{dt} = \frac{i\, di}{dq}.$$

After solving for i, replace i by dq/dt and solve for q.

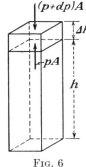

FIG. 6

29. Air pressure

To obtain an expression for air pressure at height h above the earth, consider a vertical column of air (see Fig. 6) having a small square cross section of area A and extending from the ground upward indefinitely. An element of this column bounded above and below by two horizontal planes at heights h ft. and $h + \Delta h$ ft., respectively, from the ground is subjected to an upward force on its lower side of p lb./in.^{2}, to a downward force on its upper side of $p + \Delta p$ lb./in.^{2}, to the weight of the element, and to horizontal forces. Since the element is in equilibrium, the vertical forces balance. Equating the algebraic sum of the vertical forces to zero, we have

$$pA - (p + \Delta p)A - \bar{\rho}A\, \Delta h = 0, \tag{6}$$

where $\bar{\rho}$ represents the average density of the element of air. Canceling A, dividing by Δh, and finding the limit approached as Δh approaches zero, we obtain

$$dp + \rho\, dh = 0. \tag{7}$$

If the air obeys Boyle's law for perfect gases,

$$\rho = kp.^* \tag{8}$$

Solving (7) and (8) as simultaneous equations, we obtain

$$p = ce^{-kh}, \qquad \rho = kce^{-kh}.$$

PROBLEMS

1. Assuming that the atmosphere obeys Boyle's law, find the air pressure at a height of 70,000 ft. Assume that the pressure at the surface of the earth is 14.7 lb./in.^{2}, and that it is 10.08 lb./in.^{2} at an altitude of 10,000 ft.

2. Find air pressure at an altitude h, if air obeys the adiabatic law $p = k\rho^{1.4}$. Show that in this case the pressure would become zero at a finite height. Find this height in terms of k and the pressure p_0 at the surface of the earth.

3. Compute the theoretical height of an atmosphere which obeys the adiabatic law $p = k\rho^{1.4}$, assuming that pressure at height zero is 14.7 lb./in.^{2} and pressure at a height of 10,000 ft. is 10.08 lb./in.^{2}

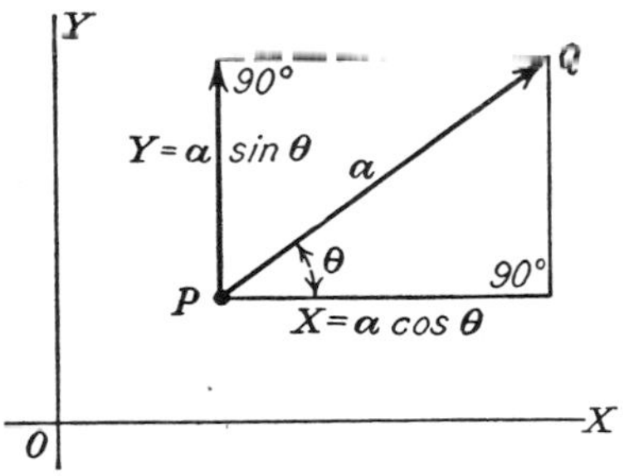

30. Applications involving forces and velocities

The applications of this section deal with forces acting in a plane and with velocities of particles moving in a plane.

FIG. 7

The directed line segment, or vector **PQ**, in Fig. 7 represents a force having a *magnitude* of a units of force and a direction specified by the

---

* A good approximation to air pressure is not to be expected by assuming Boyle's law or the law of adiabatic expansion because the density of a gas depends on its temperature and many other factors.

angle θ through which the directed X-axis must be turned so as to point in the direction from P to Q. The signed numbers

$$X = a \cos \theta, \qquad Y = a \sin \theta \qquad (9)$$

are called, respectively, the **X-component** and the **Y-component** of the force. X may be considered as a force having the direction of the X-axis or the opposite direction according as X is positive or negative, and a similar statement applies to Y. Thus if $a = 10$ lb. and $\theta = 120°$, $X = 10 \cos 120 = -5$ lb., $Y = 10 \sin 120° = 8.66$ lb.

Observe that a force is determined in magnitude and direction by the values X and Y of its components. *A force with components* **X** *and* **Y** *will be represented by* [**X**,**Y**]. Thus [$-5,8.66$] denotes the force having $X = -5$, $Y = 8.66$. *The sum* [**X**,**Y**] *of the forces* [**X₁**,**Y₁**], [**X₂**,**Y₂**], . . . , [**Xₙ**,**Yₙ**] *is defined, in magnitude and direction, by*

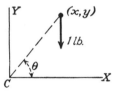

$$[\mathbf{X},\mathbf{Y}] = [\mathbf{X}_1 + \mathbf{X}_2 + \cdots + \mathbf{X}_n, \mathbf{Y}_1 + \mathbf{Y}_2 + \cdots + \mathbf{Y}_n]. \quad (10)$$

Fɪɢ. 8

Let $X(x,y)$, $Y(x,y)$ represent functions of X and Y, and let [$X(x,y)$, $Y(x,y)$] represent a force acting at (x,y). Then the corresponding set of forces for the points (x,y) of a region is called a **field of force**. For example,

$$[X(x,y), \ Y(x,y)] = [0, -1] \qquad (11)$$

represents the field (see Fig. 8) of a constant force of 1 lb. acting at each point in a fixed direction, like gravity.
Likewise (see Fig. 9),

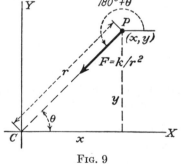

$$\left[\frac{k}{r^2} \cos (180° + \theta), \frac{k}{r^2} \sin (180° + \theta)\right]$$

$$= \left[\frac{-kx}{(x^2 + y^2)^{\frac{3}{2}}}, \frac{-ky}{(x^2 + y^2)^{\frac{3}{2}}}\right] \quad (12)$$

represents the field of force due to the attraction of a charge of positive electricity at C on a constant charge of negative electricity at (x,y).

Fɪɢ. 9

A line of force *is a curve in the field of force which has at each point on it the direction of the force acting at the point.* Evidently the differential equation for the lines of force of a field [$X(x,y)$, $Y(x,y)$] is

$$\frac{\mathbf{dy}}{\mathbf{dx}} = \frac{\mathbf{Y}}{\mathbf{X}}, \qquad \text{or} \qquad -\mathbf{Y} \, \mathbf{dx} + \mathbf{X} \, \mathbf{dy} = 0. \qquad (13)$$

The **work** U done on a particle by a field of force $[X(x,y),\ Y(x,y)]$ while the particle is moving in the field from a point (a,b) to a point (x,y) may be defined by the line integral*

$$U = \int_{(a,b)}^{(x,y)} (X\ dx + Y\ dy), \qquad (14)$$

evaluated along the path (see Fig. 10) of the particle.   If the work is independent of the path of the particle, $X\ dx + Y\ dy$ must be an exact differential. When $X\ dx + Y\ dy$ is an exact differential and when (a,b) represents a standard, or reference, position, the function $V(x,y)$ defined by

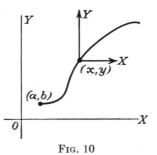

$$V(x,y) = -\int_{(a,b)}^{(x,y)} (X\ dx + Y\ dy) \qquad (15)$$

FIG. 10

is called the **potential function,**† or merely the **potential.**   The curves along which potential is constant are called **equipotential,** or **level, curves.**   When V is a constant, $dV = 0$.   Hence, from (15) we deduce that *the differential equation of the equipotential curves is*

$$\textbf{X dx} + \textbf{Y dy} = \textbf{0}, \qquad \textbf{(16)}$$

provided that (16) *is exact.*

Comparing dy/dx from (16) with dy/dx from (13) we see that *the equipotential curves are orthogonal trajectories of the lines of force.*

Example.   Find the equations of the lines of force and of the equipotential curves for the field defined by (*a*) equation (11); (*b*) equation (12).

Solution.   (*a*) For field $[0, -1]$, $X = 0$, $Y = -1$, and equation (13) becomes

$$dx + 0\ dy = 0.$$

The equation of the lines of force is, therefore,

$$\textbf{x} = \textbf{c.}$$

---

* The reader can find discussions of line integrals in books on advanced calculus. The only kinds needed for this discussion are of the type represented by

$$\int_{a,b)}^{(x,y)} \left(\frac{\partial f(x,y)}{\partial x}\ dx + \frac{\partial f(x,y)}{\partial y}\ dy \right) = f(x,y) - f(a,b),$$

where $f(x,y)$ and its derivatives of the first and second orders are continuous except at a few points.

† Fields of force and velocity fields having a potential function play a prominent role in physical theories.

The equation of the equipotential curves, obtained by substituting 0 for X and -1 for Y in (16) and solving the resulting differential equation, is

$$\mathbf{y} = \mathbf{c}.$$

Figure 11 shows these curves.

(b) Substituting for X and Y in (13) the values from (12) and solving the resulting differential equation, obtain

$$\frac{k(y\,dx - x\,dy)}{(x^2 + y^2)^{\frac{3}{2}}} = 0,$$

$$\mathbf{y} = \mathbf{cx}.$$

This equation represents the lines of force. Substituting for X and Y

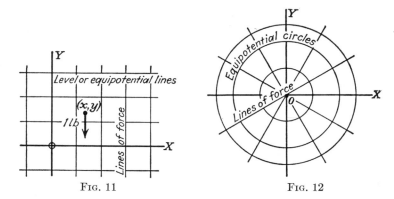

FIG. 11   FIG. 12

in (16) the values from (12) and solving the resulting exact differential equation, obtain as the equation of the equipotential curves

$$\mathbf{x}^2 + \mathbf{y}^2 = \mathbf{c}.$$

Figure 12 shows the lines of force $y = cx$ and equipotential circles $x^2 + y^2 = c$.

Velocities, like forces, are represented by vectors. If the velocity of a particle at (x,y) has x-component $u(x,y)$ and y-component $v(x,y)$, then a velocity field for particles moving in a region is defined by

$$[u(x,y),\, v(x,y)]. \tag{17}$$

The **streamlines** *corresponding to lines of force are defined by*

$$\frac{dy}{dx} = \frac{v}{u}, \quad \text{or} \quad \mathbf{v}\,d\mathbf{x} - \mathbf{u}\,d\mathbf{y} = 0, \tag{18}$$

and the velocity equipotential curves are defined by

$$u\ dx + v\ dy = 0, \tag{19}$$

when $u\ dx + v\ dy$ is an exact differential.

EXERCISES

Using differential equations (13) and (16), find the equations of the equipotential curves and of the lines of force for the fields numbered 1 to 6:

1. $[2x, 2y]$ **2.** $[2x, 6y]$

3. $[2y, 2x]$ **4.** $[2xy,\ x^2 - y^2]$

5. $\left[\dfrac{-y}{x^2 + y^2},\ 2 + \dfrac{x}{x^2 + y^2} \right]$ **6.** $[x^2 + y^2,\ 2xy]$

7. Figure 13 represents the constant field of force $[10, -32]$. Find the equations of its equipotential lines and of its lines of force. Draw a few curves of each family.

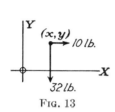

Fig. 13

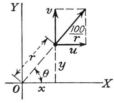

Fig. 14

8. If water has issued from the origin for a long time at π ft.³/sec. and has spread in a uniform sheet 0.01 ft. thick on the smooth XY-plane so that the velocity of the particle at (x,y) is that indicated in Fig. 14, check that the velocity field is defined by

$$[u,v] = \left[\frac{100}{r} \cos \theta,\ \frac{100}{r} \sin \theta \right] = \left[\frac{100x}{x^2 + y^2}, \frac{100y}{x^2 + y^2} \right] \qquad (r \neq 0).$$

Find the equations of the velocity equipotential curves and of the streamlines. Sketch a few curves of each family.

9. The gravitational field of force for a particle inside the earth obeys approximately the law suggested by Fig. 15. Write a bracket representation of the field and find the corresponding equations of the equipotential curves and of the lines of force.

★10. If water has issued from $(-3,0)$ at π ft.³/sec. and has disappeared at $(3,0)$ at π ft.³/sec. for a long time, so that the velocity of a particle at (x,y) is as indicated in Fig. 16(a), check that the velocity field is defined by

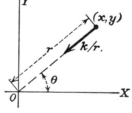

Fig. 15

$$\left[\frac{100(x + 3)}{r_1^2} - \frac{100(x - 3)}{r_2^2},\ \frac{100y}{r_1^2} - \frac{100y}{r_2^2} \right].$$

Find the equations of the velocity equipotential curves and of the streamlines. Figure 16(b) shows a few curves from each family. Describe the family of streamline circles.

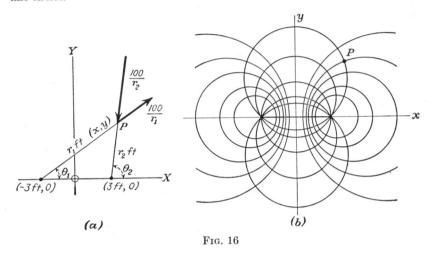

(a)

(b)

FIG. 16

★**11.** If $z = x + iy$, $i = \sqrt{-1}$, and $f(z) = \varphi(x,y) + i\psi(x,y)$, where φ and ψ are real functions having continuous partial derivatives of the first and second orders, and if $f(z)$ is a differentiable function of z, it can be shown that

$$\frac{\partial\varphi}{\partial x} = \frac{\partial\psi}{\partial y}, \qquad \frac{\partial\varphi}{\partial y} = -\frac{\partial\psi}{\partial x}.* \tag{I}$$

(a) Prove that

$$\frac{\partial^2\varphi}{\partial x^2} + \frac{\partial^2\varphi}{\partial y^2} = 0, \qquad \frac{\partial^2\psi}{\partial x^2} + \frac{\partial^2\psi}{\partial y^2} = 0.†$$

(b) Show that the differential equations for the velocity equipotential curves and for the streamlines of the two velocity fields

$$[\psi(x,y),\ \varphi(x,y)] \qquad \text{and} \qquad [-\varphi(x,y),\ \psi(x,y)]$$

are exact.

12. From exercise 11 it appear that a velocity field derived from $z^2 = (x + iy)^2 = x^2 - y^2 + 2xyi$ is represented by $[2xy,\ x^2 - y^2]$. (a) Derive a bracket representation of a velocity field from $z^3 = (x + iy)^3$. (b) Find the equations of the equipotential curves and of the streamlines for each of the velocity fields.

* These are the celebrated Cauchy-Riemann equations.

† These equations, called Laplace's equations, are of basic importance in many theories of modern physics. To prove them, use (I) and the fact that $\dfrac{\partial^2\varphi}{\partial x\,\partial y}$

$= \dfrac{\partial^2\varphi}{\partial y\,\partial x}$.

13. Using the method of exercise 12, write bracket representations of velocity fields and find the equations of their velocity equipotential curves and of their streamlines from

(a) $\dfrac{1}{z} = \dfrac{1}{x + iy} = \dfrac{x - iy}{x^2 + y^2}$ (b) $2 + \dfrac{3}{z}$ (c) $\dfrac{1}{z^2}$.

★14. Figure 17 represents a field of force due to electrical charges, an attraction

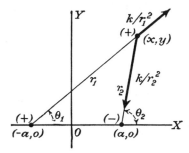

FIG. 17

at $(a,0)$ and a repulsion at $(-a,0)$.   Check that the field of force is defined by

$$\left[\frac{k(x + a)}{r_1^3} - \frac{k(x - a)}{r_2^3}, \frac{ky}{r_1^3} - \frac{ky}{r_2^3} \right].$$

Find the equations of the equipotential curves and of the lines of force.

CHAPTER V

FIRST-ORDER EQUATIONS OF DEGREE HIGHER THAN THE FIRST

31. Foreword

This chapter relates mainly to four types of differential equations of the first order and degree higher than the first. Since certain special solutions, called *singular solutions*, involve envelopes of families of curves, a little theory of envelopes will be reviewed and used.

32. Equations solvable for dy/dx

This section deals with a type of first-order differential equation which can be resolved into factors linear in dy/dx. The notation

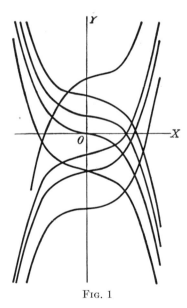

$$p = \frac{dy}{dx} \qquad (1)$$

will be used throughout this chapter. An equation which can be reduced to the form

$$(p - A_1)(p - A_2) \cdots (p - A_n) = 0, \qquad (2)$$

where the $A_1, A_2, \ldots, A_n$ are functions of x and y, may be solved by equating each factor to zero and integrating the resulting equations. The solutions thus obtained

$$\varphi_1(x,y,c_1) = 0, \qquad \varphi_2(x,y,c_2) = 0,$$
$$\ldots, \qquad \varphi_n(x,y,c_n) = 0 \qquad (3)$$

may be regarded as the result required, or we may use

FIG. 1

$$\varphi_1(x,y,c) \cdot \varphi_2(x,y,c) \cdots \varphi_n(x,y,c) = 0 \qquad (4)$$

as the general solution; for (4) represents all curves defined by (3) and no others.

64

Take, for example,

$$9p^2 - x^4 = 0. \tag{5}$$

From this write $(3p - x^2)(3p + x^2) = 0$ and solve the equations $3p - x^2 = 0,\ 3p + x^2 = 0$ to obtain

$$9y = x^3 + c_1, \qquad 9y = -x^3 + c_2, \tag{6}$$

$$(9y - x^3 - c)(9y + x^3 + c) = 0. \tag{7}$$

Figure 1 represents the solution (6) or (7).

EXERCISES

1. $(p - x)(p - y) = 0,\ p = \dfrac{dy}{dx}$ **2.** $(p - x^2)(p - xy)(p - y^2) = 0$

3. $4p^2 = 9x$ **4.** $p^2 - y^2 = 0$

5. $y^2(1 + p^2) = 1$ **6.** $8ap^3 = 27y$

7. $x^2p^2 + 3xyp + 2y^2 = 0$ **8.** $p^2 + py = x^2 + xy$

9. $xp^2 - 2yp - x = 0$

10. $(x + 2y)p^3 + 3(x + y)p^2 + (y + 2x)p = 0$

11. $(a^2 - x^2)p^3 + bx(a^2 - x^2)p^2 - p - bx = 0$

12. If, from the equation $x^2p^2 + 5xyp + 6y^2 = 0$, we form a new equation by replacing p by $-1/p$, what will be the relation between the systems of curves represented by the solutions of the two equations?

13. Find the equation of the curves for which the length of the segment of the tangent line between the point of contact and the intersection with the X-axis is a constant.

33. Envelopes

Since the equations of envelopes appear as particular solutions of differential equations, a brief review of the pertinent facts of envelopes is in order.

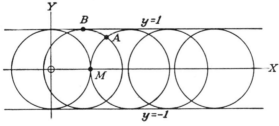

Fig. 2

Any curve which is tangent to an infinite number of members of a singly infinite family of curves and which is tangent at each of its points to a finite number of these curves, is a part of the **envelope** *of the family.*

For example (see Fig. 2), the envelope of the circles

$$(x - c)^2 + y^2 = 1$$

consists of the lines

$$y = \pm 1.$$

It is proved in calculus* that, with suitable restrictions, the envelope of a family of curves $f(x,y,c) = 0$ is a part or the whole of the locus satisfying

$$f(x,y,c) = 0, \qquad \frac{\partial f(x,y,c)}{\partial c} = 0. \tag{8}$$

The result of eliminating c from (8) is called the **c-discriminant** of $f(x,y,c) = 0$. One can perceive intuitively that (8) represents the envelope of $f(x,y,c) = 0$. For, when (8) holds at a point (x_0,y_0), c is a multiple root of $f(x_0,y_0,c) = 0$; this indicates that there is a smaller number of values of c than usual, and therefore that fewer curves than usual pass through (x_0,y_0). Note in Fig. 2 that two circles pass through point A, but that only one passes through point B on the envelope of the family of circles.

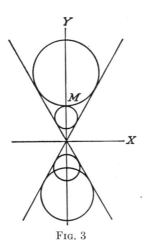

For example, the envelope of the circles

$$x^2 + (y - 10c)^2 = 20c^2 \tag{9}$$

is defined by

$$x^2 + (y - 10c)^2 = 20c^2,$$
$$2(y - 10c)(-10) = 40c. \tag{10}$$

The result of eliminating c from (10) is

$$x = \pm\tfrac{1}{2}y. \tag{11}$$

These are the equations of the envelope. Figure 3 represents the system of circles and the enveloping lines.

FIG. 3

34. Envelope from differential equation

Consider a differential equation

$$\psi(x,y,p) = 0, \tag{12}$$

having $F(x,y,c) = 0$ as general solution. Substitution of (x_0,y_0) in $F(x,y,c) = 0$ gives $F(x_0,y_0,c) = 0$, an equation in c having, let us suppose, n roots. Since a curve is associated with each of these n values of c,

---

* See the author's "Calculus," pp. 338–342, and "Advanced Calculus" by W. B. Fite, pp. 324–326.

we conclude that, in general, n curves of the family $F(x,y,c) = 0$ pass through (x_0,y_0). If now $F_c(x_0,y_0,c_0) = 0$, then c_0 is a multiple root of $F(x_0,y_0,c) = 0$, and therefore fewer curves than usual pass through (x_0,y_0). This condition may be described by saying that *a smaller number of curves than usual pass through a point on the envelope of the solution.* Since the slopes of curves of the general solution through a point (x_0,y_0) on its envelope are given by $\psi(x_0,y_0,p) = 0$ and since there are fewer than usual, $\psi(x_0,y_0,p) = 0$ must have a multiple root, p_0. Therefore $\psi_p(x_0,y_0,p_0) = 0$. Hence along the envelope of $F(x,y,c) = 0$ we have

$$\psi(\mathbf{x,y,p}) = \mathbf{0}, \qquad \psi_p(\mathbf{x,y,p}) = \mathbf{0}. \tag{13}$$

The result of eliminating p from (13) is called the **p-discriminant** of the differential equation $\psi(x,y,\,dy/dx) = 0$. It includes the equation of the envelope. In general, *this equation of the envelope satisfies the differential equation* because the slope of the envelope at each of its points is the same as that of a curve belonging to the general solution; it is called the **singular solution.** A part of an envelope defined by $x = c$, a constant, would not ordinarily satisfy the differential equation, since along such a curve, p does not exist.

The name **tac-locus** is given to a locus of points at each of which two or more curves of a family have the same tangent. In Fig. 3 of §33, $x = 0$ is a tac-locus of points such as M for the system of circles. Since, at a point on the tac-locus, two of the values of p associated to the point by the differential equation are equal, the coordinates of the point must satisfy the p-discriminant, that is, *the graph of the p-discriminant must contain the tac-locus.* The equation of the tac-locus generally does not satisfy the differential equation but may do so in special cases. Also, at a cusp, the values of p for each of the two branches are equal. Hence *the graph of the p-discriminant contains any locus of cusps belonging to the corresponding family.* The cuspidal locus generally does not satisfy the differential equation.

As an example, consider the system of circles (9). The differential equation of (9) is found by the method of §4 to be

$$(5x^2 - y^2)p^2 - 2xyp + 4x^2 = 0. \tag{14}$$

For this, equations (13) are

$$(5x^2 - y^2)p^2 - 2xyp + 4x^2 = 0, \qquad 2(5x^2 - y^2)p - 2xy = 0. \tag{15}$$

Replacing p in the first equation by its value from the second, obtain, after simplification,

$$20x^2(4x^2 - y^2) = 0. \tag{16}$$

Here $4x^2 - y^2 = 0$, or $y = \pm 2x$, represents the envelope, and $x = 0$ represents the tac-locus.

EXERCISES

1. Show that the p-discriminant of $y = x^3 p^2 - 2xp$, obtained by using (13) with $\psi = y - x^3 p^2 + 2xp$, is $y = -x^{-1}$. Prove that $y = -x^{-1}$ satisfies $y = x^3 p^2 - 2xp$ and is therefore a singular solution of it.

2. Show that the p-discriminant of $y = 2px + p^2$ is $y + x^2 = 0$. Show that this does not satisfy the differential equation and conclude that $y = 2px + p^2$ has no singular solution.

3. The differential equation of the circles $(x - c)^2 + y^2 = 1$ (see Fig. 2) is $y^2(1 + p^2) = 1$. Show that the p-discriminant represents the envelope $y = \pm 1$ and also the tac-locus $y = 0$. Does $y = 0$ satisfy the differential equation?

4. Find the p-discriminant of $y = 2px - yp^2$. Is the p-discriminant a singular solution of $y = 2px - yp^2$?

5. Differentiate partially with respect to p

$$(p^2 + 1)(2y - x)^2 = (x + py)^2 \qquad (a)$$

to obtain

$$2p(2y - x)^2 = 2(x + py)y. \qquad (b)$$

Replace $(2y - x)^2$ in (a) by its values from (b) and simplify to obtain $y = px$; then eliminate p between $y = px$ and (a) to obtain the singular solution $y(3y - 4x) = 0$. Prove that this singular solution satisfies (a). Also replace $x + py$ in (a) by its value from (b), thus showing that $2y - x = 0$ is part of the p-discriminant. Prove that $2y - x = 0$ does not satisfy (a). It defines a tac-locus. The solution of (a) is

$$(x - 2c)^2 + (y - c)^2 = c^2. \qquad (c)$$

Show that the c-discriminant, representing the envelope of (c), is $y(3y - 4x) = 0$. Plot the c-discriminant, the tac-locus, and a few of the circles (c).

35. Equations solvable for y

When a first-order differential equation is solvable for y, it may be written in the form

$$y = f(x,p). \qquad (17)$$

Taking the total derivative of this equation with respect to x, we get

$$\frac{dy}{dx} = p = \frac{\partial f}{\partial x} + \frac{\partial f}{\partial p}\frac{dp}{dx}. \qquad (18)$$

This equation, since y does not appear in it, may be solved as an equation in x and p to get

$$\psi(x,p,c) = 0. \qquad (19)$$

Equations (17) and (19) may be thought of as the parametric equations (p being the parameter) of a system of curves and therefore as the general solution of (17).

The result of eliminating p between the equations (17) and (19) gives the general solution as an equation in x, y, and an arbitrary constant. If one suspects that the eliminant contains, as it may, extraneous factors that do not represent solutions, he should check by substitution in the differential equation. An extraneous factor may yield a singular solution; the following example illustrates this case.

Example. Solve

$$y = \tfrac{9}{2}xp^{-1} + \tfrac{1}{2}px. \tag{a}$$

Solution. Differentiating (a) with respect to x, obtain

$$p = \left(-\frac{9}{2}xp^{-2} + \frac{1}{2}x\right)\frac{dp}{dx} + \frac{9}{2}p^{-1} + \frac{1}{2}p, \tag{b}$$

or, rearranged,

$$\left(-\frac{9}{2}p^{-2} + \frac{1}{2}\right)x\frac{dp}{dx} - p\left(-\frac{9}{2}p^{-2} + \frac{1}{2}\right) = 0. \tag{c}$$

Equation (c) will be satisfied if either of the equations

$$x\frac{dp}{dx} - p = 0, \qquad -\frac{9}{2}p^{-2} + \frac{1}{2} = 0 \tag{d}$$

holds true. From the first of (d) obtain

$$x = cp. \tag{e}$$

Parametric equations of the solution, obtained by solving (a) and (e) for x and y in terms of p, are

$$\mathbf{x = cp}, \qquad \mathbf{y = \tfrac{9}{2}c + \tfrac{1}{2}cp^2}. \tag{f}$$

To get the solution in terms of x and y, eliminate p from (f). Replacing p in the second equation of (f) by its value from the first and simplifying, obtain

$$\mathbf{2cy = 9c^2 + x^2}. \tag{g}$$

The **singular solution** is obtained by eliminating p between (a) and the second equation of (d) and simplifying. This gives

$$\mathbf{y = \pm 3x}. \tag{h}$$

Observe that the p-discriminant, found by using (13) with $\psi(x,y,p) = y - \tfrac{9}{2}xp^{-1} - \tfrac{1}{2}px$, is $y = \pm 3x$. Also the c-discriminant, from equations (8) and (g), is the same thing. There is no tac-locus.

EXERCISES

1. Solve each equation by the method of this article. Also in each case equate to zero the factor that may be canceled from the equation in x, p, and dp/dx, and eliminate p between the result and the original equation to obtain a singular solution. Compare the singular solution thus obtained with the c-discriminant and with the p-discriminant.

(a) $2yp = 3x + xp^2$ (b) $y = x^4p^2 - xp$

2. Find solutions of the following equations in parametric form:

(a) $y = 2xp - 3p^2$ (b) $2y + px = 6p^2$

Using the p-discriminant, show that neither equation has a singular solution.

3. Solve $x^2(y - px) = yp^2$. Show that it does not have a singular solution.

★4. Solve $p^2 - 4px + 6y = 0$. Find the p-discriminant and show that it is not a solution of the given differential equation.

5. Solve $y = x^3p^2 - 2xp$

6. Solve $y = 2px - xp^2$

7. Solve $y = 2px + 4xp^2$

36. Equations solvable for x

A first-order differential equation which is solvable for x may be written in the form

$$x = f(y,p). \tag{20}$$

Taking the total derivative of this equation with respect to y, we get

$$\frac{dx}{dy} = \frac{1}{p} = \frac{\partial f}{\partial y} + \frac{\partial f}{\partial p}\frac{dp}{dy}. \tag{21}$$

This equation may be solved as an equation in y and p to obtain

$$\psi(y,p,c) = 0. \tag{22}$$

Equations (20) and (22) may be considered as the general solution in parametric form, or we may eliminate p between (20) and (22) to obtain the solution as a relation between x, y, and a constant of integration.

Example. Solve

$$y = 2px + y^2p^3. \tag{a}$$

Solution. Solving for x, we get

$$x = \frac{y}{2p} - \frac{y^2p^2}{2}. \tag{b}$$

The derivative of (b) with respect to y is

$$\frac{dx}{dy} = \frac{1}{p} = \frac{1}{2p} - yp^2 - \left(\frac{y}{2p^2} + y^2p\right)\frac{dp}{dy}, \qquad (c)$$

or, simplified,

$$\frac{1}{2p} + yp^2 = -\frac{y}{p}\left(\frac{1}{2p} + yp^2\right)\frac{dp}{dy}. \qquad (d)$$

Dividing out $(1/2p) + yp^2$ and integrating, we obtain

$$py = c, \qquad \text{or} \qquad y = \frac{c}{p}. \qquad (e)$$

Substituting y from (e) in (b), we get

$$x = \frac{c}{2p^2} - \frac{c^2}{2}. \qquad (f)$$

Equations (e) and (f) give, in parametric form, the general solution required. Eliminating p between (e) and (f), we find the solution in rectangular form to be

$$x = \frac{y^2}{2c} - \frac{c^2}{2}, \qquad \text{or} \qquad \mathbf{y^2 = 2cx + c^3}.$$

Equation (d) is satisfied if $(1/2p) + yp^2 = 0$. Eliminating p between this equation and (a), we obtain the singular solution,

$$\mathbf{27y^4 = -32x^3}.$$

EXERCISES

1. Solve the following equations by the method of this article:

(a) $x = y + \log p$ (b) $y - 2px - p^2y = 0$

     (c) $xp^2 - 2yp + x + 2y = 0$

2. Find the solutions of the following equations in parametric form:

(a) $x = y + p^2$ (b) $4px = y + a^2p^2y$

3. Solve each equation by the method of this article. Also in each case equate to zero the factor that may be canceled from the equation in y, p, and dp/dy, and eliminate p between the result and the original equation to obtain a singular solution. In each case compare this singular solution with the p-discriminant and with the c-discriminant.

(a) $4pxy = 8y^2 + p^3$ (b) $py = p^2x + 1$ (c) $p^3 = y^5 + xpy^4$

4. Solve (a) $a^2yp^2 + y = 2xp$;   (b) $xy^2p^2 - y^3p = x$.

5. Solve, in three ways, $xp^2 - 2yp - x = 0$.

6. $p^3 + 4xyp - 8y^2 = 0$

37. Clairaut's equation

The equation

$$\mathbf{y = px + f(p)}, \tag{23}$$

known as **Clairaut's equation,** is named after Alexis Claude Clairaut (1713–1765). He was the first man to differentiate a differential equation, as we have done in §§35 and 36, in order to solve it.

Let us apply the method of §35 to equation (23). Differentiation with respect to x gives

$$\frac{dy}{dx} = p = p + \left(x + \frac{df}{dp}\right)\frac{dp}{dx}, \quad \text{or} \quad \left(x + \frac{df}{dp}\right)\frac{dp}{dx} = 0. \tag{24}$$

Then

$$\frac{dp}{dx} = 0 \quad \text{and} \quad p = c.$$

Substituting c for p in equation (23), we have

$$y = cx + f(c) \tag{25}$$

as the general solution. Thus, it appears that *to solve Clairaut's equation, it is necessary only to replace p by c.*

The particular solution arising from equating $x + (df/dp)$ to zero and eliminating p between the result and (23) gives a singular solution. In general, *the systems of lines represented by the general solution are the tangent lines of the graph of the singular solution.*

Since the equation

$$f(y - px, p) = 0, \tag{26}$$

when solved for $y - px$, takes the form

$$y - px = \psi(p),$$

it is really Clairaut's equation, and its solution is

$$f(y - cx, c) = 0. \tag{27}$$

Example. Find the equation of a curve having the sum of the intercepts on the tangent equal to a constant k.

Solution. Let $y = px + f(p)$ represent the tangents. Since the y-intercept is $f(p)$ and the x-intercept is $-f(p)/p$, we have

$$f(p) - \frac{f(p)}{p} = k, \quad \text{or} \quad f(p) = \frac{pk}{p - 1}. \tag{a}$$

Hence

$$y = px + \frac{kp}{p - 1}. \tag{b}$$

The singular solution of this is the required answer. Differentiation of (b) partially with respect to p gives $0 = x - k/(p - 1)^2$. Solving this and (b) simultaneously for x and y in terms of p, obtain

$$x = \frac{k}{(p-1)^2}, \qquad y = \frac{p^2k}{(p-1)^2}. \qquad (c)$$

EXERCISES

Find the solutions, general and singular, of the equations numbered 1 to 6:

1. $y = px + p^2$ **2.** $y = px + p^3$

3. $y = px \pm a \sqrt{1 + p^2}$ **4.** $3p^2e^y - px + 1 = 0$; let $z = e^y$

5. $y = 2px + y^2p^3$; let $z = y^2$ **6.** $y = 10px + y^{18}p^3$; let $z = y^{10}$

7. Using a method suggested by the illustrative example, find in each case the equation of the curve having the property that:

(a) Each of its tangent lines has intercepts whose difference is constant and equal to k.

(b) Each of its tangent lines together with the coordinate axes encloses a constant area equal to a^2.

(c) The distance from the origin to any tangent line is numerically equal to the square root of the square of the slope increased by 1.

8. Remembering that the distance from (m,n) to $y = px + f(p)$ is $\pm[n - mp - f(p)]/\sqrt{1 + p^2}$, find the equation of a curve such that the perpendiculars drawn from $(a,0)$ and $(-a,0)$ to the tangent have:

(a) The difference of their squares constant.

(b) The sum of their squares constant.

(c) Their sum constant.

(d) Their product constant.

9. To find the differential equation of the tangent lines to $F(x,y) = 0$, let $y = px + f(p)$ be the required equation and find $f(p)$ by using the fact that at any point (x_1, y_1) on the curve

$$f(p) = y_1 - px_1, \quad F(x_1, y_1) = 0, \quad \frac{\partial F(x_1, y_1)}{\partial x} + \frac{\partial F(x_1, y_1)}{\partial y}\, p = 0.$$

Find the differential equation of the tangent lines to

(a) $y^2 = x$ (b) $x^2 + y^2 = k^2$ (c) $xy + m = 0$

(d) $3y = x^3$ (e) $y = x^4$ (f) $x = 2y^4$

10. To find the equation of the evolute, or envelope of the normals, to $F(x,y) = 0$, find the p-discriminant of $y = px + f(p)$, where at any point (x_1, y_1) on $F(x,y) = 0$,

$$f(p) = y_1 - px_1, \quad F(x_1, y_1) = 0, \quad \frac{\partial F(x_1, y_1)}{\partial x} + \frac{\partial F(x_1, y_1)}{\partial y}\left(\frac{-1}{p}\right) = 0.$$

Find the equation of the evolute of

(a) $y^2 = 4x$ (b) $x^2 = 2y + 2$ (c) $2x^2y = 1$

CHAPTER VI

LINEAR DIFFERENTIAL EQUATIONS WITH
CONSTANT COEFFICIENTS

38. Operators

The operators discussed below furnish powerful and timesaving methods of solving many differential equations of outstanding importance.

We define operation D by

$$Du = \frac{du}{dx}, \; D^2u = \frac{d^2u}{dx^2}, \; \ldots, \; D^k u = \frac{d^k u}{dx^k}, \tag{1}$$

where u is a function of x. In general, if $f(D)$ and $\varphi(D)$ represent any two operations which we know how to perform on a function of x, $u(x)$, we speak of $f(D)$ and $\varphi(D)$ as operators,* and define the sum and the product of $f(D)$ and $\varphi(D)$ by

$$\begin{aligned} [\mathbf{f(D)} + \varphi\mathbf{(D)}]\mathbf{u} &= \mathbf{f(D)u} + \varphi\mathbf{(D)u}, \\ \mathbf{f(D)}\varphi\mathbf{(D)u} &= \mathbf{f(D)}[\varphi\mathbf{(D)u}]. \end{aligned} \tag{2}$$

Observe in the product formula that the operator adjacent to u is applied first. Illustrations of (2) are

$$(D^2 + 2D - 3)y = D^2y + 2\,Dy - 3y = \frac{d^2y}{dx^2} + 2\frac{dy}{dx} - 3y,$$

$$(D + 2)\,D(x^2 + 3x) = (D + 2)(2x + 3) = D(2x + 3) + 2(2x + 3)$$
$$= 4x + 8.$$

The elementary operators D^k obey the fundamental laws of algebra, for we have from calculus

$$\begin{aligned} (D^m + D^n)u &= (D^n + D^m)u, \\ [(D^m + D^n) + D^r]u &= [D^m + (D^n + D^r)]u, \\ D^m \cdot D^n u &= (D^n \cdot D^m)u = D^{m+n}u, \\ D^m(D^n \cdot D^r)u &= (D^m \cdot D^n)D^r u = D^{m+n+r}u, \\ D^m(D^n + D^r)u &= (D^m \cdot D^n + D^m \cdot D^r)u. \end{aligned}$$

* We shall be interested mainly in operators having the form of rational fractions in D.

Two operators are called equal if they produce equal results when applied to any function of the independent variable. Because of the fundamental laws, we may obtain from *a given operator other equal operators by multiplication, factorization, and introduction or removal of parentheses, just as in algebra.* Thus

$$(D^2 + 2D - 3)x^3 = -3x^3 + 6x^2 + 6x,$$
$$(D + 3)[(D - 1)x^3] = (D + 3)(-x^3 + 3x^2) = -3x^3 + 6x^2 + 6x.$$

Also negative indices will be used. We *define* $D^{-1}u = (1/D)u = v$ *to be such an expression v that* $Dv = u$, that is, an operator with a negative index is equivalent to an integration. We write then

$$v = D^{-1}u, \qquad Dv = D(D^{-1}u) = u, \qquad D \cdot D^{-1} = 1. \qquad (3)$$

These negative indices obey the laws of algebra except in considerations relating to the constants of integration. In general, if $f(y)$ represents a polynomial, $f(D)$ will be an operator, and the symbol $f^{-1}(D)$, or $1/f(D)$, will represent another operator such that

$$\mathbf{f(D)f^{-1}(D)u(x) = f(D)\frac{1}{f(D)}u = u.} \qquad (4)$$

Thus $y = (D - a)^{-1}u(x) = [1/(D - a)]u(x)$ is defined to be a function y such that

$$(D - a)y = (D - a)[(D - a)^{-1}u(x)] = u(x).$$

In other words $(D - a)^{-1}u(x)$ is the general solution of the differential equation $(D - a)y = u(x)$.

From the definitions and laws just stated it appears that many elementary transformations involving operators of the type $f_1(D)/f_2(D)$ may be carried out in accordance with the fundamental laws of algebra.

Example 1. Perform the operations indicated in

$$(D^2 - 2aD + a^2)(e^{ax} \sin x).$$

Solution

$$(D^2 - 2aD + a^2)(e^{ax} \sin x)$$
$$= (D - a)[(D - a)(e^{ax} \sin x)]$$
$$= (D - a)\left[\frac{d}{dx}(e^{ax} \sin x) - ae^{ax} \sin x\right]$$
$$= (D - a)[e^{ax} \cos x + ae^{ax} \sin x - ae^{ax} \sin x]$$
$$= -e^{ax} \sin x + ae^{ax} \cos x - ae^{ax} \cos x = \mathbf{-e^{ax} \sin x.}$$

Example 2. Express $y = (D - a)^{-1}x$ without operators.
Solution. Since $y = (D - a)^{-1}x$, we have

$$(D - a)y = (D - a)(D - a)^{-1}x = x.$$

The solution of this differential equation, found by the method of §22, is

$$\mathbf{y} = (\mathbf{D} - \mathbf{a})^{-1}\mathbf{x} = \frac{-1}{a^2}(\mathbf{ax} + 1) + \mathbf{ce}^{ax}.$$

EXERCISES

Perform the operations indicated in the following exercises:

1. (a) Dx^2 (b) $(D + 1)6x^2$ (c) $(D^2 - aD)e^{ax}$

2. (a) D^2e^{3x} (b) $(D - a)e^{ax}$

    (c) $(D^2 - a^2)\sin ax$ (d) $(D^2 - a^2)[(D^2 - a^2)\cos ax]$

    (e) $(D + 1)[(D + 1)(xe^{-x})]$ (f) $(D - 1)(D - 1)(x\cos x)$

3. (a) $(D + 4)^2e^{-3x}$ (b) $(D^2 + 4D + 4)^2(\cos 2x)$

    (c) $(D + 1)(D + 2)(D + 3)e^{-x}$ (d) $(D + 2)^2(D^2 - 4)(\sin 2x)$

4. (a) $D^{-1}(2x)$ (b) $D^{-2}(6x) = D^{-1}[D^{-1}(6x)]$

    (c) $D^{-3}\cos x = D^{-2}[D^{-1}(\cos x)]$ (d) $D^{-3}\sin 2x = D^{-2}[D^{-1}(\sin 2x)]$

5. (a) $(D - 1)^{-1}e^x$ (b) $(D + 3)^{-1}e^{3x}$ (c) $(3D - 4)^{-1}(xe^{\frac{4}{3}x})$

★**6.** $D^{-1}(D + 1)^{-1}e^{-x}$.   *Hint:* $D^{-1}(D + 1)^{-1}e^{-x} = D^{-1}[(D + 1)^{-1}e^{-x}]$.   First find a value for the bracket and then integrate it.

★**7.** (a) $(D - 1)^{-1}(D - 1)^{-1}e^x$ (b) $D^{-1}(D - 1)^{-1}e^x$

8. Does $D^2(xy)$ equal $xD^2y + y D^2x$? If u and v are functions of x, does $f(D)(uv)$ equal $uf(D)v + vf(D)u$? Does $f(D)(au)$ equal $af(D)u$, where a is a constant?

39. A basic theorem relating to operators

THEOREM. *If $\varphi(y)$ represents a polynomial, then*

$$\varphi(\mathbf{D})(\mathbf{e}^{ax}\mathbf{X}) = \mathbf{e}^{ax}\varphi(\mathbf{D} + \mathbf{a})\mathbf{X}, \tag{5}$$

where X is any function of x possessing all the derivatives indicated in (5).

    Proof. First we shall use mathematical induction in proving that

$$D^n(e^{ax}X) = e^{ax}(D + a)^nX. \tag{6}$$

When $n = 0$, each member of (6) is equal to $e^{ax}X$. Hence (6) is true when $n = 0$. Let k be any non-negative integer for which (6) holds. Then

$$D^k(e^{ax}X) = e^{ax}(D + a)^kX,$$

and, differentiating this, obtain

$$D^{k+1}(e^{ax}X) = D[e^{ax}(D + a)^kX] = e^{ax}D(D + a)^kX + ae^{ax}(D + a)^kX$$
$$= e^{ax}(D + a)^{k+1}X.$$

That is, if (6) holds when $n = k$, it holds when $n = k + 1$. Therefore, by complete induction, (6) is true when $n = 0$ or a positive integer.

Consequently, (5) holds, because each term in the left member equals the corresponding term in the right member.

As an illustration of (5), consider that

$$(D^2 + D)(e^{2x}x^3) = e^{2x}[(D + 2)^2 + D + 2]x^3 = e^{2x}(D^2 + 5D + 6)x^3$$
$$= e^{2x}(6x + 15x^2 + 6x^3).$$

The following special cases of (5) are useful. If $X = 1$, equation (5) becomes

$$\varphi(\mathbf{D})\mathbf{e}^{ax} = \mathbf{e}^{ax}\varphi(\mathbf{a}). \tag{7}$$

The result of replacing $\varphi(D)$ in (5) by $(D - a)^n$ is

$$(\mathbf{D} - \mathbf{a})^n(\mathbf{e}^{ax}\mathbf{X}) = \mathbf{e}^{ax}(\mathbf{D} - \mathbf{a} + \mathbf{a})^n\mathbf{X} = \mathbf{e}^{ax}\mathbf{D}^n\mathbf{X}, \tag{8}$$

and if X_{n-1} represents a polynomial of degree $n - 1$ or less, (8) becomes

$$(\mathbf{D} - \mathbf{a})^n(\mathbf{e}^{ax}\mathbf{X}_{n-1}) = \mathbf{e}^{ax}\mathbf{D}^n(\mathbf{X}_{n-1}) = \mathbf{0}. \tag{9}$$

Illustrations of (7), (8), and (9) follow:

$$(D^3 + 3D^2 + D - 1)e^{ax} = e^{ax}(a^3 + 3a^2 + a - 1),$$
$$(D - a)^5(e^{ax}x^6) = e^{ax}D^5x^6 = 6 \cdot 5 \cdot 4 \cdot 3 \cdot 2xe^{ax},$$
$$(D - 4)^7[e^{4x}(x^6 + 7x^2)] = e^{4x}D^7(x^6 + 7x^2) = 0.$$

EXERCISES

1. Use (7) to carry out the indicated operations:

(a) $(D^3 + 3D^2 - 21)e^{2x}$

(b) $(D - 2a)^5e^{ax}$

(c) $(D + a)^5e^{ax}$

(d) $(D^2 + 7D + 7)e^{-2x}$

(e) $(D + a)(D - a)e^{-ax}$

(f) $(D - 1)(D - 2)(D - 3)e^{-3x}$

2. Use (8) to carry out the indicated operations:

(a) $(D - 3)^3(x^2e^{3x})$

(b) $(D - 2)^3(x^4e^{2x})$

(c) $(D + 1)^8(e^{-x}\sin x)$

(d) $(D + 2)^4(e^{-2x}\cos x)$

(e) $(D + 1)^5[(D + 3)^3(x^3e^{-3x})]$

(f) $(D + 1)^n(x^ne^{-x})$

3. Use (9) to prove that (a) $y = e^{3x}(ax^3 + bx^2 + cx + d)$ is a solution of $(D - 3)^4y = 0$; (b) $y = e^{-x}(ax^2 + bx + c)$ is a solution of $(D + 2)(D + 1)^3y = 0$.

4. Use (5) to show that:

(a) $(D - 2)^4(e^{2x}\sin x) = e^{2x}D^4 \sin x = e^{2x}\sin x.$

(b) $[(D + 3)^5 + 2(D + 3)^3](e^{-3x}\cos 2x) = e^{-3x}(D^5 + 2D^3)\cos 2x$
$= -16e^{-3x}\sin 2x.$

(c) $(D^2 + D - 2)(e^{2x}\sin 2x) = e^{2x}(D^2 + 5D + 4)\sin 2x = 10e^{2x}\cos 2x.$

5. Using (5), carry out the indicated operations:

(a) $(D^3 + 1)(x^4 e^{-x})$ (b) $(D^3 - 3D^2 + 3D - 7)(e^x \cos x)$

(c) $(D^2 - 6D + 7)(e^{3x} \tan x)$ (d) $[(D - 1)^3 + D + 3)](x^2 e^x)$

6. Show that:

(a) $y = (x^3 + ax + b)e^x$ is a solution of $(D - 1)^2 y = 6xe^x$.

(b) $y = (x^4 + ax^2 + bx + c)e^{-2x}$ is a solution of $(D + 2)^3 y = 24xe^{-2x}$.

(c) $y = (x \log x + c_1 x + c_2)e^{2x}$ is a solution of $(D - 2)^2 y = x^{-1}e^{2x}$.

40. Linear differential equation

A **linear differential equation** *contains the dependent variable and all its derivatives to the first degree only.* Its general form is

$$L(D)y = (a_0 D^n + a_1 D^{n-1} + \cdots + a_{n-1}D + a_n)y = X, \quad (10)$$

where the a's and X are functions of x. If $X = 0$, the equation is said to be **homogeneous,** since each term is of the first degree in y and its derivatives.

A very important theorem relating to the operator $L(D)$ may be expressed by writing

$$L(D)(y_1 + y_2 + \cdots + y_m) = L(D)y_1 + L(D)y_2 + \cdots + L(D)y_m, \quad (11)$$

where $y_1, y_2, \ldots, y_m$ represent functions of x. To prove (11), observe that

$$D^k(y_1 + y_2 + \cdots + y_m) = D^k y_1 + D^k y_2 + \cdots + D^k y_m,$$

multiply both members of this by a_0 with $k = m$, by a_1 with $k = m - 1$, $\cdots$, by a_m with $k = 0$, in succession, and add the results to obtain (11).

Let $y_1(x), y_2(x), \ldots$ be solutions of (10) with $X = 0$. For these functions, the right member, and therefore the left member of (11), will be zero. Hence the following theorem is true:

THEOREM. *If $y_1(x), y_2(x), \ldots$ are solutions of a linear homogeneous equation, then their sum $y_1(x) + y_2(x) + \cdots$ is also a solution.*

If we think of $L(D)y$ as a force producing the displacement y, then (11) expresses that several forces $L(D)y_1, L(D)y_2 \ldots$ producing respective displacements $y_1, y_2, \ldots$ produce, when acting in combination, the displacement $y_1 + y_2 + \cdots$. This relation is often referred to as **superposition.** As an example, consider a beam projecting horizontally from a wall acted upon by its weight and a load hung on its end. Its total deflection y is $y_1 + y_2$, where y_1 is the deflection produced by its weight when acting alone and y_2 is the deflection produced by the load at its end. In the applications of linear differential equations, numerous illustrations of superposition are found.

41. Homogeneous linear differential equation with constant coefficients

We shall first find a method of solving equations of the type

$$(a_0D^n + a_1D^{n-1} + \cdots + a_{n-1}D + a_n)y = 0, \tag{12}$$

where the a's are constants.

A very special case of equation (12) is $Dy + ay = 0$, and its solution is $y = ce^{-ax}$. This suggests that an equation of the form

$$y = ce^{mx} \tag{13}$$

might be a solution of (12). Substituting $y = ce^{mx}$, $dy/dx = cme^{mx}$, $\ldots$, $d^ky/dx^k = cm^ke^{mx}$ in (12), we obtain

$$ce^{mx}(a_0m^n + a_1m^{n-1} + \cdots + a_{n-1}m + a_n) = 0.$$

This equation will be satisfied if m is a root of the equation

$$\mathbf{a_0m^n + a_1m^{n-1} + \cdots + a_{n-1}m + a_n = 0.} \tag{14}$$

Equation (14) is referred to as the **auxiliary equation**. Therefore, if $r_1, r_2, \ldots, r_n$ are the roots of (14), then the equations

$$y = c_1e^{r_1x}, \; y = c_2e^{r_2x}, \; \ldots, \; y = c_ne^{r_nx} \tag{15}$$

are all solutions of (12). Therefore, in accordance with the theorem of §40,

$$\mathbf{y = c_1e^{r_1x} + c_2e^{r_2x} + \cdots + c_ne^{r_nx}} \tag{16}$$

is a solution of (12). Since (16) contains n arbitrary constants, it is the general solution of (12) provided no two of the roots of (14) are equal.

Example. Solve

$$\frac{d^3y}{dx^3} + 2\frac{d^2y}{dx^2} - 3\frac{dy}{dx} = 0. \tag{a}$$

Solution. The auxiliary equation (14) in this case is

$$m^3 + 2m^2 - 3m = 0. \tag{b}$$

The roots of (b) are $1, -3, 0$. Hence the solution of (a), in accordance with (16), is

$$\mathbf{y = c_1e^x + c_2e^{-3x} + c_3.}$$

EXERCISES

1. $(D^2 - 3D + 2)y = 0$
2. $(D^2 + 4D - 5)y = 0$
3. $(D^2 + 4D + 3)y = 0$
4. $D^2y + 3y = 5Dy$
5. $(4D^3 - 5D)y = 0$ ✓
6. $D^3y = Dy$
7. $D^2y = k^2y$
8. $(D^3 - 3D^2 - D + 3)y = 0$ ✓
9. $(D^3 - 7D + 6)y = 0$
10. $(D^4 - D^3 - 7D^2 + 3D)y = 0$

42. Auxiliary equation has repeated roots

Let $r_1, r_2, \ldots, r_n$ be the roots of the auxiliary equation, and for convenience let us write

$$
\begin{aligned}
f(m) &= a_0 m^n + a_1 m^{n-1} + \cdots + a_{n-1} m + a_n \\
&= a_0 (m - r_1)(m - r_2) \cdots (m - r_n).
\end{aligned}
\tag{17}
$$

Equation (12) may then be written

$$
a_0 (D - r_1)(D - r_2) \cdots (D - r_n)y = f(D)y = 0.
\tag{18}
$$

If $f(m) = 0$ has a double root r, then by §41 the solution of (18) contains the two terms $c_1 e^{rx} + c_2 e^{rx}$; but since this may be written $(c_1 + c_2)e^{rx} = (\text{constant})e^{rx}$, only one arbitrary constant is involved. The solution, got by using (16) of §41, involves fewer than n independent arbitrary constants and consequently is not the general solution. Suppose that equation (14) contains r as a p-fold root. Equation (18) may then be written

$$
a_0 (D - r_1)(D - r_2) \cdots (D - r_{n-p})[(D - r)^p y] = 0.
\tag{19}
$$

Substituting

$$
y = (c_0 + c_1 x + c_2 x^2 + \cdots + c_{p-1} x^{p-1}) e^{rx}
\tag{20}
$$

in (19), and noting that, in accordance with equation (9) of §39, $(D - r)^p [(c_0 + c_1 x + \cdots + c_{p-1} x^{p-1})e^{rx}] = 0$, we obtain

$$
a_0 (D - r_1)(D - r_2) \cdots (D - r_{n-p})(0) = 0.
$$

Evidently this equation is true. Hence (20) is a particular solution of (18) corresponding to the p-fold root r. Since a like expression will apply for any other multiple root, it appears that, *if the roots of the auxiliary equation are*

$$
r(p\text{-fold}), \; s(q\text{-fold}), \; \ldots,
$$

the general solution is

$$
\begin{aligned}
\mathbf{y} = \mathbf{e}^{rx}(\mathbf{c}_0 + \mathbf{c}_1 \mathbf{x} + \cdots + \mathbf{c}_{p-1}\mathbf{x}^{p-1}) \\
+ \mathbf{e}^{sx}(\mathbf{b}_0 + \mathbf{b}_1 \mathbf{x} + \cdots + \mathbf{b}_{q-1}\mathbf{x}^{q-1}) + \cdots.
\end{aligned}
\tag{21}
$$

Example. Find the general solution of $(D^5 - 2D^4 + D^3)y = 0$.

Solution. The auxiliary equation is $m^5 - 2m^4 + m^3 = 0$, and its roots are 0, 0, 0, 1, 1. Hence in accordance with (21) the general solution is

$$
\mathbf{y} = \mathbf{c}_0 + \mathbf{c}_1 \mathbf{x} + \mathbf{c}_2 \mathbf{x}^2 + \mathbf{e}^x(\mathbf{c}_3 + \mathbf{c}_4 \mathbf{x}).
$$

43. Constants of integration from initial conditions

To determine the constants of integration from the general solution of a differential equation, replace the variables in the solution and the derivatives of the solution by given corresponding values, and solve the resulting equations for the required constants.

Example. Find the particular solution of $(D^3 - 6D^2 + 9D)y = 0$ which satisfies the initial conditions $y = 0$, $Dy = 2$, $D^2y = -6$ when $x = 0$.

Solution.   The auxiliary equation is $m^3 - 6m^2 + 9m = 0$, its roots are 0, 3, 3, and the general solution of the given equation is

$$y = c_1 + e^{3x}(c_2 + c_3x). \qquad (a)$$

By differentiation we obtain from (a)

$$Dy = e^{3x}(3c_2 + c_3 + 3c_3x),$$
$$D^2y = e^{3x}(9c_2 + 6c_3 + 9c_3x). \qquad (b)$$

Substitution of the initial conditions in (a) and (b) gives

$$0 = c_1 + e^0(c_2 + c_3 \cdot 0) = c_1 + c_2,$$
$$2 = 3c_2 + c_3, \qquad -6 = 9c_2 + 6c_3. \qquad (c)$$

Solving these equations for c_1, c_2, and c_3, we get

$$c_1 = -2, \qquad c_2 = 2, \qquad c_3 = -4.$$

The required particular solution, obtained by substituting these values of the c's in (a), is

$$y = -2 + e^{3x}(2 - 4x).$$

EXERCISES

For each of the following equations, find the general solution and, for each of exercises 11 to 16, the particular solution satisfying the given initial conditions:

1. $(D^2 - 6D + 9)y = 0$
2. $(D^2 + 4D + 4)y = 0$
3. $(D^3 - D^2)y = 0$
4. $(D^5 - 4D^3)y = 0$
5. $(D^3 - 2D^2 + D)y = 0$
6. $D^3y = 0$
7. $(D^3 - D^2 - D + 1)y = 0$
8. $(D^3 - 3D^2 + 3D - 1)y = 0$
9. $(D^6 - 8D^4 + 16D^2)y = 0$
10. $(D^5 - 12D^3 + 16D^2)y = 0$

11. $(D^2 - 2D + 1)y = 0$; $y = 5$, $Dy = -9$ when $x = 0$
12. $(D^2 + 2D + 1)y = 0$; $y = 1$, $Dy = -1$ when $x = 0$
13. $(D^2)(D - 1)y = 0$; $y = 2$, $Dy = 3$, $D^2y = 2$ when $x = 0$
14. $(D^3 + D^2)y = 0$; $y = 4$, $Dy = -2$, $D^2y = 4$ when $x = 0$
15. $(D^3 - 4D^2 + 4D)y = 0$; $y = 1$, $Dy = 2$, $D^2y = 8$ when $x = 0$
16. $(D^3 - D^2 - D + 1)y = 0$; $y = 0$, $Dy = 0$, $D^2y = 4$ when $x = 0$

44. Auxiliary equation has imaginary roots

If the coefficients of the auxiliary equation $f(m) = 0$ are real, and if $a + ib$ ($i = \sqrt{-1}$) is a root of it, then $a - ib$ is also a root. The corresponding terms of the general solution are

$$A e^{(a+ib)x} + B e^{(a-ib)x}, \quad \text{or} \quad e^{ax}(A e^{ibx} + B e^{-ibx}), \tag{22}$$

since $A e^{(a+ib)x} + B e^{(a-ib)x}$ may be written

$$A e^{ax} e^{ibx} + B e^{ax} e^{-ibx}.$$

By applying the following equation from complex-variable theory:

$$e^{i\theta} = \cos \theta + i \sin \theta \quad (i = \sqrt{-1}),$$

to (22), we get

$$e^{ax}(A \cos bx + Ai \sin bx + B \cos bx - Bi \sin bx),$$

or

$$e^{ax}[(A + B) \cos bx + i(A - B) \sin bx]. \tag{23}$$

Now letting $A = (c_2 - ic_1)/2$, $B = (c_2 + ic_1)/2$ in (23), we obtain

$$e^{ax}(c_2 \cos bx + c_1 \sin bx). \tag{24}$$

If we take $c = \sqrt{c_1^2 + c_2^2}$ and $\tan \alpha = c_2/c_1$, then (see Fig. 1)

$$\sin \alpha = \frac{c_2}{\sqrt{c_1^2 + c_2^2}}, \quad \cos \alpha = \frac{c_1}{\sqrt{c_1^2 + c_2^2}}.$$

Hence (24) may be written

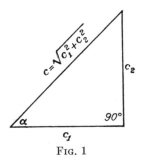

FIG. 1

$$e^{ax} \sqrt{c_1^2 + c_2^2} \left(\frac{c_2}{\sqrt{c_1^2 + c_2^2}} \cos bx + \frac{c_1}{\sqrt{c_1^2 + c_2^2}} \sin bx \right), \tag{25}$$

or

$$c e^{ax}(\sin \alpha \cos bx + \cos \alpha \sin bx), \tag{26}$$

or

$$c e^{ax} \sin (bx + \alpha), \tag{27}$$

where c and α are arbitrary constants. The part of the general solution corresponding to a pair of complex roots $a \pm ib$ is generally written in the form (24) or (27).

In the case of a double pair of complex roots, the corresponding terms of the general solution are

$$e^{ax}[(A_0 + A_1x) \cos bx + (B_0 + B_1x) \sin bx],* \tag{28}$$

or

$$e^{ax}[c_0 \sin (bx + \alpha_0) + c_1x \sin (bx + \alpha_1)], \tag{29}$$

and a similar extension applies for a p-fold multiple pair of complex roots.

Example.   Solve $(D^3 - 3D^2 + 9D + 13)y = 0$.

Solution.   The roots of the auxiliary equation are -1, $2 \pm 3i$. Hence the general solution is

$$y = c_1e^{-x} + e^{2x}(c_2 \sin 3x + c_3 \cos 3x),$$

or

$$y = c_1e^{-x} + ce^{2x} \sin (3x + \alpha).$$

EXERCISES

Solve the following equations and determine the constants of integration where initial conditions are given:

1. $(D^2 - 2D + 2)y = 0$
2. $D(D^2 - 4D + 5)y = 0$
3. $(D - 2)(D^2 + 2D + 10)y = 0$
4. $(D^2 + 4)y = 0$
5. $(D^2 + k^2)y = 0$
6. $(D^4 - a^4)y = 0$
7. $(D^4 + 8D^2 + 16)y = 0$
8. $(D^4 + D^2)y = 0$
9. $(D^6 + 6D^4 + 9D^2)y = 0$
10. $(D^3 + a^3)y = 0$

11. $(D^4 - D^2 - 18D - 18)y = 0$
12. $(D^2 + 1)y = 0$; $y = 1$, $Dy = -1$ when $x = \pi$
13. $(D^2 + 9)y = 0$; $y = 2$, $Dy = 0$ when $x = \pi/6$
14. $(D^2 + 2D + 2)y = 0$; $y = 0$, $Dy = 1$ when $x = 0$
15. $(D^3 - 2D^2 + 2D)y = 0$; $y = 1$, $Dy = 1$, $D^2y = 2$ when $x = 0$
★16. $(D^3 - 2D + 4)y = 0$; $y = -2$, $Dy = 8$, $D^2y = 0$ when $x = 0$
17. $(D^2 + 4)y = 0$; $y = 4$, $Dy = 0$ when $x = 1$.   *Hint:* Write the solution in the form $y = c_1 \sin 2(x - 1) + c_2 \cos 2(x - 1)$.

45. Right-hand member not zero

To solve the equation

$$(a_0D^n + a_1D^{n-1} + \cdots + a_{n-1}D + a_n)y = X, \tag{30}$$

where the a's are constants and X is a function of x, we shall write

$$y = y_c + y_p, \tag{31}$$

where $y = y_c$ is the general solution of (30) with X replaced by zero, and $y = y_p$ is a particular solution of (30).   Equation (31) is a solution of (30) involving n independent arbitrary constants and hence is the

---

* This may be proved by substituting expression (28) or (29) for y in $[(D - a)^2 + b^2]^2y = 0$.

general solution. y_c is referred to as the *complementary function* and is found as in §§41 to 44. y_p may be found by various methods, one of which, the *method of undetermined coefficients,* is illustrated below. *This method applies when the right-hand member consists of terms from which only a finite number of terms can be got by differentiation.* Many of the equations arising in practice may be solved by this method.

Consider the solution of the equation

$$(D^2 + 3D + 2)y = 4x - 20 \cos 2x. \tag{a}$$

Solving the equation obtained by replacing the right member by zero, we get

$$y_c = c_1 e^{-x} + c_2 e^{-2x}. \tag{b}$$

To get a particular solution of (*a*), let

$$y_p = Ax + B + C \cos 2x + E \sin 2x, \tag{c}$$

and try to find numbers for A, B, C, and E such that y_p from (*c*), when substituted for y in (*a*), satisfies it.   Substituting y_p from (*c*) and

$$\begin{aligned} Dy_p &= A - 2C \sin 2x + 2E \cos 2x, \\ D^2 y_p &= -4C \cos 2x - 4E \sin 2x \end{aligned} \tag{d}$$

in (*a*) for y, Dy, D^2y, we obtain after simplification

$$2Ax + (2B + 3A) + (6E - 2C) \cos 2x - (6C + 2E) \sin 2x$$
$$= 4x + 0 - 20 \cos 2x + 0 \sin 2x. \tag{e}$$

Since (*e*) is to be an identity, the coefficients of like terms must be equal.   Hence

$$2A = 4, \quad 2B + 3A = 0, \quad 6E - 2C = -20, \quad -6C - 2E = 0. \tag{f}$$

Solving (*f*) for A, B, C, and E, we get

$$A = 2, \quad B = -3, \quad C = 1, \quad E = -3. \tag{g}$$

Hence, from (*c*) and (*g*), $y_p = 2x - 3 + \cos 2x - 3 \sin 2x$, and the general solution is

$$\mathbf{y = y_c + y_p = c_1 e^{-x} + c_2 e^{-2x} + 2x - 3 + \cos 2x - 3 \sin 2x.}$$

The question arises: What terms are assumed in the trial y_p?   *To get the trial form of y_p, write the variable part* of each term in the right-hand member X together with the variable parts of any terms that may be derived by differentiating X repeatedly, multiply each of these terms by an*

---

* It is assumed that the variable part of a constant term is 1.

arbitrary constant, and equate y_p to the sum of the terms thus obtained.
Observe that, in forming y_p in (c), we chose a term Ax and a term C
$\cos 2x$, also a constant term B since $Dx = 1$, a constant, and a term E
$\sin 2x$ because $D \cos 2x = -2 \sin 2x$. If any of these terms had been
omitted, the corresponding number of equations would have been
greater than the number of unknowns and there would have been no
solution.

EXERCISES

Solve the following equations and determine the constants of integration where
initial conditions are given:

1. $(D^2 + 4)y = 8x + 4$.   *Hint: Let $y_p = Ax + B$*

2. $(D^2 + D - 2)y = 3 - 6x$ ✓   **3.** $(D^2 + 2D - 8)y = 16x - 12$
4. $(D^2 - D - 2)y = 6e^x$ **5.** $(D^2 + 1)y = 3 + 6e^x$
6. $(D + 2)^2y = x + 8e^{2x}$ ✓   **7.** $(D^3 + D)y = 6 \sin 2x$
8. $(D^3 - D^2)y = 2 \cos x$ ✓   **9.** $(D^2 + 1)y = 10e^x \sin x$

10. $(D^2 - 1)y = 2x^2$. Let $y = Ax^2 + Bx + C$
11. $(D^2 - 9)y = 18 \cos 3x + 9$; $y = -1$, $Dy = 3$ when $x = 0$
12. $(D^2 + D - 6)y = 2 - 12x$; $y = 3$, $Dy = -7$ when $x = 0$
13. $(D^2 + D)y = e^x$; $y = 3$, $Dy = 0$ when $x = \log 2$
★14. $(D^2 + 4D + 3)y = 8xe^x - 6$; $y = -\frac{11}{4}$, $Dy = \frac{1}{4}$ when $x = 0$
★15. $(D^3 - 4D)y = 6e^{-x} - 3e^x$; $y = 7$, $Dy = 9$, $D^2y = 19$ when $x = \log 2$

46. Special case when the right-hand member is not zero

Terms having the same variable part will be referred to as **like terms.**
Thus, $5 \sin 2x$, $A \sin 2x$, and $(3B + C) \sin 2x$ are like terms.

It may happen that a term in the trial solution of $f(D)y = X$, found
in accordance with the method of §45, is like a term in the complementary function. Such a term will give zero when substituted in the
left member $f(D)y$ because it is a solution of $f(D)y = 0$; hence it cannot
function to give a term like itself. For example, consider the equation

$$(D^2 + 4)y = \sin 2x. \tag{32}$$

Here $y_c = c_1 \sin 2x + c_2 \cos 2x$. Letting $y_p = A \sin 2x + B \cos 2x$
and substituting in (32), we get the impossible equation $0 \equiv \sin 2x$.
The process for multiple roots suggest that a factor x be introduced.
Hence we use

$$y_p = x(A \sin 2x + B \cos 2x). \tag{33}$$

Substituting this value of y_p in (32), we obtain after slight simplification

$$4A \cos 2x - 4B \sin 2x = \sin 2x.$$

Hence

$$4A = 0, \quad -4B = 1, \quad \text{or} \quad A = 0, B = -\tfrac{1}{4},$$

and the solution of (32) is

$$y = y_c + y_p = c_1 \sin 2x + c_2 \cos 2x - \tfrac{1}{4}x \cos 2x. \tag{34}$$

As another example, consider

$$(D^2 - 2D + 1)y = xe^x + 5. \tag{35}$$

The complementary function is

$$y_c = (c_1 + c_2 x)e^x. \tag{36}$$

Divide the task of finding y_p into two parts: that of finding the particular solution relating to xe^x, and that relating to 5. For the part xe^x we write

$$y_{p_1} = x^2(A + Bx)e^x. \tag{37}$$

The part $(A + Bx)e^x$ was written in accordance with §45, and the factor x^2 was supplied to make y_{p_1} unlike the complementary function. Substituting y_{p_1} from (37) in the left member of (35) and equating the result to xe^x, we obtain after simplification

$$e^x(6Bx + 2A) = xe^x.$$

Equating the coefficients of like terms, we get $B = \tfrac{1}{6}$, $A = 0$, and $y_{p_1} = \tfrac{1}{6}x^3 e^x$. The particular solution of (35) relating to 5, found by the regular procedure of §45, is $y_{p_2} = 5$. Hence the solution of (35) is

$$y = y_c + y_{p_1} + y_{p_2} = (c_1 + c_2 x)e^x + \tfrac{1}{6}x^3 e^x + 5.$$

Observe that, in forming a trial y_p for any term in the right-hand member, it is first formed by the method of §45 and then multiplied by x^n, where n is the least integer that will make each term of the trial y_p unlike any term in the complementary function.

EXERCISES

  1. $(D^2 + D)y = 4x.$ *Hint:* Take $y_p = x(Ax + B)$
  2. $(D^2 - 1)y = 5e^x.$ *Hint:* Take $y_p = Axe^x$

Find a particular solution of each of the following differential equations.

  3. $(D^2 + D)y = e^{-x}$ **4.** $(D^3 + D^2 - 2D)y = 8x$
  5. $(D^2 + 1)y = \sin x$ **6.** $(D^2 - 1)y = e^{-x}$
  7. $(D^2 + 4D + 3)y = 3x + e^{-x}$ **8.** $(D^2 - 2D + 1)y = e^x + 3$
  9. $(D^2 + 4D + 3)y = 4e^{-3x} - 2e^{-x}$ **10.** $(D^2 + 4)y = \cos 2x$
  11. $(D^2 + 2D)y = 8x + e^{-2x}$ **12.** $(D^3 + 4D)y = 16 \sin 2x$

13. $(D^3 + 4D)y = 8 \cos 2x + 4$
★14. $(D^3 - 2D^2 + 5D)y = 10 + 15 \cos 2x$
★15. $(D^2 - 2D + 1)y = 6xe^x$
★16. $(D^2 - 2D + 2)y = e^x \sin x$

47. Methods using symbolic operators

The student should review §§38 and 39 at this point, especially equations (4) and (5). Throughout this article $f(D)$, $\varphi(D)$, and $\psi(D)$ refer to polynomials in D, and X refers to a function of x possessing all derivatives and integrals involved.

First let us prove that the equation

$$\varphi(D)y = e^{ax}X, \quad \text{or} \quad y = \varphi^{-1}(D)(e^{ax}X) = \frac{1}{\varphi(D)}(e^{ax}X) \quad (38)$$

has $y = e^{ax}[1/\varphi(D + a)]X$ as a solution; in other words

$$\frac{1}{\varphi(D)}(Xe^{ax}) = e^{ax}\frac{1}{\varphi(D + a)}X, \quad (39)$$

where $=$ *means* **equivalent** *in the sense that both are solutions of* (38). The left member of (39) is a solution of (38) by definition. Operating on the right member of (39) with $\varphi(D)$, we get

$$\varphi(D)\left[e^{ax}\frac{1}{\varphi(D + a)}X\right] = e^{ax}\varphi(D + a)\frac{1}{\varphi(D + a)}X = e^{ax}X,$$

by (5) of §39 and by definition. Hence (39) is true.

Another useful equation will be obtained. Since

$$D^2(\sin ax) = -a^2 \sin ax, \quad D^2(\cos ax) = -a^2 \cos ax,$$

it appears that

$$\varphi(D^2) \sin ax = \varphi(-a^2) \sin ax, \quad \varphi(D^2)(\cos ax) = \varphi(-a^2) \cos ax. \quad (40)$$

For example

$$(D^2 + 1)^2 \sin 2x = (-2^2 + 1)^2 \sin 2x = 9 \sin 2x.$$

Furthermore *a solution of* $\varphi(D^2)y = \sin ax$ is

$$y = \frac{1}{\varphi(D^2)} \sin ax = \frac{1}{\varphi(-a^2)} \sin ax, \quad (41)$$

provided $\varphi(-a^2) \neq 0$; for

$$\varphi(D^2)\left[\frac{1}{\varphi(-a^2)}\sin ax\right] = \varphi(-a^2)\frac{1}{\varphi(-a^2)}\sin ax = \sin ax.$$

A similar argument shows that the result of replacing $\sin ax$ by $\cos ax$ in (41) holds true. Two other simple results are useful. First

$$\frac{1}{D}X = \int X\,dx, \qquad \frac{1}{D^2}X = \int (\textstyle\int X\,dx)\,dx, \qquad \cdots \qquad (42)$$

Also when X is a polynomial of degree n in x, a solution of $(D + a)y = X$, or $y = [1/(D + a)]X$ is given by

$$y = \frac{1}{D + a}X = \frac{1}{a}\left(\frac{1}{1 + D/a}\right)X = \frac{1}{a}\left[1 - \frac{D}{a} + \frac{D^2}{a^2} - \cdots\right.$$

$$\left. + (-1)^n\frac{D^n}{a^n}\right]X; \quad (43)$$

for, operating on the third member of (43), we get

$$(D + a)\left[\frac{1}{a}\left(1 - \frac{D}{a} + \cdots + (-1)^n\frac{D^n}{a^n}\right)X\right] = \left[1 - \left(\frac{D}{a}\right)^{n+1}\right]X,$$

and since $D^{n+1}X = 0$, this is equal to X.

Example 1. Find a particular solution of

$$(D - 2)^2 y = x^5 e^{2x}.$$

Solution. Using (39) and (42) in succession, we have

$$y = \frac{1}{(D - 2)^2}(x^5 e^{2x}) = e^{2x}\frac{1}{D^2}x^5 = \frac{x^7 e^{2x}}{42}.$$

Example 2. Find a particular solution of

$$(D - 2)^3(D - 1)y = 6(x^2 + 2x)e^{2x}.$$

Solution. Using (39), (43), and (42) in order, we get

$$y = \frac{1}{(D - 2)^3(D - 1)}(6x^2 + 12x)e^{2x}$$

$$= e^{2x}\frac{1}{D^3(D + 1)}(6x^2 + 12x)$$

$$= e^{2x}\left(\frac{1}{D^3}\right)(6x^2 + 12x - 12x - 12 + 12)$$

$$= \frac{1}{10}x^5 e^{2x}.$$

Example 3. Find a particular solution of $(D^2 + 1)y = e^x \sin x.$ ✓
Solution. Using (39) and (41) in succession, obtain

$$y = \frac{1}{D^2 + 1}(e^x \sin x) = e^x \frac{1}{(D + 1)^2 + 1} \sin x$$

$$= e^x \frac{1}{(D^2 + 2) + 2D} \sin x = \frac{(D^2 + 2) - 2D}{(D^2 + 2)^2 - 4D^2} \sin x*$$

$$= e^x \frac{(-1 + 2) - 2D}{(-1 + 2)^2 + 4} \sin x = \frac{1}{5} e^x (\sin x - 2 \cos x). ✓$$

Example 4. To solve $(D - 1)(D - 2)y = x^2 e^{2x}$, break

$$\frac{1}{(D - 1)(D - 2)}$$

into fractions and use the result to operate on $x^2 e^{2x}$.

Solution. $1/[(D - 1)(D - 2)] = 1/(D - 2) - 1/(D - 1)$. For zero constants of integration, the two members of this operator equation give equivalent results, as may be seen by applying $(D - 1)(D - 2)$ to each member operating on $u(x)$. Hence, using partial fractions, (39), (42), and (43) in succession, obtain

$$y = \frac{1}{(D - 1)(D - 2)} x^2 e^{2x} = \left(\frac{1}{D - 2} - \frac{1}{D - 1}\right) x^2 e^{2x}$$

$$= e^{2x}\left(\frac{1}{D} - \frac{1}{D + 1}\right) x^2 = e^{2x}\left[\frac{x^3}{3} - (1 - D + D^2)x^2\right]$$

$$= e^{2x}\left(\frac{x^3}{3} - x^2 + 2x - 2\right).$$

* Consider the operator got by multiplying numerator and denominator of an operator by the same polynomial in D. Let $f(D)$ and $\varphi(D)$ be polynomials. From equation (4) of §38

$$f(D)\left[\frac{1}{f(D)}\right]u(x) = u(x). \tag{a}$$

Denote the value of $[1/f(D)]f(D) u(x)$ by $u(x) + g(x)$; then

$$\left[\frac{1}{f(D)}\right]f(D)u = u + g. \tag{b}$$

Operating on both members of (b) by $f(D)$, obtain

$$f(D)u = f(D)u + f(D)g. \tag{c}$$

Equation (c) will hold if $f(D)g = 0$, and $f(D)g = 0$ provided that all constants of integration are zero. Hence in *finding a particular solution of* $\varphi(D)y = V(x)$, *we may use*

$$y = \frac{V}{\varphi(D)} = \frac{f(D)}{f(D)\varphi(D)} V \tag{d}$$

and carry out the operations in any order provided that all constants of integration are taken to be zero.

EXERCISES

In exercises 1 to 3, take all constants of integration zero.

1. Using (39), carry out the indicated operations:

(a) $\dfrac{1}{(D - 1)^3}(xe^x)$ (b) $\dfrac{1}{(D + 3)^2}(e^{-3x}\sin x)$ (c) $\dfrac{2D - 2}{(D - 2)^2}(e^{2x}\cos x)$

2. Use (40) and (41) to carry out the indicated operations:

(a) $\left[\dfrac{1}{(D^2 + 4)^2}\right]\sin 3x$ (b) $\dfrac{D + 1}{D^2 + 9}\sin 2x$ (c) $\dfrac{1}{(D^2 + 1) + 2D}\cos x$

3. Use (42) and (43) to carry out the indicated operations:

(a) $(D - 1)^{-1}x^2$ (b) $(D + 4)^{-1}x^2$ (c) $[(D + 3)D]^{-1}x$

Find a particular solution of each differential equation:

4. $(D - 3)^2y = 48xe^{3x}$. Write $y = [1/(D - 3)^2](48xe^{3x})$ and use (39) and (42).

5. $(D - 1)^2y = x^5e^x$. Use (39) and (42).

6. $(D + 1)^3y = 16(2x + 3)^{-3}e^{-x}$

7. $(D + 2)(D - 2)y = 64xe^{2x}$. Write $y = [1/(D^2 - 4)](64xe^{2x}) = 64e^{2x}[1/(D + 4)](1/D)x$. Use (39), (42), and (43).

8. $(D^2 - 2D - 3)y = 64xe^{3x}$

9. $(D^4 + 2D^2 + 1)y = \sin 2x$. Write $[1/(D^2 + 1)^2]\sin 2x$ and use (41).

10. $(D^2 + 1)y = \sin 2x + \cos 3x$. Use (41) on each term of the right-hand member.

11. $(D^4 - 1)y = 40 \sin 3x - 30 \cos 2x$. Use (41).

12. $(D - 1)^3y = e^x \cos x$. Use (39) and (42).

13. $[(D - 1)^2 + 1]y = 24e^x \sin 3x$. Use (39) and (41).

★**14.** $(D^2 + 4)y = 9e^x \sin 2x$. Read Example 3.

★**15.** $(D^2 - D + 2)y = 58e^x \cos 3x$. Read Example 3.

16. $(D - 1)^2y = e^x \sin x + e^{2x} \cos x$

17. $D(D - 1)^2y = xe^x$ **18.** $[(D - 1)^2 + 2]^3y = e^x \cos x$

19. $(D^2 + 4)y = e^x \sin 2x$ **20.** $(D^2 - 4D + 2)y = 8e^x \cos x$

Using the method of Example 4, solve the differential equations numbered 21 to 25:

21. $(D - 1)(D - 2)y = x^2e^{3x}$ **22.** $(D^2 - 4)y = 27x^2e^{2x}$

23. $(D + 1)(D - 3)y = 16xe^{3x}$ **24.** $(D - 3)(D + 2)y = e^{2x}(2 + 6x - 4x^2)$

25. $D(D + 1)(D + 3)y = e^{-3x}(12x - 10)$

26. In the solution of this exercise, it is assumed (a) that the regular methods of operators applying for real variables apply also to functions containing complex variables and constants; and (b) that, with $\overline{RP}$ denoting *real part of*,

$$\frac{f(D)}{\varphi(D)}\overline{RP}u = \overline{RP}\,\frac{f(D)}{\varphi(D)}u.$$

Check the steps of the following indicated solution of $(D^2 + 4)y = 32 \cos 2x$:

$$y = \frac{1}{D^2 + 4}\,(\overline{RP}32e^{i2x})^* = \overline{RP}\left(e^{i2x}\,\frac{32}{D^2 + 4iD}\right) = \overline{RP}\left(e^{i2x}\,\frac{D - 4i}{D^2 + 16}\,32x\right)$$

$$= \overline{RP}(\cos 2x + i \sin 2x)\frac{32}{16}\left(1 - \frac{D^2}{16}\right)(1 - 4ix) = \mathbf{2 \cos 2x + 8x \sin 2x}.$$

Using the method of exercise 26, solve the differential equations numbered 27 to 30:

27. $(D^2 + 1)y = 4 \cos x$ 28. $(D^2 + 9)y = 36 \sin 3x$
29. $(D^2 + 1)y = 16x \cos x$ ★30. $(D^2 + 4)y = 64x \sin 2x + 32 \cos 2x$

48. Variation of parameters ✓✓

The methods used in §§45 to 47 generally fail to give a solution when the derivatives of the right-hand member X do not contain a finite number of terms. We shall therefore consider the general method of variation of parameters. The following solution illustrates this method.

Example. Solve

$$(D^3 + D)y = \sec x. \tag{a}$$

Solution. The solution of $(D^3 + D)y = 0$ is

$$y = A \sin x + B \cos x + C. \tag{b}$$

Now we assume that (b) is the solution of (a) where A, B, C are functions of x to be determined. From (b)

$$D(y) = A \cos x - B \sin x + A' \sin x + B' \cos x + C', \tag{c}$$

where the primes denote derivatives with respect to x. A, B, and C, being three arbitrary functions, may be subjected to three conditions; hence let us assume further that

$$A' \sin x + B' \cos x + C' = 0. \tag{d}$$

Then

$$D^2y = -A \sin x - B \cos x + A' \cos x - B' \sin x. \tag{e}$$

Let

$$A' \cos x - B' \sin x = 0. \tag{f}$$

Then

$$D^3y = -A \cos x + B \sin x - A' \sin x - B' \cos x. \tag{g}$$

Substituting y and its derivatives from (b), (c), (e), and (g) in (a) while taking account of (d) and (f), we get, after slight simplification,

$$-A' \sin x - B' \cos x = \sec x. \tag{h}$$

* Since $e^{ikx} = \cos kx + i \sin kx$, we have

$$\cos kx = \overline{RP}e^{ikx}, \qquad \sin kx = \overline{RP}(-ie^{ikx}).$$

The solution of (d), (f), and (h) for A', B', and C' is

$$A' = -\tan x, \qquad B' = -1, \qquad C' = \sin x \tan x + \cos x = \sec x. \qquad (i)$$

Solving (i) for A, B, and C, obtain

$$A = \log\cos x + c_1, \qquad B = -x + c_2, \qquad C = \log(\sec x + \tan x) + c_3. \qquad (j)$$

Substituting the values of A, B, and C from (j) in (b), obtain

$$\mathbf{y = (\log \cos x + c_1)\sin x + (c_2 - x)\cos x + \log(\sec x + \tan x) + c_3.}$$

EXERCISES

1. To solve $(D^2 + 1)y = \tan x$, write

$$y = A\sin x + B\cos x, \qquad (a)$$

find Dy treating A, B, and x as variables, and take

$$A'\sin x + B'\cos x = 0. \qquad (b)$$

Find D^2y and substitute Dy and D^2y in the given differential equation to obtain, after simplification,

$$A'\cos x - B'\sin x = \tan x. \qquad (c)$$

Solve (b) and (c) for A' and B', integrate the results to find A and B, and then replace A and B in (a) by these values.

Solve exercise 1, and then solve the following differential equations by using the same methods:

2. $(D^2 + 1)y = \sec x$ **3.** $(D^2 + 4)y = 4\cot 2x$
4. $(D^2 + 2D + 2)y = e^{-x}\sec x$ ★**5.** $(D - 2)^2y = x^ne^{2x}$
6. $(D + 2)^2y = x^{-2}e^{-2x}$ **7.** $(D + 1)^2y = x^{-2}e^{-x}\log x$

8. $(D^2 - 2D + 2)y = e^x(\tan x + \cot x)$
★**9.** $(D^3 - 3D^2 + 4D - 2)y = e^x\sec x$
★**10.** $(D - 1)^3y = 18x^{-4}e^x\log x$

49. Summary

In this section a linear differential equation with constant coefficients will be referred to as $L(D)y = X$. The general solution of $L(D)y = X$ is

$$y = y_c + y_p,$$

where y_c refers to the general solution of $L(D)y = 0$ and y_p is a particular solution of $L(D)y = X$.

To solve an equation of the type $L(D)y = 0$, find the roots of the auxiliary equation $L(m) = 0$ and then write the solution in accordance with (16) of §41, (21) of §42, and (24) and (27) of §44.

The shortest methods of finding particular solutions of equations coming under the type $L(D)y = X$ are the operator methods based on equations (39), (40), (42), and (43) of §47. The method of exercise 26 of §47 is especially powerful when equation (40) fails. The methods of §§45 and 46 are instructive but generally cumbersome.

When D^kX, $k = 1, 2, 3, \ldots$, has an endless array of variable parts, the method of variation of parameters, §48, should be used.

EXERCISES

Solve the differential equations 1 to 10 and determine the constants of integration from the given conditions.

 1. $(D^2 - 4)y = 0$; $y = 3$, $Dy = 6$, when $x = 0$
 2. $D^2(D - 3)y = 6$; $y = 1$, $Dy = -1$, $D^2y = -2$, when $x = 1$
 3. $(D - 1)^2y = x^2 - 3x$; $y = 0$, $Dy = 2$, when $x = 0$
 4. $(D^2 - 1)y = \sin x$; $y = 1$, $Dy = -\frac{0}{2}$, when $x = 0$
 5. $(D^2 - 4)y = 25e^{3x}$; $y = 0$, $Dy = 5$, when $x = 0$
 6. $D(D^2 + 1)y = -6 \cos 2x$; $y = 1$, $Dy = -3$, $D^2y = 0$, when $x = \frac{\pi}{2}$
★7. $(D - 1)(D^2 + 1)y = 5e^x \sin x$; $y = 0$, $Dy = -2$, $D^2y = -3$, when $x = 0$
★8. $D^2(D + 1)y = 4xe^x$; $y = -4$, $Dy = -4$, $D^2y = 0$, when $x = 0$
★9. $D(D - 1)(D + 1)y = 6 + 130 \cos 5x$; $y = 1$, $Dy = -12$, $D^2y = 1$, when $x = 0$
★10. $(D^2 + 2D + 2)y = e^x(\cos 2x - 8 \sin 2x)$; $y = 0$, $Dy = 2$, when $x = 0$

Find particular solutions of the following differential equations:

11. $(D^2 - 4)y = 48e^{2x}$ 12. $(D^2 - 4)y = 64xe^{2x}$
13. $(4D^2 + 9D + 5)y = e^{-x} + 5$ 14. $D^2(D + 1)y = x^2e^{-x}$
15. $(2D^2 + D - 3)y = 15e^x + 20e^{-\frac{3}{2}x}$ 16. $(D^2 + 1)y - 3 \sin 2x + 8 \cos 3x$
17. $(D^2 + D + 14)y = 50 \sin 4x$ 18. $D(D^2 + 11)y = 40(\sin 4x + \cos 4x)$

Use the method suggested by exercise 26 of §47 to solve equations 19 to 22.

19. $(D^2 + 9)y = 12 \cos 3x$ 20. $(D^2 + 9)y = 72x \cos 3x$
21. $(D^2 - 2D + 2)y = 4e^x \sin x$ 22. $(D^2 + 4D + 5)y = 12e^{-2x} \cos x$

23. $(D^2 + 1)y = -x^{-2} \sin x + 2x^{-1} \cos x$ 24. $(D^2 + 1)y = 2 \sec^3 x$

25. $(D^2 + 4)y - 8 \tan^2 2x$ 26. $(D^2 + 2D - 8)y = (6x^{-1} - x^{-2})e^{2x}$

50. Simultaneous differential equations *omit*

A solution of n simultaneous equations in $n + 1$ unknowns consists of n independent relations involving one or more of these unknowns but not their derivatives; if these n relations are solved for n of the unknown quantities in terms of the remaining one, and if the results are substituted in the given differential equations, identities must result. *The first object in solving such a system is so to combine the given equations and other equations derived from them as to obtain an equation in two unknowns.* This may be integrated to obtain one relation, and the result may be used to obtain other relations. In the process of eliminating variables, we often find that operators can be used to advantage., Using the facts relating to operators in §§38, 39, and 47, we shall find the process of elimination in the case of linear equations with constant coefficients to be very much like an analogous process of elimination used in algebra.

Example. Solve

$$\frac{dx}{dt} + \frac{dy}{dt} + y - x = e^{2t},$$

$$\frac{d^2x}{dt^2} + \frac{dy}{dt} = 3e^{2t}. \tag{a}$$

Solution. Replacing d/dt by D, we may write the equations (a) in the form

$$(D - 1)x + (D + 1)y = e^{2t},$$
$$D^2x + Dy = 3e^{2t}. \tag{b}$$

Operating on the first of equations (b) with D and on the second with $(D + 1)$, we obtain

$$(D^2 - D)x + D(D + 1)y = De^{2t} = 2e^{2t},$$
$$(D^3 + D^2)x + (D + 1)\,Dy = D(3e^{2t}) + 3e^{2t} = 9e^{2t}. \tag{c}$$

Subtracting the first of equations (c) from the second, we get

$$(D^3 + D)x = 7e^{2t}. \tag{d}$$

The solution of this equation is

$$x = c_1 + c_2 \sin t + c_3 \cos t + \tfrac{7}{10}e^{2t}. \tag{e}$$

Substituting the value of x from (e) in the second equation of (b) and integrating the resulting equation, we obtain

$$y = \tfrac{1}{10}e^{2t} - c_2 \cos t + c_3 \sin t + c_4. \tag{f}$$

There may be too many constants of integration in the solution given by (e) and (f). It can be shown* that the number of constants of integration to be expected in the general solution of a system of simultaneous linear differential equations with constant coefficients is the same as the degree in D of the determinant of the equations. Thus the determinant of (b) is

$$\begin{vmatrix} D - 1 & D + 1 \\ D^2 & D \end{vmatrix},$$

---

* See INCE, E. L., "Ordinary Differential Equations," p. 150.

its degree is three, and there should be only three constants of integration in the solution of (a).

The general procedure in finding any relation that may exist between the constants is to substitute the solution in one of the original equations, simplify as much as possible, and equate the coefficients of like terms in the two members of the result. Substituting the value of x from (e) and y from (f) in the first equation of (b), we obtain after simplification

$$c_4 - c_1 = 0, \qquad \text{or} \qquad c_4 = c_1.$$

It therefore appears that the solution is

$$x = c_1 + c_2 \sin t + c_3 \cos t + \tfrac{7}{10}e^{2t},$$
$$y = c_1 + c_3 \sin t - c_2 \cos t + \tfrac{1}{10}e^{2t}.$$

Remark. Extraneous constants of integration can often be avoided by deriving from the given set of equations an equation of low order to be used in finding the expression for an additional variable after the expressions for several variables have already been found. Thus, after equation (e) was obtained, y could have been found without introducing another constant, by subtracting the second equation of (b) from the first, substituting x from (e) in the result, and solving for y.

EXERCISES

Solve the following systems of differential equations, with $D = d/dt$:

1. $x + Dy = 0$, $(D - 1)x + (D - 1)y = 2t$
2. $(D - 1)x + Dy = 0$, $Dx + 2Dy = 4e^{2t}$
3. $(D - 7)x + y = 0$, $Dy + 3x - 5y = 0$
4. $Dx + Dy + 3x = \sin t$, $Dx + y - x = \cos t$
5. $D^2x = y$, $D^2y = x + 1$
6. $(D^2 - 3)x - 4y = 0$, $x + (D^2 + 1)y = 0$
7. $(2D^2 - 4)y - Dx = 4t$, $(4D - 3)x + 2Dy = 0$
8. $D^2x + (D^2 - D)y = 0$, $(D - 1)x + Dy = 2t^2 + 4t + 4$
9. $(D^2 - 1)x + 8Dy = 16e^t$, $Dx + 3(D^2 + 1)y = 0$

10. Find the particular solution of the system

$$(D^2 - 3)x - 4y + 3 = 0, \qquad (D^2 + 1)y + x + 5 = 0$$

for which $x = y = Dx = Dy = 0$ when $t = 0$.

11. $Dx - 3y = 0$, $Dy + z = x$, $Dz + y = 0$
12. $x + y + z = t$, $Dx + z = 0$, $2x - Dy = 0$
13. $Dx + Dy - x - y = 2e^t$, $Dx - Dz = 0$, $D(x + y + z) = e^t$
★14. $(D^2 - 1)x + 2(D + 1)y + (D + 1)z = e^t$, $(D + 1)^2x + 2(D + 1)y - (D + 1)z = 0$, $(D - 1)x - 2y - z = 0$

CHAPTER VII

APPLICATIONS OF LINEAR EQUATIONS WITH CONSTANT COEFFICIENTS

51. Harmonic motion. Damping

For convenience of reference we shall recall, at this point, a few facts concerning harmonic motion and damping.

If, as a particle moves in a straight line, its motion is defined by

$$y = c \sin (\omega t + \varphi) + a, \tag{1}$$

where a is a constant, y is the distance of the particle from a fixed point on the line, and t is the time, its motion is called **simple harmonic motion.** The number c, representing the greatest value of $y - a$, is called the **amplitude of the motion.** Because of the periodic nature of $\sin (\omega t + \varphi)$, it is clear that the motion consists of an endless repetition of the movement that takes place while the angle $\omega t + \varphi$ changes by 2π radians; hence the motion is called **periodic.** The time T required for the angle $\omega t + \varphi$ to change by 2π radians is called the **period of the motion.** Therefore we must have

$$\omega(t + T) + \varphi - (\omega t + \varphi) = 2\pi,$$

or
$$\text{Period } T = \frac{2\pi}{\omega}. \tag{2}$$

The number n of repetitions of the least complete motion, that is, the number of cycles per unit of time, is called the **frequency.** Hence

$$\text{Frequency } n = \frac{1}{T} = \frac{\omega}{2\pi}. \tag{3}$$

The angle φ is often referred to as the **angle of epoch,** and $\omega t + \varphi$ as the phase. Figure 1 represents the motion. The heavy part of the curve between A and B represents one period of the motion, the length c is the amplitude, and the distance from A to B represents the period $T = (2\pi - \varphi)/\omega - (-\varphi/\omega) = 2\pi/\omega.$

96

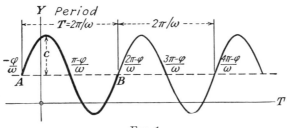

FIG. 1

An equation having the form $y - a = c_1 \sin \omega t + c_2 \cos \omega t$ may be written in the form (1).   For

$$c_1 \sin \omega t + c_2 \cos \omega t = \sqrt{c_1^2 + c_2^2} \left(\frac{c_1 \sin \omega t}{\sqrt{c_1^2 + c_2^2}} + \frac{c_2 \cos \omega t}{\sqrt{c_1^2 + c_2^2}} \right),$$

and this, in view of Fig. 2, may be written

$$\sqrt{c_1^2 + c_2^2} \, (\sin \omega t \cos \varphi + \cos \omega t \sin \varphi) = \sqrt{c_1^2 + c_2^2} \sin (\omega t + \varphi). \quad (4)$$

Hence, it appears from Fig. 2 that

$$y - a = c_1 \sin \omega t + c_2 \cos \omega t$$
$$= c \sin (\omega t + \varphi), \quad (5)$$

where

$$c = \sqrt{c_1^2 + c_2^2}, \qquad \varphi = \tan^{-1} \frac{c_2}{c_1}. \quad (6)$$

A very important damped oscillatory motion is represented by

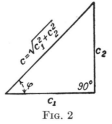

FIG. 2

$$y = ce^{-at} \sin (\omega t + \varphi), \qquad (a > 0).$$

Observe that the factor $\sin (\omega t + \varphi)$ describes an oscillatory kind of motion, and e^{-at} becomes smaller and smaller as t increases so that the oscillations become smaller and smaller in magnitude.   Figure 3 represents the motion.   Observe that the length of time for each wave is the same, but that the heights of the waves become smaller and smaller with increasing t; that is, the motion is damped.   *The factor e^{-at} is called the* **damping factor,** *a the* **damping constant,** $2\pi/\omega$ *the* **period of oscillation,** *and* $\omega/2\pi$ *the* **frequency of y.**   For example, if

$$y = 10e^{-0.02t} \sin \left(120\pi t - \frac{\pi}{2} \right),$$

the period is $2\pi/(120\pi) = \frac{1}{60}$, the frequency is 60 cycles, 0.02 is the damping constant, and $e^{-0.02t}$ is the damping factor.   To find the time required by the damping factor to decrease one-half its value, we have $e^{-0.02t} = \frac{1}{2}$; hence $\log e^{-0.02t} = \log(\frac{1}{2})$, or $-0.02t = -\log 2 = -0.6931$, and $t = 34.7$. This shows that the magnitude of the damping factor

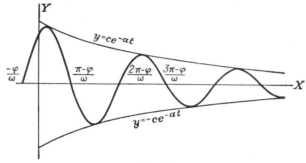

FIG. 3

at the end of a 34.7-sec. interval is one-half its magnitude at the beginning.

EXERCISES

In the following exercises assume distance in feet and time in seconds.

1. For a straight-line motion represented by $y = 5 \sin(12\pi t + \pi/6)$, find the amplitude, the period, the frequency, and two positive values of t for which $y = 0$.

2. For a straight-line motion represented by $y = 5 \sin 32t + 12 \cos 32t$, find the period, frequency, and amplitude, and show that the maximum value of dy/dt is 416.

3. The equation $(d^2y/dt^2) + 100y = 0$ represents a simple harmonic motion. Find the general solution of the equation and determine the constants of integration if $y = 10$, $dy/dt = 50$, when $t = 0$. Tell the frequency, the period, and the amplitude of the motion represented.

4. The equation $(d^2y/dt^2) + y = 0$ represents a simple harmonic motion. Find its period, frequency, and amplitude if $y = 5$, $dy/dt = 0$, when $t = 0$.

5. For a straight-line motion represented by $y = 25e^{-0.035t} \sin(377t + 1)$, find the period and frequency and show that the damping factor decreases from 1 when $t = 0$ to $\frac{1}{2}$ when t is approximately 20 units of time.

6. What must be true of k in the equation $(d^2s/dt^2) + (k \, ds/dt) + 30s = 0$, if the motion represented is vibratory?

7. An oscillatory motion is represented by

$$\frac{d^2y}{dt^2} + \frac{1}{10}\frac{dy}{dt} + 10y = 0.$$

Find the period of oscillation of y, the damping factor, and the time required for the damping factor to decrease 50 per cent.

8. Solve the differential equation

$$\frac{d^2x}{dt^2} + \frac{dx}{dt} + \frac{37}{4}x = 0,$$

and determine the constants of integration by using the conditions $x = 0$, $dx/dt = 6$, when $t = 0$. Find x in terms of the time, the period of oscillation of x, and the magnitude of the damping factor after 3 sec.

9. Solve the differential equation

$$9\frac{d^2x}{dt^2} + 3a\frac{dx}{dt} + 82x = 0,$$

and determine a and the constants of integration if $dx/dt = 6$, $x = 0$, when $t = 0$ and if the damping factor decreases 50 per cent in 2.08 units of time. Also find the period.

10. An oscillatory motion represented by an equation of the form

$$\frac{d^2x}{dt^2} + b\frac{dx}{dt} + cx = 0$$

has a frequency of oscillation $n = 60$ and a damping constant $a = \frac{1}{10}$. Find b and c.

11. Find b and c in the differential equation of exercise 10 if the period of oscillation of x is $\frac{1}{10}$ sec. and the damping factor decreases 50 per cent in 30 sec.

52. Forces, accelerations, and moments

Forces, their components along the coordinate axes, and their sum in magnitude and direction were discussed in §30, page 58. The first three paragraphs of §30 should now be reviewed. In what follows we shall use the concept of a force along a directed line or in the direction of the line. *If a force F of magnitude f makes an angle θ with a directed line AB, the* **component of F** *in the direction of AB is a force of magnitude f* cos *θ, and it has the same direction as AB or the opposite direction according as* cos *θ is positive or negative.* Thus in Fig. 4, $P_1'Q_1'$ represents the component of force P_1Q_1 and $P_2'Q_2'$ that of P_2Q_2 in the di-

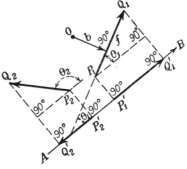

Fig. 4

rection of AB. Also, if we think of the direction of the X-axis in §30 as any direction, then equation (10) of §30 indicates that *the* **component of the sum** *of n forces in any direction is the sum of their components in that direction.*

For example, the forces indicated in Fig. 5 have, as the sum of their components along OA, a vector of magnitude $10 \cos 0 + 5 \cos 90° + 7 \cos 240° + 5 \cos (-135°) = 10 - 3.50 - 3.54 = 2.96$ lb. directed along OA; and, as sum of components along OB, a vector of $10 \cos 90° +$

$5 \cos 0° + 7 \cos 150° + 5 \cos 135° = 5 - (7/\sqrt{3}/2) - 5/\sqrt{2} = -4.60$ lb.
along OB, or 4.60 lb. in the direction opposite to that of OB.

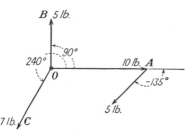

FIG. 5

Acceleration a, *like force, is a directed quantity which has components* $\mathbf{a}_x$ *and* $\mathbf{a}_y$ *in the directions of the coordinate axes*

$$a_x = \frac{d^2x}{dt^2}, \qquad a_y = \frac{d^2y}{dt^2},$$

where t represents time. The statements made about forces apply generally to accelerations.

Again, consider a force represented by a vector P_1Q_1 lying in a fixed plane, and an axis which is perpendicular to the plane and cuts it in point O (see Fig. 4). *The* **moment,** or **torque,** *of the force about the axis, also referred to as the* **torque about O,** *is defined to be the magnitude f of the force multiplied by the distance b from O to the line of action P_1Q_1 of the force.* Moment measures the tendency to cause turning. Two forces, one tending to turn a body about O in one sense and the other tending to turn it about O in the opposite sense, would have moments about O opposite in sign. For example, forces P_1Q_1 and P_2Q_2 in Fig. 4 have moments about O opposite in sign. In general, *if θ is the angle through which a body attached to the axis is turned from some fixed position of reference, the torque of a force is considered as positive when it tends to turn the body in the sense of increasing angle θ and negative when it tends to turn the body in the opposite sense.*

53. Some fundamental equations of motion

Plane motion of a rigid body is a motion such that each point in the body remains at a constant distance from a fixed plane; for example, a wheel on an automobile has plane motion when the car is moving in a straight line.

When all the particles of the body, rigid or not, have plane motion with respect to the same plane, the sum ΣF_d of the components in any direction of all the external forces acting on it is equal to the product of the component a_d in the same direction of the acceleration of the center of gravity of the body and the mass m* of the body; that is,

$$\Sigma F_d = ma_d. \tag{7}$$

* The acceleration g of a body given it by the pull of the earth is nearly 32.2 ft./sec.[2] For many problems in this book the unit of mass will be that of a g-lb. body. Hence for a w-lb. weight the mass m will be w/g slugs.

Applying this rule for the direction of the X-axis and for the direction of the Y-axis, we obtain

$$\sum \mathbf{F}_x = \mathbf{ma}_x = \mathbf{m}\frac{d^2\mathbf{x}}{dt^2}, \qquad \sum \mathbf{F}_y = \mathbf{ma}_y = \mathbf{m}\frac{d^2\mathbf{y}}{dt^2}. \tag{8}$$

When a rigid body has plane motion, the moment, or torque, T_g of the external forces acting on it about an axis through the center of gravity of the body and perpendicular to the plane of its motion is equal to the product of the moment of inertia I_g* of the body with respect to the same axis and the angular acceleration α of the body; that is,

$$\mathbf{T}_g = \mathbf{I}_g\alpha = \mathbf{I}_g\frac{d^2\theta}{dt^2}, \tag{9}$$

where θ is the angle through which the body is turned from some fixed position of reference. When the motion is pure rotation, we may write

$$\mathbf{T} = \mathbf{I}\alpha = \mathbf{I}\frac{d^2\theta}{dt^2}, \tag{10}$$

where T is the torque of the external forces about the axis of rotation and I is the moment of inertia of the body with respect to the same axis. Note that the axis associated with (10) is not necessarily an axis through the center of gravity.

54. Vibratory motion

Three very important types of motion are referred to as **free** motion, **damped** motion, and **forced** motion. Thus, a weight supported in a vacuum by a spring would tend to move with an oscillatory motion when displaced vertically; if air were admitted, it would tend to slow down or *damp* the motion; and if the supporting structure were moved up and down, a motion would be *forced* on the weight. These three types of motion or their counterparts occur in a great many physical phenomena. The example below will show how they are associated with the respective terms Bx, $A\ dx/dt$, and $f(t)$ in the equation

$$\frac{d^2x}{dt^2} + A\frac{dx}{dt} + Bx = f(t).$$

Later we shall find the term Bx associated with the oscillatory flow of electricity to and from a condenser, $A\ dx/dt$ with a damped flow of electricity due to resistance, and $f(t)$ with the forced flow of electricity due to a dynamo or other source of electric energy.

* For force in pounds and length in feet, I is in slug-feet^2.

Example. The force exerted by a certain spring is proportional to the amount it is stretched, and a force of 8 lb. stretches it 3 in.   A 16.1-lb. weight hanging at rest on the spring is drawn down 6 in. and released.   Describe the motion (*a*) if there is no air resistance; (*b*) if the air resistance in pounds and one-hundredth of the speed in feet per second are equal numerically; (*c*) if, in addition to the air resistance, the supporting structure is given a motion $y = \frac{1}{2} \sin 7t$.

Solution. (*a*) Let *x* be the number of feet the spring is stretched [see Fig. 6(*a*)], and let *f* represent the force exerted by the spring.

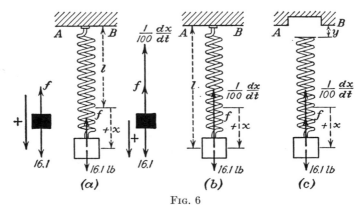

Fig. 6

Then, in accordance with Hooke's law, $f = kx$.   Since $f = 8$ lb. when $x = \frac{1}{4}$ ft., it appears that $8 = k\frac{1}{4}$ and $k = 32$.   Hence

$$f = 32x. \tag{a}$$

From the first equation of (8), with downward considered as the positive direction, we get

$$16.1 - f = 16.1 - 32x = \frac{16.1}{32.2} \frac{d^2x}{dt^2}. \tag{b}$$

The solution of this equation is

$$x = c_1 \sin 8t + c_2 \cos 8t + 0.503, \tag{c}$$

and

$$v = \frac{dx}{dt} = 8(c_1 \cos 8t - c_2 \sin 8t). \tag{d}$$

The initial conditions are

$$v = \frac{dx}{dt} = 0, \qquad x = 0.503 + 0.5 = 1.003 \text{ ft.} \qquad when \; t = 0. \tag{e}$$

Substituting these values in (c) and (d), we get

$$1.003 = c_2 + 0.503, \qquad 0 = 8c_1, \tag{f}$$

or

$$c_2 = \tfrac{1}{2}, \qquad c_1 = 0.$$

Substituting these values in (c), we get the solution

$$\mathbf{x - 0.503} = \tfrac{1}{2} \cos 8t. \tag{g}$$

This represents a harmonic motion with amplitude $\tfrac{1}{2}$ ft. and period $2\pi/8 = \mathbf{0.785}$ **sec.**, or frequency $8/(2\pi) = \mathbf{1.27}$ cycles/sec.

(b) From Fig. 6(b), equation (a), and the first equation of (8), we have

$$16.1 - \frac{1}{100}\frac{dx}{dt} - 32x = \frac{16.1}{32.2}\frac{d^2x}{dt^2}. \tag{h}$$

The general solution of (h) is

$$\mathbf{x = e^{-0.01t}(c_1 \sin 8t + c_2 \cos 8t) + 0.503}. \tag{i}$$

Differentiating this and using the initial conditions (e) to determine the constants of integration, we finally obtain

$$x = e^{-0.01t}(0.000625 \sin 8t + \tfrac{1}{2} \cos 8t) + 0.503. \tag{j}$$

Here the period is the same as before, accurate to three figures. The damping factor is $e^{-0.01t}$. To get an idea of the rate of damping, notice that the damping factor is $\tfrac{1}{2}$ when $e^{-0.01t} = \tfrac{1}{2}$, or when $-0.01t = -\log 2 = -0.693$ and $t = 69.3$ sec.; that is, the magnitude of the damping factor at the end of a 69.3-sec. period is one-half its magnitude at the beginning.

(c) In this case [see Fig. 6(c)] let $x - y$ be the amount the spring is stretched. Then

$$f = 32(x - y) = 32x - 16 \sin 7t,$$

and the equation of motion is

$$16.1 - 32x + 16 \sin 7t - 0.01\frac{dx}{dt} = \frac{16.1}{32.2}\frac{d^2x}{dt^2}. \tag{k}$$

The solution of (k), subject to the initial conditions (e), is found by the usual procedure to be

$$\mathbf{x = e^{-0.01t}(0.512 \cos 8t - 1.863 \sin 8t) + 0.503 + 2.13 \sin 7t}$$
$$\mathbf{- 0.020 \cos 7t,}$$

approximately. Observe that the motion of the weight is made up of two motions: a damped oscillatory motion and a harmonic motion.

As time increases, the damped harmonic motion dies away while the harmonic motion $0.503 + 2.13 \sin 7t - 0.020 \cos 7t$ remains. The flow of electricity in many circuits follows this same plan, being made up of two parts, a **transient part,** which quickly dies out, and a **steady-state part,** which remains indefinitely.

PROBLEMS

1. Solve parts (a) and (b) of the example, referring as little as possible to the solution given.

2. The force exerted by a spring is proportional to the amount the spring is stretched and is 200 lb. when the spring is stretched 1 ft. A 64-lb. weight suspended by the spring as indicated in Fig. 7 is moved down until the spring is stretched 0.72 ft. and released from rest. Find the equation, the amplitude, the period, and the frequency of the resulting motion. Take mass m as $\frac{64}{32} = 2$ slugs.

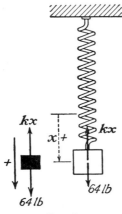

FIG. 7

3. Assume in problem 2 an additional vertical resisting force numerically equal to $0.04v$, where velocity v is in feet per second, and solve the resulting problem. Omit the part referring to amplitude. Also find the damping factor and the time it takes it to decrease to 50 per cent of its initial value.

4. Assume the situation of problem 2, together with the additional requirement that the upper end of the spring be given the motion $y = 0.64 \sin 6t$, where y ft. represents distance below the point of suspension at t seconds after motion starts. Find (a) the equation of the motion of the 64-lb. weight, (b) the period of the complementary solution, that of the particular solution, and that of the motion, and (c) the amount the spring is stretched 1 sec. after motion starts.

5. A particle of mass 1 slug moves toward a fixed center of force which repels it with a magnitude in pounds equal to k times the distance of the particle from the center. Initially the particle is distant a from the center and is moving toward it with a velocity equal in magnitude to $\sqrt{ka^2}$. Prove that the particle will continually approach but never reach the center.

6. A rubber band of natural length $AB = l$ (see Fig. 8) is suspended vertically from a point A, and a weight is attached to it at B. The weight stretches the band to a length $AO = l + h$. The weight is given a displacement $OP = a$ $(a < h)$ and then released. Find the equation of the motion.

7. A spring is stretched 1 in. when a 4-lb. weight is hung on it. If a 12-lb. weight is hanging at rest on the spring when the upper end of the spring is given the motion $y = \sin \sqrt{3g}\, t$, find a differential equation of the motion of the weight, solve

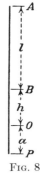

FIG. 8

this equation, and determine all constants of integration. Find the position of the weight $50\pi/\sqrt{g}$ sec. after the motion starts. *Hint:* At time t (see Fig. 9), y is the distance of the upper end above its initial position, and we let x be the distance of the weight above its initial position. Hence, at time t, the spring is stretched $y + \frac{1}{4} - x$, and the upward force on the weight is $48(y + \frac{1}{4} - x) - 12$.

8. Solve the preceding problem when $y = \sin\sqrt{3g}\,t$ is replaced by $y = \sin 2\sqrt{g}\,t$. Is there a theoretical upper limit to the distance of the weight from the starting point?

9. A rigid body suspended by a wire (see Fig. 10) has a motion of pure rotation about the line of the wire as an axis. If the only torque acting is a torque in the wire proportional to the angle that the body is turned from the position in which

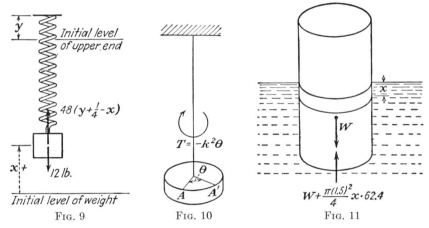

Fig. 9   Fig. 10   Fig. 11

it hangs in equilibrium, find the period of the motion. *Hint:* Let θ be the angle through which the body is turned from equilibrium. Then use (9) to obtain

$$-k^2\theta = I\frac{d^2\theta}{dt^2}.$$

10. A uniform sphere rotates about a supporting wire as an axis. If the number expressing the torque in the wire in pound-feet is equal to the number of radians through which the sphere is turned from the position in which it will hang in equilibrium, and if the sphere makes two complete oscillations per second, find the moment of inertia of the sphere with respect to the line of the wire.

11. If, for the sphere and wire of problem 10, change of motion is caused by a frictional torque proportional to the angular velocity together with the torque in the wire, and if the corresponding damping factor decreases to 25 per cent of its initial value during the first 2 sec. of motion, find the equation and the period of the motion. Use the value of I found in problem 10.

12. A cylindrical spar buoy 18 in. in diameter stands in fresh water with its axis vertical (see Fig. 11). When depressed slightly and released, its period of vibration is found to be 2.7 sec. Find the weight of the cylinder.

13. A rectangular block of wood 2 by 2 by 1 ft. floats in fresh water with its 1-ft. edge vertical. If the block weighs 160 lb., find the time of vibration when it is

depressed slightly and released.   Find also the time of vibration of the same block
in a liquid of specific gravity ρ.

14. Find, approximately, the period of vibration of a simple pendulum l ft.
long.   Assume that the angle θ between the vertical and the cord of the pendulum
is always so small that $\sin \theta$ may be replaced by θ without
appreciable error.   *Hint:* Use Fig. 12 and apply equation (10).

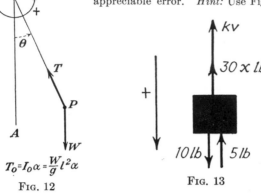

$$T_0 = I_0 \alpha = \frac{W}{g} l^2 \alpha$$

FIG. 12

FIG. 13

15. A 10-lb. weight
having specific gravity
2 is immersed in water
and supported by a spring
which it stretches 2 in.
It is drawn down 1 ft.
from its position of equilibrium and let go.   The
resistance of the liquid
to the motion of the
weight is proportional to
its velocity.   If, at the
end of two complete
vibrations, the value
of the damping factor is 25 per cent of its initial value, find the equation of the
motion and its period.   Figure 13 indicates the forces acting on the body.

16. A particle below the earth's surface is attracted toward the center of the
earth with a force proportional to the distance of the particle from the center.
If a particle were dropped into a smooth straight vacuum passing through the
earth's center, how long would it take the particle to reach the center?   Assume
that the radius of the earth is 3960 statute miles.   *Hint:* $(W/32.2)a = ks$, and
$a = -32.2$ ft./sec.^{2} when $s = R$.

17. A body falling from rest in a heavy fluid acquires a velocity which approaches
10 ft./sec. as a limit.   Assuming the resistance of the medium to be proportional
to the velocity, and the buoyancy of the fluid to be one-half the weight of the body,
find the factor of proportionality and the distance traversed during the first 10 sec.

18. A body of weight w lb. moves vertically under the force of gravity and under
the action of a force opposite to the direction of motion and equal numerically to
$0.4wv/32.2$, where v is the speed in feet per second.   Taking y as the distance above
the ground, study the motion under the conditions $y = 0$, $v = 100$, when $t = 0$.

★19. Figure 14 represents a 96-lb. weight and a 64-lb. weight moving on a smooth,
straight, horizontal track subject to the action of springs, as indicated.   The

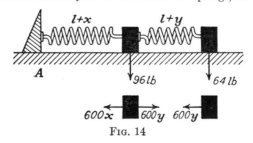

FIG. 14

force exerted by each spring is 600s, where s ft. represents elongation of the spring. Assume that, when $t = 0$, the springs are unstretched, the 96-lb. weight is moving away from A at 600 ft./sec., and the 64-lb. weight is at rest. Take 3 slugs and 2 slugs as the respective masses. Find the equations of motion of the weights.

20. If I ton-ft.^{2} is the moment of inertia of a W-ton ship about a longitudinal water-line axis, G is the center of gravity of the ship, and M a fixed point in the ship through which the buoyancy of the water acts, the differential equation

$$I \frac{d^2\theta}{dt^2} = -gW\overline{GM}\,\theta$$

applies approximately. (*a*) Find I for a 30,000-ton battleship having $\overline{GM} = 7.7$ ft. and period 17 sec. (*b*) Find the period of a 1600-ton destroyer having $\overline{GM} = 2.3$ ft. and $I = 2.9 \times 10^5$ ton-ft.^{2}

★21. In Fig. 14 replace 96 lb. by W lb., 64 lb. by w lb., 600x by Kx, 600y by ky, and then assume a force $a \sin \omega t$ acting to the right on the W-lb. block. Show that the motion of the W-lb. block due to the force $a \sin \omega t$ will be annulled by the w-lb. weight provided $gk/w = \omega^2$.*

22. Figure 15 shows schematically a w-lb. car moving over a corduroy road, so that the road imparts to the bottom of the springs the motion

$$y = a + b \sin \omega t$$

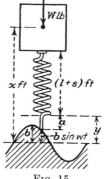

FIG. 15

where a, b, and ω are constants. Assuming that x, s, l, and y have the meanings suggested by the figure and that the force of the spring is Ks lb., show that approximately

$$\frac{w}{g} \frac{d^2x}{dt^2} = -Kx + Ky + c - Ka,$$

where c is a constant. Show that the motion x_p of the car due to the motion $y = a + b \sin \omega t$ is given by

$$x_p - \frac{c}{K} = \frac{b\omega_1^2}{(\omega_1^2 - \omega^2)} \sin \omega t, \qquad \omega_1^2 = \frac{Kg}{W}.$$

Assume that ω/ω_1 will generally be fairly large. (*a*) For only slight effect, should K be large or small? (*b*) If the speed of the car is increased, will the average value of $x_p - c/K$ increase or decrease? (*c*) If $\omega_1 = 0.1\omega$, find the ratio of dy/dt to dx_p/dt and interpret. (*d*) Discuss the effect $x_p - c/K$ when ω_1 is nearly equal to ω.

55. Plane motions of bodies

In §54 motions in a straight line and simple rotary motions were considered. The equations of §53 will now be applied to the curved-line motion of projectiles and to bodies rotating and translating at the

---

* This problem illustrates the use of auxiliary masses to eliminate or reduce vibratory disturbances.

same time.   In Fig. 16 the curve ODH is the path, or trajectory, of a projectile fired from a gun at O, φ is the angle of departure, V_0 is the initial velocity, θ is the inclination of the tangent line to the X-axis (taken horizontal), OH is the range, vector W represents the force of gravity acting on the projectile, and vector R represents the force due

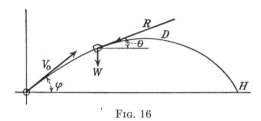

Fig. 16

to air resistance assumed to be acting along the tangent to the trajectory in a direction opposite to that in which the projectile is moving.

If $\dot{x} = dx/dt$ and $\dot{y} = dy/dt$, the relations between components $\dot{x}$ and $\dot{y}$ of the velocity are shown in Fig. 17.   From Fig. 17 we read

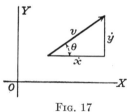

Fig. 17

$$\cos \theta = \frac{\dot{x}}{v}, \qquad \sin \theta = \frac{\dot{y}}{v}.$$

Applying equations (8) of §53, we obtain

$$\frac{W}{g} \frac{d\dot{x}}{dt} = -R\frac{\dot{x}}{v}, \qquad \frac{W}{g} \frac{d\dot{y}}{dt} = -W - R\frac{\dot{y}}{v}, \quad (11)$$

where $\dot{x}$ and $\dot{y}$ represent, respectively, the horizontal and the vertical components of the velocity.   The force R is a very complex quantity, so complex, in fact, that only approximations to the solutions of equations (11) can be found.   Some rough approximations of special cases will appear as solutions of problems in the list of this article.

The following example will illustrate a type involving both rotation and translation.

Example.   A homogeneous cylinder, having radius $= r$ ft., weight $= W$ lb., $I_g = \dfrac{W}{g} \dfrac{r^2}{2}$ (where $g = 32.2$), has a flexible cord wrapped around its central plane.   One end of the cord is attached to a fixed plane as shown in Fig. 18.   As the

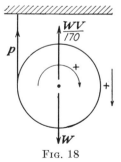

Fig. 18

body falls, an air resistance in pounds equal numerically to $W/170$ times its velocity in feet per second retards its motion.   If it starts from rest, find distance y fallen in t sec., limiting velocity, and percentage of limiting velocity acquired in 20 sec.

Solution. If y is the distance fallen from rest and θ the angle through which the body has turned, we have

$$y = r\theta, \qquad v = \frac{dy}{dt} = r\frac{d\theta}{dt}, \qquad a = \frac{d^2y}{dt^2} = r\frac{d^2\theta}{dt^2} = r\alpha. \qquad (a)$$

Here downward is considered as the positive direction and clockwise as the positive sense of rotation. Applying equations (8) and (9) to the system represented by Fig. 18, we get

$$-p - \frac{W}{170}v + W = \frac{W}{g}\frac{d^2y}{dt^2}, \qquad (b)$$

$$pr = \frac{W}{g}\frac{r^2}{2}\alpha = \frac{Wr}{2g}r\alpha = \frac{Wr}{2g}\frac{d^2y}{dt^2}. \qquad (c)$$

Substituting p from (c) in (b) and simplifying slightly, we obtain

$$\frac{3W}{2g}\frac{d^2y}{dt^2} + \frac{W}{170}\frac{dy}{dt} = W. \qquad (d)$$

The solution of (d) is

$$y = A + Be^{-(g/255)t} + 170t; \qquad (e)$$

hence

$$v = \frac{dy}{dt} = \frac{-Bg}{255}e^{-(g/255)t} + 170. \qquad (f)$$

Using the conditions $y = 0$, $v = 0$, when $t = 0$ in (e) and (f), we have

$$0 = A + B, \qquad 0 = \frac{-Bg}{255} + 170,$$

or

$$\frac{3(170)^2}{2g} = B = -A. \qquad (g)$$

Substituting A and B from (g) in (e) and (f) and simplifying, we obtain

$$\mathbf{y} = \frac{3(\mathbf{170})^2}{\mathbf{2g}}(e^{-gt/255} - \mathbf{1}) + \mathbf{170t}, \qquad (h)$$

$$v = 170(1 - e^{-(g/255)t}). \qquad (i)$$

Substituting $t = \infty$ in (i), we get

$$\lim_{t \to \infty} v = \mathbf{170 \ ft./sec.}$$

Again,

$$\frac{170[1 - e^{-20(32.2)/255}]}{170}\ (100\%) = \mathbf{92\%}.$$

PROBLEMS

1. Solve equations (11) for x and y in terms of t if $R = 0$. Determine the constants of integration from the initial conditions $\dot{x} = v_0 \cos \varphi$, $\dot{y} = v_0 \sin \varphi$, $x = 0$, $y = 0$, all when $t = 0$.

2. Solve equations (11) for the special case where R is numerically equal to $0.02wv/g$, and v is the speed in feet per second. Assume that $v_0 = 3000$ ft./sec., $\varphi = 30°$, and note that, when $t = 0$, $x = y = 0$, $\dot{x} = 3000 \cos 30°$ft./sec. and $\dot{y} = 3000 \sin 30°$ ft./sec. Find the greatest height reached by the projectile.

3. When a projectile is fired at a small angle of elevation, the vertical component of its velocity is small, and consequently the vertical component of air resistance is small. A 100-lb. shell is fired with initial velocity $v_0 = 2000$ ft./sec. and with angle of departure $\varphi = 5°$. Assuming in this case that air resistance is horizontal and equal numerically to $\dfrac{100}{25g} \dfrac{dx}{dt}$, derive equations similar to (11); solve these equations for dx/dt, dy/dt, x, and y, and determine the constants of integration.

4. If a projectile is fired at an angle of departure nearly equal to 90°, the horizontal component of air resistance is small. An anti-aircraft gun fires a projectile of weight W with initial velocity $v_0 = 2000$ ft./sec. and angle of departure $\varphi = 80°$. Assume air resistance to be vertical and equal numerically to $\dfrac{W}{1200} \dfrac{dy}{dt}$. Find the equations of the trajectory, the maximum height attained by the projectile, and the height of the projectile when the vertical component of its velocity is 500 ft./sec.

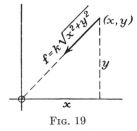

Fig. 19

5. A particle of mass m slugs moves in a plane under the action of a force (see Fig. 19) always directed to a fixed point in the plane and equal in magnitude to k times the distance of the particle from the fixed point. At a certain instant the particle is moving with velocity v_0 at right angles to a line connecting it with the fixed point and is a units from it. Find the equations of motion and tell the nature of the path. *Hint:* Apply equations (8), to obtain $m\ddot{x} = -kx$, etc.

6. A fixed plane contains a variable point P and two fixed points A and B. P is the position of a particle of unit mass which is acted on by two forces, one equal numerically to the magnitude of BP and exerted in the direction from B toward P, a second equal numerically to the magnitude of $2PA$ and exerted in the direction from P toward A. Find the equations of motion if $AB = 2$ ft. and if the particle is initially at A moving 3 ft./sec. in a direction making (a) an angle of 90° with AB; (b) an angle of 45° with AB. *Hint:* In Fig. 20, $\Sigma F_x = \overline{BP} \cos \theta - 2AP \cos \varphi = \overline{BP}(x/\overline{BP}) - 2\overline{AP}(x/\overline{AP}) = x - 2x = -x$, etc.

7. A circular cylinder having radius r, weight W, and I with respect to its axis $\dfrac{W}{g} \dfrac{r^2}{2}$ is rolling on a rough horizontal plane when two horizontal forces perpendicular to its axis are impressed on it: a constant force equal to $\frac{1}{10}W$ in the direction of motion and an oppositely directed air resistance proportional to the velocity of its axis. If no slipping occurs, if the limiting speed is 60 ft./sec., and if the initial speed is zero, describe the motion and find how far the cylinder rolls during the first minute of motion (see Fig. 21). *Hint:* Apply equations (8) and (9) of §53, eliminate f, and integrate the resulting equations.

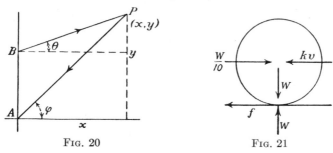

FIG. 20   FIG. 21

8. The cylinder of problem 7 rolls without slipping and with axis horizontal on a rough plane inclined 30° to the horizontal. If air resistance is opposite to the direction of motion and is numerically equal to $W/600$ times the magnitude of the velocity of the axis in feet per second, find the limiting speed and the distance traversed during the first minute of motion from rest.

56. Kirchhoff's current law and electromotive-force law*

A few facts about electricity were considered in §28. Here a more extensive treatment will be given.

Electricity may be thought of as a substance. A practical unit of electricity is called the **coulomb.**† If electricity is flowing along a conductor, like a copper wire, the number of coulombs per second flowing past a cross section is called the **current.** A current of 1 coulomb/sec. is called an **ampere.**

KIRCHHOFF'S CURRENT LAW. *The excess of the current flowing into a given region at a given time over the current flowing out at the same time is the time rate of increase of quantity of electricity within the region at that time.*

If there is no accumulation of electricity within a given region, current flowing into this region equals current flowing out of it; for example, in Fig. 22,

$$i_1 = i_2 + i_3 + i_4. \tag{12}$$

* Good reference books are:
PIERCE, G. W., "Electric Oscillations and Waves."
BEDELL, F., and A. C. CREHORE, "Alternating Currents."
SEARS, F. W., "Principles of Physics II."
† The electron, an elemental building block of nature, carries a fixed charge of negative electricity. A coulomb consists approximately of the sum of the charges on 6.24×10^{18} electrons.

If the region is the positive plate of a condenser, electricity flows into the region, but none, theoretically, flows out. Hence

$$q = \int_c i\, dt, \tag{13}$$

where q is the charge (quantity of electricity) on the positive plate of the condenser, i is the current, t is the time, and the subscript c on the integral sign indicates that limits are to be taken so as to obtain the total quantity of electricity on the condenser at time t. Differentiating (13) with respect to the time, we obtain

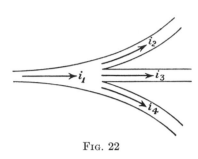

FIG. 22

$$\frac{dq}{dt} = i, \qquad \frac{d^2q}{dt^2} = \frac{di}{dt}. \tag{14}$$

Electromotive force, also called **voltage** and **difference of potential,** causes electricity to move just as physical force causes bodies to move· The **volt** will be used as the unit.

When electricity is flowing through a coil, any change in current sets up a counter electromotive force opposing the change in current. For this reason an electromotive force e_L of magnitude $e_L = L(di/dt)$ must act to cause the current to flow. L is a constant, called **inductance.** It is analogous to the mass of a body. The practical unit of inductance is the **henry.**

Conductors offer **resistance** to the flow of electricity through them. The practical unit of resistance is the **ohm.** Resistance depends upon such things as size and kind of material. If a conductor has a resistance of R *ohms*, an electromotive force e_R of magnitude $e_R = Ri$ volts is required to cause a current of i amperes to flow through it. Resistance is analogous to friction.

A **condenser** consists essentially of two plates separated by a nonconducting substance, or insulator. When a current flows to one plate of a condenser, a charge is deposited there; an equal charge opposite in sign appears at the other plate; and the current away from the condenser is equal to the current flowing to it. The electromotive force e_c across a condenser having a charge of q coulombs and a capacity of C **farads** is given by

$$e_c = \frac{q}{C} = \frac{1}{C} \int_c i\, dt.$$

Figure 23 represents the elements mentioned above, and Kirchhoff's electromotive-force law, which follows, gives an equation connecting them.

ELECTROMOTIVE-FORCE LAW.   *When several elements, resistance R, inductance L, and capacity C, all constant, are connected in series, and when an instantaneous current i is flowing in them, there is impressed in*

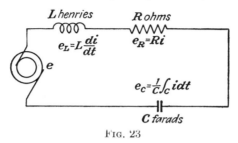

FIG. 23

the direction of i at the terminals of this series from a source of power external to the elements a difference of potential e such that

$$e = L\frac{di}{dt} + Ri + \frac{1}{C}\int_c i\, dt, \tag{15}$$

where $\int_c i\, dt$ represents the total quantity of electricity on the condenser considered.

It is worthy of note that *Kirchhoff's laws may be applied to any part or the whole of a circuit but that, in such application, fall of potential must be considered positive in the direction of the current and negative in the opposite direction.* Also L, R, and C do not necessarily apply to concentrated elements in a circuit but are sums of inductances, resistances, or capacities for the part of the circuit considered.

Substitution of q for $\int_c i\, dt$, dq/dt for i, and d^2q/dt^2 for di/dt in (15) gives

$$L\frac{d^2q}{dt^2} + R\frac{dq}{dt} + \frac{q}{C} = e, \tag{16}$$

and differentiation of (15) with respect to the time gives

$$L\frac{d^2i}{dt^2} + R\frac{di}{dt} + \frac{1}{C}i = \frac{de}{dt}. \tag{17}$$

57. Simple circuits containing constant electromotive force

To illustrate the use of equations (16) and (17), consider the charging of a condenser of capacity C through a resistance R and an inductance

L by a constant electromotive force E. For this case equation (16) becomes

$$L D^2 q + R Dq + \frac{1}{C} q = E, \tag{18}$$

where $D = d/dt$. Assume as initial conditions $q = 0$, $i = 0$, when $t = 0$. The roots of the auxiliary equation $Lm^2 + Rm + 1/C = 0$ are

$$m = \frac{-R}{2L} \pm \sqrt{\frac{R^2}{4L^2} - \frac{1}{LC}}, \quad \text{or} \quad \frac{-R}{2L} \pm \sqrt{\frac{1}{LC} - \frac{R^2}{4L^2}} j, \tag{19}$$

where $j = \sqrt{-1}$. First let us assume that the roots are imaginary and let

$$a = \frac{R}{2L}, \quad \omega_1 = \sqrt{\frac{1}{LC} - \frac{R^2}{4L^2}}. \tag{20}$$

Then we have $m = -a \pm \omega_1 j$, and the solution of (18) is

$$q = \epsilon^{-at}(c_1 \sin \omega_1 t + c_2 \cos \omega_1 t) + CE.* \tag{21}$$

Differentiating this, remembering that $i = dq/dt$, and using the initial conditions $q = 0$, $i = 0$, when $t = 0$, obtain from (21)

$$q = \frac{-CE}{\omega_1} \epsilon^{-at}(a \sin \omega_1 t + \omega_1 \cos \omega_1 t) + CE,$$

$$i = \frac{E}{L\omega_1} \epsilon^{-at} \sin \omega_1 t. \tag{22}$$

EXERCISES

1. Carry out the solution required to derive (22) from (21), initial conditions, and $i = dq/dt$.

2. Taking account of (20), find the solution (22) when $R = 0$, and give the period and amplitude of both i and q.

3. If the roots of $Lm^2 + Rm + 1/C = 0$ are the real numbers α_1 and α_2, show from (17) that both are negative, and that the corresponding values for q and i shrink toward zero without oscillation as t increases.

4. If $1/(LC) - R^2/(4L^2) = 0$, write the corresponding solution of (18) and show that there is no oscillation of q or i, that q approaches CE, and that i approaches 0 as t increases without bound.

5. Solve (18) and $i = dq/dt$ simultaneously under the assumptions $R = 0$, $E = 0$, and initially $t = 0$, $q = q_0$, $i = 0$.

6. Solve equations (16) and (14) to find i and q for a circuit in which $L = 0.1$ henry, $R = 1$ ohm, $C = 250 \times 10^{-6}$ farad, $e = E = 100$ volts, if the initial conditions are $q = 0$, $i = 0$, when $t = 0$. In what time does the damping factor of

---

* Here ϵ ($= 2.7183$, approximately) is used to represent the base of natural logarithms.

the current decrease to one-tenth of its value when $t = 0$, and what is the period of the current? What are the limiting values of q and i?

7. Solve equations (14) and (16) to find i and q in terms of t for a circuit in which $L = 1$ henry, $R = 1$ ohm, $C = 4$ farads, and $e = E = 100$ volts, if $q = 0$, $i = 0$, when $t = 0$. Show that the maximum value of the current is $200\epsilon^{-1}$ (where $\epsilon = 2.718$, nearly) and that the ratio of the current when $t = 10$ sec. to this maximum value is $5\epsilon^{-4} < 0.1$.

8. To find i and q for a circuit during the discharge of a condenser, take $L = 0.1$ henry, $R = 1$ ohm, $C = 250 \times 10^{-6}$ farad, $e = 0$, and the initial conditions $q = 0.05$ coulomb, $i = -0.25$ ampere, when $t = 0$. What are the period of the current and the limiting values of i and q?

9. A circuit consists of an impedance coil of inductance L and negligible resistance connected in series with a condenser of capacity C. Use equations (14) and (16) to find the charge q on the condenser and current i at time t, if t is the number of seconds since i was zero and q was q_0. Describe the fluctuation of i and q. *Hint: e = 0.*

10. Solve equations (16) and (14), with e replaced by the constant E and R by zero, for i and q in terms of t. Assume that $i = 0$, $q = 0$, when $t = 0$.

11. A circuit consists of an impedance coil having an inductance L and resistance R connected in series with a condenser having a capacity C. Initially the current is zero, and the charge on the condenser is q_0. Find i and q at any time if $4L > CR^2$.

58. Simple circuits containing a sinusoidal electromotive force

The type of equation to be considered in this article has the form

$$LD^2q + RDq + \frac{1}{C} q = E \sin \omega t. \tag{23}$$

The current i is found from the equation $i = dq/dt$. The electromotive force $e = E \sin \omega t$ is generally supplied by a dynamo.

In what follows it will be convenient to let

$$X = L\omega - \frac{1}{C\omega}, \qquad Z = \sqrt{R^2 + X^2}. \tag{24}$$

X is called the **reactance** and Z the **impedance.**

A particular solution of (23) could be found by using any of the methods discussed in §§45 to 48. That using the symbolic operator (§47) is the shortest. From (23), by using first equation (41) of §47 and then (24), and after a slight simplification, obtain

$$
\begin{aligned}
q_p &= \frac{E \sin \omega t}{(LD^2 + 1/C) + RD} = \frac{LD^2 + 1/C - RD}{(LD^2 + 1/C)^2 - R^2D^2} E \sin \omega t \\
&= \frac{(-L\omega^2 + 1/C)E \sin \omega t - RE\omega \cos \omega t}{(-L\omega^2 + 1/C)^2 + R^2\omega^2} \\
&= \frac{-E}{\omega Z^2} (X \sin \omega t + R \cos \omega t).
\end{aligned}
$$

Supplying the solution of the auxiliary equation, we obtain the general solution of (23),

$$q = q_c + q_p = \epsilon^{-at}(c_1 \sin \omega_1 t + c_2 \cos \omega_1 t) - \frac{E}{\omega Z^2} (X \sin \omega t + R \cos \omega t).$$

(25)

The equation of the current is obtained by differentiating (25) and replacing dq/dt by i.

The part containing the factor ϵ^{-at} generally becomes negligible in a very short time. It is called a **transient**. Transients are important in the theory of radio and of radar. The other part of the solution is permanent and is called the **steady-state solution.** Dropping the transient term from (25), we have for the steady state

$$q = \frac{-E}{\omega Z^2} (X \sin \omega t + R \cos \omega t),$$

(26)

and, since $i = dq/dt$, for the *steady-state value* of i

$$i = \frac{dq}{dt} = \frac{E}{Z^2} (R \sin \omega t - X \cos \omega t).$$

(27)

59. Resonance

Equation (27) may be written in the form

$$i = \frac{E}{Z} \sin \left(\omega t - \tan^{-1} \frac{X}{R} \right),$$

(28)

where the quadrant of $\tan^{-1} (X/R)$ is that of point (X,R) when plotted in rectangular coordinates. Observe that the amplitude of i,

$$\frac{E}{Z} = \frac{E}{\sqrt{R^2 + X^2}} = \frac{E}{\sqrt{R^2 + [L\omega - 1/(C\omega)]^2}},$$

(29)

will be a maximum for given values of L, R, E, and ω when C is chosen so that $X = 0$, that is, so that

$$L\omega - \frac{1}{C\omega} = 0, \quad \text{or} \quad \omega = \frac{1}{\sqrt{LC}}.$$

(30)

With this condition is associated the name *current resonance*. A person tuning a radio in to a station takes advantage of current resonance.

EXERCISES

1. Reproduce the solution of (23) to obtain (25) without using the text.

2. Obtain the steady-state equation for i by differentiating (25) while omitting the term having ϵ^{-at} as a factor.

3. A sinusoidal electromotive force of frequency $200/\pi$ and maximum value 110 volts is connected in series in a circuit with an inductance of 0.1 henry, a resistance of 10 ohms, and a condenser of capacity 250×10^{-6} farad. Find the steady-state solution of i and q in terms of t and the maximum values of the steady-state charge on the condenser and the current.

4. If $e = E \sin \omega t$ in the circuit of Fig. 23, derive the steady-state solution for i and q (a) when $R = 0$ and there is no condenser; (b) when $L = 0$ and there is no condenser; (c) when $L = 0$ and $R = 0$; (d) when $L = 0$; (e) when there is no condenser; (f) when $R = 0$.

5. Find the expression of i in terms of t for the circuit of Fig. (23) provided $e = 20 \sin 500t$, $R = 2$ ohms, $L = 0.2$ henry, $C = 20 \times 10^{-6}$ farad, and if i and q are zero when $t = 0$. Find the value of the damping factor of the transient at time $t = 1$ sec.

6. Use (30) to find C at current resonance when the frequency is 10^5 cycles/sec. and $L = 6 \times 10^{-6}$ henry. If $R = 100$ ohms, find the ratio of the maximum current E/Z from (28) at current resonance to the current in the same circuit with no condenser.

60. Applications of Kirchhoff's laws to networks

The e.m.f. (electromotive-force) law and the current law stated in §56 may be applied when elements involving inductance, resistance,

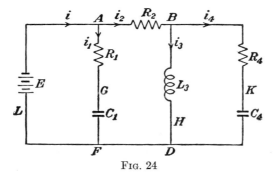

Fig. 24

and capacity are connected in a more or less complicated network. Equations can be obtained by applying the e.m.f. law to complete circuits or the current law at points where two or more conductors meet.

For example, in Fig. 24, apply the current law at A and at B to obtain

$$i = i_1 + i_2, \qquad i_2 = i_3 + i_4.$$

Apply the e.m.f. law to circuit $LAGF$ to obtain

$$R_1 i_1 + \frac{q_1}{C_1} = E, \qquad i_1 = \frac{dq_1}{dt}.$$

Also apply the e.m.f. law to the circuits $LABHDF$ and $BKDH$ to obtain

$$R_2 i_2 + L_3 \frac{di_3}{dt} = E, \qquad R_4 i_4 + \frac{q_4}{C_4} - L_3 \frac{di_3}{dt} = 0, \qquad i_4 = \frac{dq_4}{dt}.$$

Observe in this last circuit that there was no externally applied e.m.f.

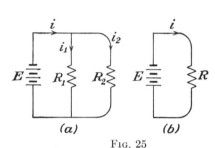

(a)   (b)

FIG. 25

and that a negative sign was given to $L_3(di_3/dt)$ because, in following the circuit in the direction B to K to D to H, the element of inductance L_3 was traversed opposite to the direction of the assumed current i_3. Solving the equations just derived, we could find the current in each branch of the network and the charge of electricity on each condenser at time t.

As another application, apply Kirchhoff's laws to the circuits of Fig. 25(a). We have

$$R_1 i_1 = E, \qquad R_2 i_2 = E, \qquad i = i_1 + i_2. \tag{31}$$

Substituting i_1 and i_2 from the first two equations of (31) in the third and transforming slightly, we have

$$i = E \left(\frac{1}{R_1} + \frac{1}{R_2} \right), \qquad \text{or} \qquad \frac{i}{1/R_1 + 1/R_2} = E. \tag{32}$$

Comparing this last equation with $Ri = E$ from Fig. 25(b), it appears that two resistances R_1 and R_2 in parallel are together equivalent to a resistance $R = \dfrac{1}{1/R_1 + 1/R_2}$.

In general, to find the currents in the branches of a network and the charges on the condensers, proceed as follows: (1) *Draw a figure representing the elements involved, indicating inductance by* ⌒⌒⌒⌒⌒, *resistance by* ⌁⌁⌁⌁⌁, *and a condenser by* —⊣⊢—; (2) *draw arrowheads to indicate the assumed directions of currents through the various branches;* (3) *apply the current law at points where conductors intersect and the e.m.f. law to complete circuits to find as many independent equations as are necessary to determine the unknown quantities involved;* (4) *solve these equations for the unknowns.* The following example will illustrate the procedure:

Example.   An impedance coil which has a resistance of 14 ohms and an inductance of 0.05 henry and a branch having a non-inductive resistance of 15 ohms and a condenser of capacity 10^{-4} farad in series are connected in parallel across the terminals of a 220-volt source of e.m.f.   Find expressions in terms of the time for the charge on the condenser, the current in the impedance coil, the current in the non-inductive resistance, and the total current.

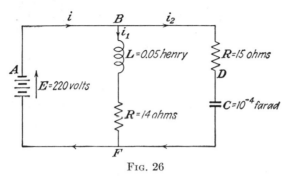

FIG. 26

Solution.   Figure 26 represents the circuit with indicated elements and currents.   The current law applied at point B gives

$$i = i_1 + i_2. \tag{a}$$

The e.m.f. law applied to circuit $ABFA$ gives

$$0.05 \frac{di_1}{dt} + 14i_1 = 220, \tag{b}$$

and, applied to circuit $ABDFA$, it gives

$$15i_2 + 10^4 \int i_2 \, dt = 220. \tag{c}$$

Finally we have from equation (13) of §56

$$q = \int_c i_2 \, dt, \qquad i_2 = \frac{dq}{dt}. \tag{d}$$

Elimination of i_2 from (c) by using (d) gives

$$15 \frac{dq}{dt} + 10^4 q = 220. \tag{e}$$

The solution of equation (e), subject to the condition $q = 0$ when $t = 0$, is

$$\mathbf{q = 0.022(1 - \epsilon^{-\frac{2000}{3}t}).}$$

Therefore

$$i_2 = \frac{dq}{dt} = \frac{44}{3} \epsilon^{-\frac{2000}{3}t}.$$

The solution of (b), subject to the condition $i_1 = 0$ when $t = 0$, is

$$i_1 = 15.71(1 - \epsilon^{-280t}).$$

Finally

$$i = i_1 + i_2 = 15.71(1 - \epsilon^{-280t}) + \frac{44}{3} \epsilon^{-\frac{2000}{3}t}.$$

As the values of ϵ^{-280t} and $\epsilon^{-\frac{2000}{3}t}$ are practically zero after a fraction of a second, it appears that the condenser very soon is practically charged and that the inductance in BF opposes the current for only a small fraction of a second. Hence we have practically $q = 0.022$ coulomb and $i = 15.71$ amperes in a very short time.

PROBLEMS

1. For the system represented in Fig. 27 obtain by the current law at point A $i = i_1 + i_2$, and from the e.m.f. law applied to circuits $AFHG$ and $ABHG$

$$L \frac{di_1}{dt} = E \sin \omega t, \qquad Ri_2 = E \sin \omega t.$$

Solve these equations for i_1, i_2, and i in terms of t and determine a constant of integration by using the condition $i = 0$ when $t = 0$.

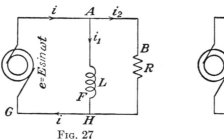

FIG. 27

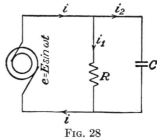

FIG. 28

2. From Fig. 28 derive by Kirchhoff's laws

$$i = i_1 + i_2, \qquad Ri_1 = E \sin \omega t, \qquad \frac{1}{C} \int_c i_2\, dt = \frac{q}{C} = E \sin \omega t.$$

Find q, i_1, i_2, and i in terms of t.

3. For the system indicated in Fig. 29 derive three equations by applying Kirchhoff's laws. Assume that the charge on the condenser is zero when $t = 0$, deduce that $i_2 = 2$ amperes always, and that $i_1 = \frac{1}{10}\epsilon^{-10t}$ and therefore rapidly approaches zero.

4. Replace the 100-volt e.m.f. in Fig. 29 by a sinusoidal e.m.f. represented by $100 \sin 400t$ and then find q, i_1, and i_2 at time t. Assume that the charge on the condenser is zero when $t = 0$.

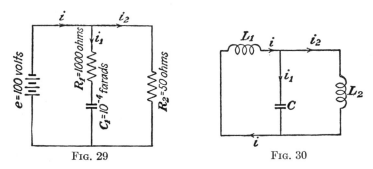

FIG. 29   FIG. 30

5. If initially the charge on the condenser of Fig. 30 is q_0 and $i_1 = 0$, show that $q = q_0 \cos \sqrt{(L_1 + L_2)/(CL_1L_2)}\ t$. *Hint:* $e = 0$.

6. Find the charge on the condenser of Fig. 31 at time t if initially there is no charge on the condenser and no current through the inductance.

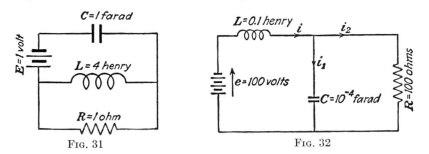

FIG. 31   FIG. 32

7. If, in the system represented by Fig. 32, there is initially no charge on the condenser and no current flowing, find i in terms of the time and describe its fluctuation.

8. Find i in terms of the time t in the system represented by Fig. 33 if all initial currents and the initial charge on the condenser are zero.

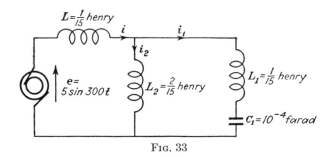

FIG. 33

9. Find i in terms of the time t in the system represented in Fig. 34 if the initial currents and the initial charges on the condensers are zero and $\omega \neq 1/\sqrt{L(C_1 + C_2)}$.

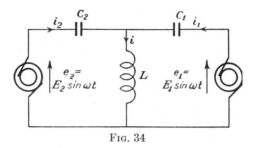

FIG. 34

10. Show that the current i indicated in Fig. 35 is the same as it would be if the three inductances were replaced by a single inductance of magnitude

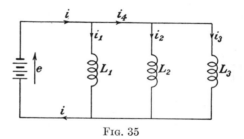

FIG. 35

$1/\left(\dfrac{1}{L_1} + \dfrac{1}{L_2} + \dfrac{1}{L_3}\right)$ in series with the e.m.f. Also show that, in the same sense, the three condensers in parallel in Fig. 36 are equivalent to a single one of capacity $C_1 + C_2 + C_3$.

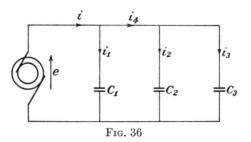

FIG. 36

★11. A hot-wire galvanometer having a resistance of 5 ohms is shunted with a condenser of capacity $C = 5 \times 10^{-8}$ farad, as indicated in Fig. 37. If effective current is $1/\sqrt{2}$ times maximum current, find the ratio of the effective current i_1

through the galvanometer to the total effective current i when (a) $\omega = 2 \times 10^4$; (b) $\omega = 2 \times 10^5$; (c) $\omega = 2 \times 10^6$; (d) $\omega = 2 \times 10^7$.

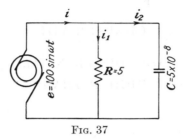

FIG. 37

★12. The following equations are important in the theory of the transformer:

$$(L_1D + R_1)i_1 + MDi_2 = E \sin \omega t,$$
$$MDi_1 + (L_2D + R_2)i_2 = 0,$$

where $D = d/dt$. Show that

$$(L_1L_2 - M^2) D^2i_1 + (L_1R_2 + L_2R_1) Di_1 + R_1R_2i_1 = R_2E \sin \omega t + E\omega L_2 \cos \omega t,$$

$$i_2 = -\frac{1}{MR_2}[L_2E \sin \omega t + (M^2D - L_1L_2D - L_2R_1)i_1].$$

CHAPTER VIII

MISCELLANEOUS DIFFERENTIAL EQUATIONS
OF ORDER HIGHER THAN THE FIRST

61. Reduction of order by substitution

In Chapter VI we found general methods for solving linear equations with constant coefficients. This was unusual, for we cannot solve most equations of order higher than the first in finite form. Certain types, however, are readily solvable. One method of attack is to *make such a substitution as to reduce the order and then try to solve the result.* For example, consider the equation

$$\frac{d^n y}{dx^n} = f(x). \tag{1}$$

To solve this, substitute p for $d^{n-1}y/dx^{n-1}$ and obtain

$$\frac{d^n y}{dx^n} = \frac{d}{dx}\left(\frac{d^{n-1}y}{dx^{n-1}}\right) = \frac{dp}{dx} = f(x). \tag{2}$$

Therefore

$$p = \int f(x)\, dx + c_1, \qquad \text{or} \qquad \frac{d^{n-1}y}{dx^{n-1}} = \int f(x)\, dx + c_1. \tag{3}$$

Clearly we can treat equation (3) in a similar manner and obtain

$$\frac{d^{n-2}y}{dx^{n-2}} = \int \left[\int f(x)\, dx\right] dx + c_1 x + c_2, \tag{4}$$

and it appears that we may continue this process until we find y in terms of x by n successive integrations.

Various types of differential equations with appropriate substitutions will be considered in the following articles.

62. Dependent variable absent

If an equation contains derivatives of the dependent variable y but does not contain y directly, then the substitution

$$p = \frac{dy}{dx}, \frac{dp}{dx} = \frac{d^2 y}{dx^2}, \cdots, \frac{d^{n-1}p}{dx^{n-1}} = \frac{d^n y}{dx^n} \tag{5}$$

will reduce the order of the equation by unity; if the result can be solved for p in terms of x,

$$p = \frac{dy}{dx} = f(x), \tag{6}$$

a single integration will give y in terms of x. In fact, if $d^k y/dx^k$ is the derivative of lowest order in an equation which does not contain y directly, then the substitution

$$p = \frac{d^k y}{dx^k}, \frac{dp}{dx} = \frac{d^{k+1}y}{dx^{k+1}}, \quad \cdots, \quad \frac{d^{n-k}p}{dx^{n-k}} = \frac{d^n y}{dx^n} \tag{7}$$

will reduce the order by k; if the result can be solved for p in terms of x,

$$p = \frac{d^k y}{dx^k} = f_1(x), \tag{8}$$

y may be found in terms of x by k successive integrations, as indicated in §61.

Example. Solve

$$(1 + x^2)\frac{d^2 y}{dx^2} + x\frac{dy}{dx} + ax = 0. \tag{a}$$

Solution. In equation (a) substitute

$$p = \frac{dy}{dx}, \qquad \frac{dp}{dx} = \frac{d^2 y}{dx^2} \tag{b}$$

and obtain

$$(1 + x^2)\frac{dp}{dx} + px + ax = 0. \tag{c}$$

Separating the variables in equation (c) and integrating, we have

$$p + a = c_1(1 + x^2)^{-\frac{1}{2}}.$$

Replacing p by dy/dx and integrating, we obtain

$$\mathbf{y = -ax + c_1 \sinh^{-1} x + c_2.}$$

EXERCISES

Solve the following differential equations and determine the constants of integration where sufficient conditions are given:

1. $\dfrac{d^2 y}{dx^2} = 12x$

2. $x^3\dfrac{d^3 y}{dx^3} = 12$

3. $x\dfrac{d^2 y}{dx^2} + \dfrac{dy}{dx} = 0$

4. $x^2\dfrac{d^2 y}{dx^2} + \left(\dfrac{dy}{dx}\right)^2 = 0$

5. $x \dfrac{d^2y}{dx^2} + \dfrac{dy}{dx} = 16x^3$ **6.** $(x + 1) \dfrac{d^2y}{dx^2} - (x + 2) \dfrac{dy}{dx} = 0$

7. $\dfrac{d^2y}{dx^2} + 24x = 0$; $y = -28$, $\dfrac{dy}{dx} = -10$, when $x = 1$

8. $\dfrac{d^2y}{dx^2} + \cos x \left(\dfrac{dy}{dx}\right)^2 = 0$; $y = 0$, $\dfrac{dy}{dx} = \dfrac{5}{8}$, when $x = \dfrac{\pi}{2}$

9. $x \dfrac{d^3y}{dx^3} - 2 \dfrac{d^2y}{dx^2} = 12x^3$; $y = 0$, $\dfrac{dy}{dx} = 1$, $\dfrac{d^2y}{dx^2} = 0$, when $x = 1$

10. $a \dfrac{d^3y}{dx^3} = \dfrac{d^2y}{dx^2}$; $y = 1$, $\dfrac{dy}{dx} = 0$, $\dfrac{d^2y}{dx^2} = \dfrac{1}{a^2}$, when $x = 0$

11. $\left(x^2 + 2 \dfrac{dy}{dx}\right) \dfrac{d^2y}{dx^2} + 2x \dfrac{dy}{dx} = 0$; $y = 1$, $\dfrac{dy}{dx} = 0$, when $x = 0$

★12. $a \dfrac{d^3y}{dx^3} = \sqrt{1 + \left(\dfrac{d^2y}{dx^2}\right)^2}$; $y = 0$, $\dfrac{dy}{dx} = -a$, $\dfrac{d^2y}{dx^2} = 0$, when $x = 0$

13. At any point a distance r from the common center of two concentric spheres, the differential equation for the potential v due to an electric charge on the inner sphere is

$$\frac{d^2v}{dr^2} + \frac{2}{r}\frac{dv}{dr} = 0.$$

Solve for v in terms of r, given $v = v_1$, when $r = r_1$, and $v = v_0$, when $r = r_0$.

63. Independent variable absent

If p is substituted for dy/dx, we have

$$\frac{dy}{dx} = p, \qquad \frac{d^2y}{dx^2} = \frac{dp}{dy}\frac{dy}{dx} = \frac{p\,dp}{dy},$$

$$\frac{d^3y}{dx^3} = \frac{d}{dy}\left(p\frac{dp}{dy}\right)\frac{dy}{dx} = p^2\frac{d^2p}{dy^2} + p\left(\frac{dp}{dy}\right)^2, \text{ etc.} \tag{9}$$

Therefore, if a differential equation does not contain x directly, the substitution (9) will give a new differential equation in p and y of order one less than that of the original equation. If this new equation can be solved for p in terms of y to get

$$p = \frac{dy}{dx} = f(y), \tag{10}$$

then x may be found in terms of y from

$$x = \int \frac{dy}{f(y)} + c. \tag{11}$$

Example. Solve

$$y \frac{d^2y}{dx^2} + \left(\frac{dy}{dx}\right)^2 = \frac{dy}{dx}. \tag{a}$$

Solution. Substitution of

$$p = \frac{dy}{dx}, \qquad \frac{p\,dp}{dy} = \frac{d^2y}{dx^2} \tag{b}$$

in (*a*) gives

$$yp\frac{dp}{dy} + p^2 = p, \qquad \text{or} \qquad p\left(y\frac{dp}{dy} + p - 1\right) = 0. \tag{c}$$

From (*c*),

$$y\frac{dp}{dy} + p - 1 = 0, \qquad p = 0. \tag{d}$$

Hence,

$$\frac{dp}{p-1} + \frac{dy}{y} = 0. \tag{e}$$

The solution of (*e*) is

$$p = 1 + \frac{c_1}{y}. \tag{f}$$

Replacing p by dy/dx and separating the variables, we obtain

$$\frac{y\,dy}{y + c_1} = dx. \tag{g}$$

The solution of (*g*) is

$$\mathbf{x = y - c_1 \log\,(y + c_1) + c_2.}$$

From the second equation of (*d*) or by inspection, it appears that $y = c$ satisfies equation (*a*).

EXERCISES

Solve the following differential equations and determine constants of integration when initial conditions are given:

1. $y\dfrac{d^2y}{dx^2} + \left(\dfrac{dy}{dx}\right)^2 = 0$

2. $y^2\dfrac{d^2y}{dx^2} + \left(\dfrac{dy}{dx}\right)^3 = 0$

3. $y\dfrac{d^2y}{dx^2} + 2\left(\dfrac{dy}{dx}\right)^2 = 0$

4. $y\dfrac{d^2y}{dx^2} + (1 + y)\left(\dfrac{dy}{dx}\right)^2 = 0$

5. $\dfrac{d^2s}{dt^2} = \dfrac{1}{s^3}$

6. $\dfrac{d^2s}{dt^2} = 64 - \left(\dfrac{ds}{dt}\right)^2$

7. $y\dfrac{d^2y}{dx^2} + 4y^2 - \dfrac{1}{2}\left(\dfrac{dy}{dx}\right)^2 = 0$; $y = 1$, $\dfrac{dy}{dx} = \sqrt{8}$, when $x = 0$

★8. $\dfrac{d^2s}{dt^2} = 100 - \left(\dfrac{ds}{dt}\right)^2$; $s = 0$, $\dfrac{ds}{dt} = 26$, when $t = 0$

9. $\dfrac{d^2s}{dt^2} = -100 - \left(\dfrac{ds}{dt}\right)^2$; $s = 0$, $\dfrac{ds}{dt} = 24$, when $t = 0$

★10. $2\dfrac{d^2y}{dx^2} = e^y$; $y = 0$, $\dfrac{dy}{dx} = 0$, when $x = 0$

11. $\dfrac{d^2y}{dx^2} + y\dfrac{dy}{dx} + \left(\dfrac{dy}{dx}\right)^2 = 0;\ y = 0,\ \dfrac{dy}{dx} = 1,$ when $x = 0$

★12. $y\dfrac{d^2y}{dx^2} + \left(\dfrac{dy}{dx}\right)^2 + \left(\dfrac{dy}{dx}\right)^3 y^2 = 0;\ y = 1,\ \dfrac{dy}{dx} = \dfrac{1}{2},$ when $x = 0$

64. Method based on factorization of the operator

Consider a differential equation which can be written in the form

$$(PD + Q)(RD + S)y = f(x),$$

where P, Q, R, and S are functions of x. It can be solved by setting $(RD + S)y = u$, solving the result to find $u = \varphi(x)$, and then solving $(RD + S)y = u = \varphi(x)$. The difficulty comes in transforming a given operator to the factored form. A few observations relating to operators will be helpful.

If N is a function of x, $(DN)y$ is defined by

$$\mathbf{(DN)y = d(Ny)/dx = N\,Dy + N'y = (ND + N')y,}$$

where $N' = dN/dx$. Also note that if O_1 and O_2 are operators, O_1O_2y may not equal O_2O_1y. For example, the two operators

$$(D - x)(D - x^2)y = D^2y - x^2\,Dy - \mathbf{2xy} - x\,Dy + x^3y$$
$$(D - x^2)(D - x)y = D^2y - x\,Dy - \mathbf{y} - x^2\,Dy + x^3y$$

are evidently different.

The following examples illustrate a method of solution involving operators:

Example 1. Solve

$$[D^2 + (x + 1)D - 2x^2 - x + 2]y = e^{\frac{1}{2}x^2}.$$

Solution. If the operator is $(D + M)(D + N)$, we have

$$(D + M)(D + N)y = [D^2 + (M + N)D + N' + MN]y. \qquad (a)$$

This will be the given operator if

$$M + N = x + 1, \qquad MN + N' = -2x^2 - x + 2. \qquad (b)$$

Replacing M in the second equation of (b) by its value from the first, obtain

$$(x + 1)N - N^2 + N' = -2x^2 - x + 2. \qquad (c)$$

Let us attempt to find a solution by letting

$$N = ax + b \qquad (d)$$

in (c), equating coefficients of like powers of x, and determining a and b. This gives

$$(x + 1)(ax + b) - (ax + b)^2 + a = -2x^2 - x + 2, \qquad (e)$$

$$a - a^2 = -2, \qquad a + b - 2ab = -1, \qquad b - b^2 + a = 2. \quad (f)$$

These are satisfied by $a = 2$, $b = 1$.   Hence

$$N = 2x + 1, \qquad M = 1 + x - N = -x, \qquad (g)$$

and the given equation may be written

$$(D - x)(D + 2x + 1)y = e^{\frac{1}{2}x^2}. \qquad (h)$$

Now let $(D + 2x + 1)y = u$, to obtain

$$(D - x)u = e^{\frac{1}{2}x^2}.$$

The solution of this (see §22) is

$$u = (x + c_1)e^{\frac{1}{2}x^2}.$$

Since $u = (D + 2x + 1)y$, we have

$$(D + 2x + 1)y = (x + c_1)e^{\frac{1}{2}x^2}.$$

The solution of this equation is:

$$\mathbf{y = e^{-x^2-x}\int (x + c_1)e^{\frac{3}{2}x^2+x}\, dx + c_2.}$$

Example 2.   Factor the operator $x^2D^2 + (x - x^2)D - 2x - 1$.
Solution.   Represent the solution by

$$(xD + M)(xD + N) = x^2D^2 + xD + xND + MxD + xN' + MN.$$

This will represent the given operator if

$$x(M + N + 1) = x - x^2, \qquad MN + xN' = -2x - 1.$$

Replace M in the second equation by its value from the first and take $N = ax + b$, to obtain

$$-x(ax + b) - (ax + b)^2 + ax = 0x^2 - 2x - 1.$$

Equating the coefficients of like powers of x, obtain

$$-a - a^2 = 0, \qquad -b - 2ab + a = -2, \qquad -b^2 = -1.$$

These are satisfied by $a = -1$, $b = -1$.   Hence

$$N = -x - 1, \qquad M = -x - N = 1,$$

and the factored operator is

$$\mathbf{(xD + 1)(xD - x - 1).}$$

EXERCISES

1. Show that $(xD - 1)(D - x^2)y = [xD^2 - (x^3 + 1)D - x^2]y$.

2. Show that $(xD + 2)[(x - 1)D + x^2]y = [x(x - 1)D^2 + (x^3 + 3x - 2)D + 4x^2]y$.

3. If $O_1 = D + x^2$ and $O_2 = xD - 4$, show that $O_1O_2y - O_2O_1y = (D - 2x^2)y$.

Factor the operators numbered 4 to 9:

4. $D^2 + D - 1 - x - x^2$ **5.** $D^2 + (x - 1)D + 2 + x - 2x^2$

6. $D^2 + (2 - x)D + 1 + 2x - 2x^2$ **7.** $x^2D^2 + x^2D - 2 - x$

8.*$xD^2 + (1 + x^2)D + 2x$ **9.** $xD^2 - (x + 1)D + 2$

10. Factor $D^2 + (4x + 1)D + 4x^2 + 2x + 2$. May the factors be written in either order?

Solve the following differential equations:

11. $(xD - 2)(xD + x + 1)y = 0$ **12.** $(xD^2 - D)y = 12$

13. $(x^2D^2 - xD + 1)y = 12x^2$ **14.** $(D - 2x)(D - 2x + 1)y = e^{x^2}$

15. $[xD^2 + (2 - x)D - 1]y = e^x$ **16.** $[xD^2 + (3 - 2x^2)D - 4x]y = 4xe^{x^2}$

65. Homogeneous linear equation

The equation

$$x^n \frac{d^n y}{dx^n} + A_1 x^{n-1} \frac{d^{n-1}y}{dx^{n-1}} + \cdots + A_{n-1}x \frac{dy}{dx} + A_n y = X, \quad (12)$$

where the A's are constant and X represents a function of x, is often referred to as the homogeneous linear equation. The substitution

$$z = \log x \quad (13)$$

reduces this to the linear equation with constant coefficients. Using the notation

$$\frac{d^k y}{dz^k} = D^k y, \quad (14)$$

we have

$$\frac{dy}{dx} = \frac{dy}{dz}\frac{dz}{dx} = \frac{1}{x}\frac{dy}{dz} = \frac{1}{x}Dy,$$

$$\frac{d^2 y}{dx^2} = \frac{d(dy/dx)}{dz}\frac{dz}{dx} = \frac{1}{x^2}\frac{d^2 y}{dz^2} - \frac{1}{x^2}\frac{dy}{dz} = \frac{1}{x^2}D(D - 1)y,$$

$$\frac{d^3 y}{dx^3} = \frac{1}{x^3}D^2(D - 1)y - \frac{2}{x^3}D(D - 1)y = \frac{1}{x^3}D(D - 1)D - 2)y, \quad (15)$$

$$\cdots \cdots \cdots \cdots \cdots \cdots \cdots \cdots \cdots \cdots \cdots \cdots$$

$$\frac{d^n y}{dx^n} = \frac{1}{x^n}D(D - 1) \cdots (D - n + 1)y.$$

* It may be necessary to try $(xD + M)(D + N)$ and $(D + M)(xD + N)$ to get a solution.

Substitution of the values of $d^k y/dx^k$ from (15) in (12) evidently gives a linear equation with constant coefficients. Solving this equation by the methods of Chapter VI, and replacing z by $\log x$ in the result, obtain the solution of (12).

Example. Solve

$$x^3 \frac{d^3y}{dx^3} + 6x^2 \frac{d^2y}{dx^2} + 8x \frac{dy}{dx} - 8y = x^2. \tag{a}$$

Solution. Using (13) to (15), we have

$$\frac{x^3}{x^3} D(D-1)(D-2)y + 6 \frac{x^2}{x^2} D(D-1)y + 8 \frac{x}{x} Dy - 8y = e^{2z}, \tag{b}$$

or

$$(D^3 + 3D^2 + 4D - 8)y = e^{2z}. \tag{c}$$

The solution of equation (c) is

$$y = c_1 e^z + e^{-2z}(c_1 \sin 2z + c_2 \cos 2z) + \tfrac{1}{20}e^{2z}. \tag{d}$$

Replacing z in (d) by $\log x$ from (13), we have

$$y = c_1 x + \frac{1}{x^2}[c_1 \sin (2 \log x) + c_2 \cos (2 \log x)] + \tfrac{1}{20}x^2.$$

EXERCISES

1. $x^3 \dfrac{d^3y}{dx^3} + 3x^2 \dfrac{d^2y}{dx^2} - 6x \dfrac{dy}{dx} - 6y = 0$

2. $x^2 \dfrac{d^2y}{dx^2} + x \dfrac{dy}{dx} - 9y = x^n \ (n \ne \pm 3)$

3. $(x-1)^3 \dfrac{d^3y}{dx^3} + 2(x-1)^2 \dfrac{d^2y}{dx^2} - 4(x-1) \dfrac{dy}{dx} + 4y = 4 \log (x-1)$; let $z = \log (x-1)$

4. $x \dfrac{d^3y}{dx^3} + 2 \dfrac{d^2y}{dx^2} = 0$

66. Second-order linear equation

The general linear equation of the second order has the form

$$\frac{d^2y}{dx^2} + f_1(x) \frac{dy}{dx} + f_2(x)y = f_3(x). \tag{16}$$

To get an idea of how this may be solved, let us try the substitution

$$y = v(x) \cdot \varphi(x). \tag{17}$$

Substituting y from (17) in (16) and rearranging the terms, we find

$$\varphi \frac{d^2v}{dx^2} + \left(2 \frac{d\varphi}{dx} + f_1\varphi\right) \frac{dv}{dx} + \left(\frac{d^2\varphi}{dx^2} + f_1 \frac{d\varphi}{dx} + f_2\varphi\right) v = f_3. \tag{18}$$

If now $\varphi(x)$ is chosen so that the coefficient of v in (18) is zero, that is, if

$$\frac{d^2\varphi}{dx^2} + f_1 \frac{d\varphi}{dx} + f_2\varphi = 0, \tag{19}$$

equation (18) does not contain v. Hence the method of §62 may be applied to solve it. In other words, *if $y = \varphi(x)$ is any particular solution of the equation obtained by setting the left-hand member of (16) equal to zero, then the substitution (17) applied to (16) reduces it to an equation that can be solved by methods already considered.*

Example. Solve

$$(1 + x)\frac{d^2y}{dx^2} + (4x + 5)\frac{dy}{dx} + (4x + 6)y = e^{-2x}. \tag{a}$$

Solution. First we try to find a particular solution of

$$(1 + x)\frac{d^2y}{dx^2} + (4x + 5)\frac{dy}{dx} + (4x + 6)y = 0. \tag{b}$$

Often particular solutions are obtained by trial. The usual plan is to substitute simple expressions, such as $y = e^{ax}$, $y = x^a$, $y = x + a$, $y =$ polynomial in x, in the equation to be solved, and then try to determine the arbitrary constants so that the equation will be satisfied. Substituting $y = e^{ax}$ in (b), we find, after slight simplification,

$$[(a^2 + 5a + 6) + x(a^2 + 4a + 4)]e^{ax} = 0. \tag{c}$$

This will be true, if

$$a^2 + 5a + 6 = 0 \quad\text{and}\quad a^2 + 4a + 4 = 0.$$

Both of these equations have a root -2. Hence $y = e^{-2x}$ is a particular solution. Therefore, in accordance with (17), we substitute

$$y = ve^{-2x} \tag{d}$$

in (a) to obtain, after considerable simplification,

$$(1 + x)\frac{d^2v}{dx^2} + \frac{dv}{dx} = 1. \tag{e}$$

The solution of this equation, found by the method of §62, is

$$v = x + c_1 \log (x + 1) + c_2. \tag{f}$$

Substitution of this value of v in (d) gives the required solution of (a):

$$y = e^{-2x}[x + c_1 \log (x + 1) + c_2].$$

EXERCISES

1. $(x^2 - 1)\dfrac{d^2y}{dx^2} + x\dfrac{dy}{dx} - y = 0$; let $y = vx$

2. $x^2\dfrac{d^2y}{dx^2} + x^2\dfrac{dy}{dx} + (x - 2)y = 0$.   *Hint:* Try $y = x^n$

3. $(x^2 + 1)\dfrac{d^2y}{dx^2} - 2x\dfrac{dy}{dx} + 2y = 6(1 + x^2)^2$; let $y = vx$

4. $x\dfrac{d^2y}{dx^2} - (x + 3)\dfrac{dy}{dx} + 3y = 4x^4e^x$

5. $\sin^2 x\dfrac{d^2y}{dx^2} - \sin x \cos x\dfrac{dy}{dx} + y + \sin^3 x = 0$

67. Exact equation

An exact equation is one that can be obtained by equating to zero the derivative of a function of x, y, dy/dx, d^2y/dx^2, ...   That the equation

$$x^2D^3y + (x^2 + 2x)\,D^2y - 2\,Dy - 2y - 10 = 0 \qquad (20)$$

is exact will now be proved.   Since

$$\frac{d}{dx}\,(x^2\,D^2y) = x^2\,D^3y + 2x\,D^2y,$$

or

$$x^2\,D^3y = \frac{d}{dx}\,(x^2\,D^2y) - 2x\,D^2y, \qquad (21)$$

replace $x^2\,D^3y$ in (20) by its value from (21) to get

$$\frac{d}{dx}\,(x^2\,D^2y) + x^2\,D^2y - 2\,Dy - 2y - 10 = 0. \qquad (22)$$

Using the same process, in (22) replace $x^2\,D^2y$ by $[d(x^2\,Dy)/dx] - 2x\,Dy$ to obtain

$$\frac{d}{dx}\,(x^2\,D^2y) + \frac{d}{dx}\,(x^2\,Dy) - (2x + 2)\,Dy - 2y - 10 = 0. \qquad (23)$$

Finally, in (23) replace $(2x + 2)\,Dy$ by $d[(2x + 2)y]/dx - 2y$ and multiply through by dx to obtain

$$d(x^2\,D^2y) + d(x^2\,Dy) - d[(2x + 2)y] + 2y - 2y - 10\,dx = 0. \qquad (24)$$

Now integrate (24) term by term to obtain

$$x^2\,D^2y + x^2\,Dy - (2x + 2)y - 10x = c. \qquad (25)$$

Equation (20) is exact because it is the derivative of the left member of (25) equated to zero.

Next consider any linear equation of the third order

$$P_0\, D^3 y + P_1\, D^2 y + P_2\, Dy + P_3 y = \varphi(x), \qquad (26)$$

where the P_i represent functions of x. Treat this as we did equation (20) to get

$$\frac{d}{dx}\,(P_0\, D^2 y) + \frac{d}{dx}\,[(P_1 - P_0')\, Dy] + \frac{d}{dx}\,[(P_2 - P_1' + P_0'')y]$$
$$+ (P_3 - P_2' + P_1'' - P_0''')y = \varphi(x), \quad (27)$$

where the primes indicate derivatives with respect to x. The process used to integrate (24) will apply to integrate (27) or will fail, according as the coefficient of y in (27) is or is not zero. *Hence the condition that* (26) *be exact is*

$$P_3 - P_2' + P_1'' - P_0''' = 0. \qquad (28)$$

Suppose that (26) is not exact but becomes exact when multiplied by $\mu(x)$. Then applying (28) to (26) multiplied through by $\mu(x)$, we get as *the condition that $\mu(x)$ be an integrating factor of* (26)

$$P_3\mu - (P_2\mu)' + (P_1\mu)'' - (P_0\mu)''' = 0. \qquad (29)$$

Equation (29) *is called the* **adjoint** *of* (26). Any solution $\mu(x)$ of (29) is an integrating factor of (26).

The theory just considered for an equation of the third order is readily extended to a linear differential equation of the nth order.

EXERCISES

1. Write the condition, similar to (28), that

$$P_0\, D^2 y + P_1\, Dy + P_2 y = \varphi(x)$$

be exact, and write its adjoint.

2. Write the condition that

$$P_0\, D^n y + P_1\, D^{n-1} y + P_2\, D^{n-2} y + \cdots + P_{n-1}\, Dy + P_n y = \varphi(x)$$

be exact and write its adjoint.

3. Show that $x^2\, D^3 y + (2x^2 + 2x)\, D^2 y + (4x - 3x^2)\, Dy - 6xy = 10$ is exact by applying (28).   From this equation derive

$$D^2 y + 2\, Dy - 3y = \frac{10}{x} + \frac{c}{x^2}.$$

4. The condition that $P_0\, D^2 y + P_1\, Dy + P_2 y = \varphi(x)$ be exact is $P_2 - P_1' + P_0'' = 0$. Show that $x^3\, D^2 y + 4x^2\, Dy + 2xy = 20x$ is exact, from it derive $x\, Dy + y = 10 + cx^{-2}$, and integrate this result to obtain $x^2 y = 10x^2 - c + c_1 x$.

5. Write the adjoint of $x^2 D^2 y + 2x Dy - 2y = 4x^2$. Show that the solution of the adjoint is $\mu = c_1 x + c_2/x^2$. Using the condition for exactness, show that both x and $1/x^2$ are integrating factors of the given equation. Derive two first-order differential equations by using the two integrating factors separately, and eliminate Dy from these to obtain the solution of the original equation.

6. Find the adjoint of $x^3 D^3 y + x^2 D^2 y - 14x Dy - 10y = 30x^4$ and show that its general solution is $\mu = c_1 x^{-6} + c_2 x + c_3$. Using the corresponding integrating factors 1, x, and x^{-6}, derive three second-order differential equations from the given one. The general solution of the given equation could be found by eliminating $D^2 y$ and Dy from these three second-order equations.

7. Show that $(x^2 + x - 3) D^3 y + (6x + 3) D^2 y + 6Dy = 0$ is exact and find its first integral. Find the solution of the given differential equation.

8. Show that $(x^3 + x) D^3 y + (7x^2 + 1) D^2 y + 10x Dy + 2y = 0$ is exact and find its first integral. Show that $1/x$ is an integrating factor of the first integral and use this information to derive another integral. Solve the original differential equation.

CHAPTER IX

APPLICATIONS

68. Radius of curvature

Some problems relating to the radius of curvature are rather interesting. As an illustration, consider the following:

Example. Find the equation of the curve whose radius of curvature is double the normal and oppositely directed.

Solution. Equating the expression for the radius of curvature and twice the expression for the normal (see Fig. 1), obtain

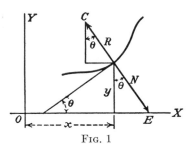

Fig. 1

$$\left[1 + \left(\frac{dy}{dx}\right)^2\right]^{\frac{3}{2}} \div \frac{d^2y}{dx^2}$$

$$= \pm\, 2y \sqrt{1 + \left(\frac{dy}{dx}\right)^2}. \quad (a)$$

Assuming that the radius of curvature R is positive and is directed from the curve toward the center of curvature, and that the normal N is directed from the curve toward the X-axis, we see that y and d^2y/dx^2 will have the same sign when R and N are directed oppositely. Hence the plus sign in (a) must be used. Substitution of p for dy/dx and $p\, dp/dy$ for d^2y/dx^2 in (a) gives

$$\frac{(1 + p^2)^{\frac{3}{2}}}{p\, dp/dy} = 2y(1 + p^2)^{\frac{1}{2}}. \quad (b)$$

Separating the variables and integrating (b), we obtain

$$\log\,(1 + p^2) = \log\frac{y}{c}, \quad \text{or} \quad \frac{dy}{dx} = \pm \sqrt{\frac{y}{c} - 1}. \quad (c)$$

Integrating (c) and simplifying, we obtain

$$(\mathbf{x} - \mathbf{c_1})^2 = \mathbf{4cy} - \mathbf{4c^2}. \quad (d)$$

This represents a system of parabolas with their axes parallel to the Y-axis.

PROBLEMS

1. Determine the curves for which the radius of curvature

   (*a*) Is equal to the normal and in the same direction.
   (*b*) Is equal to the normal and in the opposite direction.
   (*c*) Varies as the cube of the normal.
   (*d*) Projected on the *X*-axis equals the abscissa.
   (*e*) Projected on the *X*-axis is the negative of the abscissa.
   (*f*) Projected on the *X*-axis is twice the abscissa.

2. Find the equation of all plane curves which have a constant radius of curvature.
3. Integrate completely the differential equation of the curve in which the projection of the radius of curvature upon the *X*-axis is constant.
4. Find the differential equation of the curve whose radius of curvature is equal to *n* times the normal. Integrate this equation (*a*) when $n = 1$; (*b*) when $n = 3$. Is this differential equation integrable in terms of ordinary functions for all integral values of *n*?

69. Cables.   The catenary

Figure 2 represents a loaded cable. Let us assume that it is perfectly flexible, inextensible, homogeneous, and hanging from two points under the action of gravity on a load distributed along it in a continuous way. Let *H* be the tension in the cable at its lowest point *A*, *T* the tension at any point *B* of the cable, and *L* the resultant force of gravity exerted between *A* and *B*. Since the forces *T*, *H*, and *L* are in equilibrium,

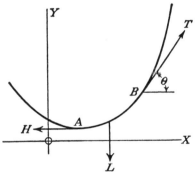

$$T \cos \theta = H, \qquad (1)$$
$$T \sin \theta = L, \qquad (2)$$

Fig. 2

where *θ* is the angle between the direction of force *T* and the horizontal.
Evidently the tension *H* at *A* is horizontal, and the tension *T* at *B* is directed along the tangent to the curve of the cable; hence, if we take the *X*-axis horizontal and the *Y*-axis vertical, we have tan $\theta = dy/dx$. Then division of (2) by (1), member by member, gives

$$\tan \theta = \frac{dy}{dx} = \frac{L}{H}. \qquad (3)$$

Differentiating both sides, we obtain

$$\frac{d^2y}{dx^2} = \frac{1}{H} \frac{dL}{dx} \tag{4}$$

as the differential equation of the curve of the cable.

The curve in which a uniform chain hangs under its own weight is called the **catenary**. In this case, we have

$$L = ws, \tag{5}$$

where s represents the arc length AB in Fig. 2 and w represents weight per unit length of the chain. Substitution of L from (5) in (4) gives

$$\frac{d^2y}{dx^2} = \frac{w}{H} \frac{ds}{dx} = \frac{w}{H} \sqrt{1 + \left(\frac{dy}{dx}\right)^2}. \tag{6}$$

Substituting in (6) p for dy/dx and dp/dx for d^2y/dx^2, we obtain

$$\frac{dp}{dx} = \frac{w}{H} \sqrt{1 + p^2}. \tag{7}$$

Integrating (7), we obtain

$$\sinh^{-1} p = \frac{w}{H} x + c_1, \qquad \text{or} \qquad p = \sinh\left(\frac{w}{H} x + c_1\right). \tag{8}$$

Replacing p by dy/dx in (8) and integrating, we find

$$y = \frac{H}{w} \cosh\left(\frac{w}{H} x + c_1\right) + c_2. \tag{9}$$

If the origin is taken at the lowest point, $y = 0$ and $dy/dx = 0$, when $x = 0$. Substitution of these values in (8) and (9) gives

$$c_1 = 0, \qquad c_2 = -\frac{H}{w}.$$

Substituting these values in (9), we obtain

$$y = \frac{H}{w} \left(\cosh \frac{w}{H} x - 1\right). \tag{10}$$

PROBLEMS

1. Find the curve in which the cable of a suspension bridge hangs, if it carries a uniform horizontal load of w lb./ft. run; neglect the weight of the cable. *Hint:* In equation (3) $L = wx$.

2. Set up the differential equation for the cable of problem 1, if its weight per running foot is assumed constant and taken into account.

3. Slender uniform rods all of the same diameter are suspended from a string to which each is knotted; two consecutive rods just touch, and they hang so that their ends are in a straight horizontal line.   Neglecting the diameter of the rods, find the equation of the curve of the string. *Hint: dL* in equation (4) = *ky dx* (see Fig. 3).

4. What would be the equation of the curve of the string in problem 3 if all the rods were of the same length instead of having their ends in a straight line?

5. Set up the differential equation for the string of problem 3, if its weight per running foot is assumed constant and taken into account.

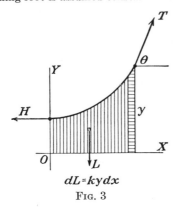

$$dL = kydx$$

Fig. 3

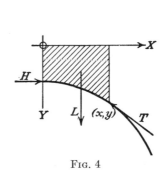

Fig. 4

6. Find the shape of the arch of a stone-arch bridge, if the resultant stress at any point of the arch due to the weight of the masonry above is directed along the tangent to the arch at the point.   Assume that the masonry is uniform in density and that the surface of the road is horizontal (see Fig. 4).

7. If an arch carries, in addition to the load of problem 6, a layer of material spread uniformly over the horizontal road surface, the density of the layer being k times that of the masonry, what would be the shape of the arch?

★8. An arch is the bottom of a canal carrying a water load.   Find the equation of its curve, assuming that the stress at each point due to the weight of the water is directed along the tangent.   Neglect the weight of the arch and note that the water pressure at each point is directed along the normal to the arch through the point (see Fig. 5).

★9. Solve problem 8 if the water is covered with a uniform layer of fluid having specific gravity k.

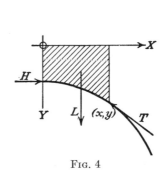

$$T \sin \theta = \int wy\,ds \cos \varphi = \int wy\,dx$$
$$T \cos \theta = H - \int wy\,dy$$

Fig. 5

★10. A uniform cable $2l$ units long has its ends attached at two points, A and B, and hangs under its own weight.   A horizontal line through B meets a vertical line through A at point C. If $AC = 2b$ units and $BC = 2c$ units, find the coordinates of the mid-point of line AB referred to a set of rectangular axes with origin at the lowest point of the cable and X-axis horizontal.

70. Equation of elastic curve. Beams

Consider a horizontal beam acted upon by vertical loads, and assume that the forces due to these loads lie in a vertical plane containing the centroidal axis (central longitudinal axis) of the beam and that they are such that no part of the beam is stressed beyond its elastic limit. These stresses cause the beam to bend, as indicated in Fig. 6, and the curve of its centroidal axis is called the **elastic curve** of the stressed

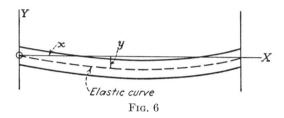

Fig. 6

beam. An important problem in the consideration of strength of materials is to find the equation of this elastic curve. If a beam is loaded as just indicated, is made of uniform material satisfying Hooke's law, and fulfills certain other conditions relating to shape and to properties of materials, it can be shown that its elastic curve satisfies approximately the differential equation

$$EI \frac{d^2y}{dx^2} = M, \tag{11}$$

where the X-axis is horizontal along the beam, the Y-axis is vertical, E is the modulus of elasticity of the material of the beam, I is the moment of inertia of the cross section of the beam perpendicular to its axis with respect to a horizontal line in the cross section passing through its centroid, and M is the **bending moment** at the cross section. Since the material of the beam is uniform, E *is constant*, and if the beam has a uniform cross section, I *is constant*.

The bending moment M at any cross section may be found by taking the algebraic sum of the moments of the external forces on the part of the beam on one side of the cross section about a horizontal line in this cross section. In finding the bending moment, *consider upward forces as giving positive moments and downward forces negative moments* about the horizontal line in the cross section. Consider, for example, the beam of Fig. 7 loaded as indicated in addition to a uniform running load of 100 lb./ft.   To find the bending moment at point A, consider the forces to the left of A:1800 lb. at O with arm x ft., and $100x$ lb. of

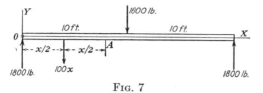

FIG. 7

running load downward and thought of as concentrated at the center of OA.   Taking moments about A, we have

$$M = 1800x - 100x\,\frac{x}{2} = 1800x - 50x^2.$$

Example.   A uniform beam (see Fig. 8) l ft. long is fixed at both ends and carries a uniformly distributed load of w lb./ft. length. Find the equation of its elastic curve and its maximum deflection.

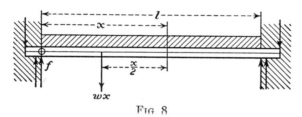

FIG. 8

Solution.   Since the beam is fixed at the ends, the elastic curve is horizontal at both ends.   Hence, taking the origin at the left end, we have

$$y = 0, \qquad \frac{dy}{dx} = 0, \qquad \text{when } x = 0,$$

$$y = 0, \qquad \frac{dy}{dx} = 0, \qquad \text{when } x = l. \tag{a}$$

The forces acting on the beam to the left of the cross section x ft. from the left end are (1) wx lb. due to the running load; (2) a supporting force at the left end; (3) a couple exerted by the masonry.   Writing f for the supporting force and A for the moment of the couple, we have for the bending moment x ft. from the left end (see Fig. 8),

$$M = A + fx - wx\,\frac{x}{2}. \tag{b}$$

Substitution of M from (b) in (11) gives

$$EI \frac{d^2y}{dx^2} = A + fx - w\frac{x^2}{2}. \tag{c}$$

Integrating (c), we obtain

$$EI \frac{dy}{dx} = Ax + f\frac{x^2}{2} - \frac{wx^3}{6} + c_1, \tag{d}$$

$$EIy = \frac{Ax^2}{2} + f\frac{x^3}{6} - w\frac{x^4}{24} + c_1x + c_2. \tag{e}$$

Substituting the conditions (a) in (d) and (e), we get

$$c_1 = 0, \qquad c_2 = 0, \qquad Al + f\frac{l^2}{2} - w\frac{l^3}{6} = 0, \qquad \frac{Al^2}{2} + \frac{fl^3}{6} - \frac{wl^4}{24} = 0,$$

or

$$c_1 = 0, \qquad c_2 = 0, \qquad f = \frac{wl}{2}, \qquad A = \frac{-wl^2}{12}. \tag{f}$$

Substituting in (e) the values of c_1, c_2, f, and A from (f) and simplifying, we have the equation of the elastic curve,

$$y = \frac{-w}{24EI} (x^2l^2 - 2x^3l + x^4). \tag{g}$$

Here $-y$ represents the deflection of the beam x ft. from the left end, and since the maximum deflection (d_{max}) will evidently be at the center of the beam where $x = l/2$, we have, from (g),

$$d_{max} = (-y)_{x=l/2} = \frac{w}{24EI} \left(\frac{l^4}{4} - 2\frac{l^4}{8} + \frac{l^4}{16} \right) = \frac{wl^4}{384EI}.$$

PROBLEMS

1. A beam (see Fig. 9) l ft. long is simply supported at its ends and carries a uniform load of w lb./ft. run. Show that the bending moment at a point x ft.

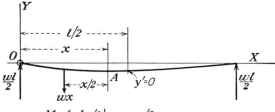

$$M_A = (wl \cdot x/2) - wx \cdot x/2$$
$$y = 0 \text{ when } x = 0,\ y' = 0 \text{ when } x = l/2$$

Fig. 9

from the left end is $\frac{1}{2}wlx - \frac{1}{2}wx^2$, and use this in equation (11) to find the deflection y at this point. Also find the maximum deflection.

2. A beam l ft. long and simply supported carries a load of P lb. at its center. Find its deflection x ft. from the left end and its maximum deflection. *Hint:* Draw a figure of the beam like Fig. 9 and observe that $M = \frac{1}{2}Px$ if $x < \frac{1}{2}l$.

3. Using the answers to problems 1 and 2, write a formula for the maximum deflection of a beam simply supported at its ends and carrying a uniformly distributed load of w lb./ft. and P lb. at its center.

4. Using the formulas from problems 1 to 3, find the maximum deflection of a simply supported steel beam 20 ft. long, having $E = 30 \times 10^6$ lb./in.^{2}, $I = 54$ in.^{4}, if the loading is (*a*) 5000 lb. at center; (*b*) 40 lb./in. uniformly distributed; (*c*) the combined loading just mentioned.

5. A beam fixed at one end and unsupported at the other (see Fig. 10) is called a **cantilever beam.** Find the deflection x ft. from the fixed end of a cantilever beam l ft. long, if it carries a load of (*a*) P lb. at the fixed end ($w = 0$ in Fig. 10); (*b*) w lb./ft. run ($P = 0$ in Fig. 10); (*c*) w lb./ft. run and P lb. at its fixed end.

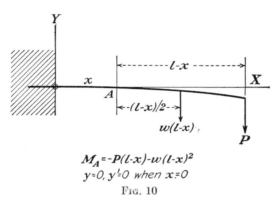

$$M_A = -P(l-x) - w(l-x)^2$$
$$y = 0,\ y' = 0 \text{ when } x = 0$$

Fig. 10

★6. Figure 11 represents a cantilever beam carrying a uniformly distributed load of w lb./ft., fixed at one end and simply supported at the other so that the right end is on a level with the left end. Since force R is unknown, it must be determined like a constant of integration by using an initial condition. Find the

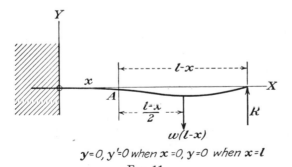

$$y = 0,\ y' = 0 \text{ when } x = 0,\ y = 0 \text{ when } x = l$$

Fig. 11

equation of the elastic curve of the beam. Also find the value of x/l at the point where the deflection is maximum.

7. Find the equation of the elastic curve of a uniform beam fixed at both ends and carrying a load P at its center.

★**8.** Figure 12 represents a uniform beam AB with a concentrated load P at C

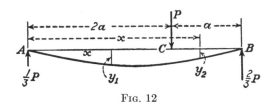

FIG. 12

twice as far from A as from B. The supporting forces $\frac{1}{3}P$ and $\frac{2}{3}P$ are indicated. If y_1 is the deflection for part AC and y_2 for part CB, we have

$$EI\,\frac{d^2y_1}{dx^2} = \frac{1}{3}\,Px, \qquad EI\,\frac{d^2y_2}{dx^2} = \frac{1}{3}\,Px - P(x - 2a),$$

with the initial conditions $y_1 = 0$ when $x = 0$, $y_2 = 0$ when $x = 3a$, $y_1 = y_2$ and $dy_1/dx = dy_2/dx$ when $x = 2a$. Integrate the two equations using the initial conditions to determine constants and thus find the equations of the elastic curves of the parts of the beam. Also find the maximum deflection.

★**9.** Solve problem 8 and then find the maximum deflection of the beam of Fig. 12 with the same loading, assuming that it is fixed at both ends. Observe in this case that the supporting force and the couple at A must be found by using initial conditions.

★**10.** A cantilever beam l ft. long carries a load of material whose width and density are uniform and whose depth is directly proportional to its distance from the free end. Find the maximum deflection of the beam.

★**11.** Find the equation of the elastic curve of a beam fixed at both ends and carrying a concentrated load P, distant a ft. from the left end and b ft. from the right end.

71. Columns

Beams placed vertically to support vertical loads are often called **columns.** This section will deal mainly with the four types represented in Figs. 13 to 16. The plane of the elastic curve of a column contains the axis of each cross section about which the moment of inertia is greatest. If now we think of the column as placed horizontally without relative change of forces acting on it, and with the plane of the elastic curve vertical (see Fig. 17), we may apply formula (11) of §70 to obtain an approximation to the equation of the elastic curve of the column.

Example. Approximate the equation of the elastic curve of a column (Fig. 17) with both ends free to turn, and find the buckling stress.

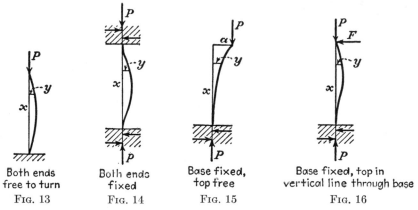

Both ends free to turn
FIG. 13

Both ends fixed
FIG. 14

Base fixed, top free
FIG. 15

Base fixed, top in vertical line through base
FIG. 16

Solution. Neglecting the weight of the beam, and applying (11) of §70, obtain (see Fig. 17)

$$EI \frac{d^2y}{dx^2} = -Py.$$

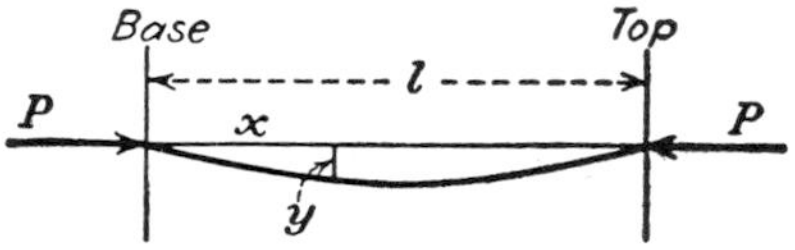

FIG. 17

The general solution of this equation is

$$y = c_1 \sin \omega x + c_2 \cos \omega x, \qquad \omega = \sqrt{\frac{P}{EI}}. \qquad (a)$$

As initial conditions we have

$$y = 0 \qquad \text{when } x = 0 \text{ and when } x = l. \qquad (b)$$

Since $y = 0$ when $x = 0$, we have from (a) $c_2 = 0$, and

$$y = c_1 \sin \omega x. \qquad (c)$$

The second condition of (b), $y = 0$ when $x = l$, will be satisfied if $c_1 = 0$. In this case $y = 0$ for all values of x, and the beam is straight. Also $y_l = c_1 \sin \omega l = 0$ if $\omega l = \pi$; or, since $\omega = \sqrt{P/(EI)}$, $P = \pi^2 EI/l^2$. Hence if A is the area of the horizontal cross section of a column, the stress p, or force per square unit for buckling, is

$$p = \frac{P}{A} = \frac{\pi^2 EI}{Al^2}. \qquad (d)$$

Since we cannot have much deflection without disagreement with the conditions of §70, a column should not be loaded so that buckling impends.*   Also note that, if l is very small, p from (d) is very large and has no design value.   Actually formula (d) is useful only for a limited range of $I/(Al^2)$.   The student may consult a book on *the strength of materials* for a detailed treatment of columns.

PROBLEMS

1. Show for the column represented by Fig. 14 that $EI\, d^2y/dx^2 = -py + G$, where G is a constant.   Check that the initial conditions are $x = 0$, $y = 0$, $dy/dx = 0$, both when $x = 0$ and when $x = l$.   Show that $y = (G/P)(1 - \cos \omega x)$, where $\omega = \sqrt{P/EI}$, and that for buckling $P = 4\pi^2 EI/l^2$.

2. In the solution of problem 1 you took $\omega l = 2\pi$ to provide that $1 - \cos \omega l = 0$. Show that, if you had used $\omega l = 4\pi$, the corresponding P would have been four times as large.   Sketch the corresponding elastic curve of the beam and thus show that it consists essentially of two beams each having one-half the length of the original one.

3. Figure 15 represents a column with fixed base and top free to move.   Show that for buckling $P = \frac{1}{4}\pi^2 EI/l^2$.

4. For problem 3 discuss the elastic curve and the strength of the beam corresponding to a value of $3\pi/2$ instead of $\pi/2$ for ωl to provide that $\cos \omega l = 0$.

★5. Figure 16 represents a column with base fixed and top free to turn but held on a vertical line through the base.   Prove that for buckling $\tan \omega l = \omega l$, where $\omega = \sqrt{P/(EI)}$.   Then show that, if A is the cross-sectional area of the column, assumed uniform, stress $p = P/A = (4.4934)^2 EI/(Al^2)$, approximately.

6. For a round steel column supported as indicated in Fig. 16 and having $E = 30 \times 10^6$ lb./in.^{2} and radius 2 in., show that $p = 6.057 \times 10^8/l^2$ lb./in.^{2}, where l is length in inches.   Show that this is greater than 30,000 lb./in.^{2} (the elastic limit of steel) when $l < 142.1$ in.

72. Motion of a particle in a plane

Polar coordinates lend themselves to the solution of certain problems more readily than rectangular coordinates.   Accordingly we shall find an expression for the component a_ρ of the acceleration in the direction of the radius vector and an expression for the component a_θ at right angles to the radius vector for the motion of a particle in a plane.   The component a_ρ is the projection of the acceleration vector a on the radius vector, or, what amounts to the same thing, the sum of the projections of the components of a on the radius vector.   Hence, denoting derivatives with respect to t by dots thus,

$$\frac{dx}{dt} = \dot{x},\ \frac{d^2x}{dt^2} = \ddot{x},\ \frac{d\rho}{dt} = \dot{\rho},\ \frac{d\theta}{dt} = \dot{\theta},\ \text{etc.,} \tag{12}$$

*Since amplitude c_1 in (c) is independent of p, it is not determined and the maximum deflection of a buckling column seems to be arbitrary.   However Professor R. P. Bailey, using a more accurate formula than (11) §70, has shown that amplitude of deflection depends on stress p.

we see from Fig. 18 that

$$a_\rho = \ddot{x} \cos \theta + \ddot{y} \sin \theta \tag{13}$$

and

$$a_\theta = -\ddot{x} \sin \theta + \ddot{y} \cos \theta. \tag{14}$$

Repeated differentiation of each of the equations

$$x = \rho \cos \theta, \qquad y = \rho \sin \theta \tag{15}$$

with respect to the time gives

$$\dot{x} = \dot{\rho} \cos \theta - \rho\dot{\theta} \sin \theta, \qquad \dot{y} = \dot{\rho} \sin \theta + \rho\dot{\theta} \cos \theta, \tag{16}$$

$$\ddot{x} = \ddot{\rho} \cos \theta - 2\dot{\rho}\dot{\theta} \sin \theta - \rho\dot{\theta}^2 \cos \theta - \rho\ddot{\theta} \sin \theta, \tag{17}$$

$$\ddot{y} = \ddot{\rho} \sin \theta + 2\dot{\rho}\dot{\theta} \cos \theta - \rho\dot{\theta}^2 \sin \theta + \rho\ddot{\theta} \cos \theta. \tag{18}$$

Substituting the values of $\ddot{x}$ and $\ddot{y}$ from (17) and (18) in (13) and (14) and simplifying, we have

$$a_\rho = \ddot{\rho} - \rho\dot{\theta}^2, \tag{19}$$

$$a_\theta = \rho\ddot{\theta} + 2\dot{\rho}\dot{\theta} = \frac{1}{\rho}\frac{d}{dt}(\rho^2\dot{\theta}). \tag{20}$$

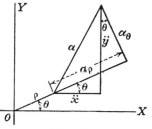

FIG. 18

Similarly, it is easy to show that the component v_ρ of the velocity along the radius vector and the component v_θ at right angles to it are

$$v_\rho = \dot{\rho}, \qquad v_\theta = \rho\dot{\theta}. \tag{21}$$

Example. A particle of mass m, whose variable distance from a fixed point S is ρ, moves under the action of a single force whose direction is always toward S and whose magnitude is $mbv_0^2/(2\rho^2)$. If it moves through fixed point B distant b units from S with velocity v_0 at right angles to SB, find the equation of its path.

Note: This problem is a simplified version of the problem of expressing in mathematical form the motion of a comet about the sun.

Solution. Taking the line SB (see Fig. 19) as initial line and S as pole, we have the initial conditions

$$\rho_0 = b, \ \dot{\rho}_0 = 0, \ b\dot{\theta}_0 = v_0, \qquad \text{when } \theta = 0. \tag{a}$$

Equation (7) in §53 applied in the direction SP of the radius vector gives

$$ma_\rho = m(\ddot{\rho} - \rho\dot{\theta}^2) = \frac{-mbv_0^2}{2\rho^2}, \tag{b}$$

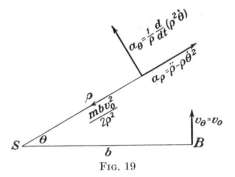

Fig. 19

and applied in the direction perpendicular to the radius vector gives

$$ma_\theta = \frac{m}{\rho} \frac{d}{dt} (\rho^2 \dot\theta) = 0. \tag{c}$$

From (c) and (a)

$$\rho^2 \dot\theta = c_1 = bv_0. \tag{d}$$

Replacing in (b) $\ddot\rho$ by $\dot\rho\, d\dot\rho/d\rho$ and, from (d), $\dot\theta$ by bv_0/ρ^2, and simplifying, we obtain

$$m\left(\frac{\dot\rho\, d\dot\rho}{d\rho} - \frac{b^2 v_0^2}{\rho^3}\right) = \frac{-mbv_0^2}{2\rho^2}. \tag{e}$$

Integrating (e), we find

$$\frac{\dot\rho^2}{2} = \frac{bv_0^2}{2\rho} - \frac{b^2 v_0^2}{2\rho^2} + c_2. \tag{f}$$

Since from (a) $\dot\rho = 0$ when $\rho = b$, it appears that $c_2 = 0$. Hence from (f)

$$\dot\rho = \frac{d\rho}{dt} = \frac{v_0}{\rho} \sqrt{b\rho - b^2}. \tag{g}$$

Replacing $\dot\theta$ in (d) by $d\theta/dt$, solving for dt, substituting the result for dt in (g), and separating the variables, we have

$$\frac{b\, d\rho}{\rho \sqrt{b\rho - b^2}} = d\theta. \tag{h}$$

Integrating (h), we obtain

$$2 \cos^{-1} \sqrt{\frac{b}{\rho}} = \theta + c_3. \tag{i}$$

Substituting zero for θ and b for ρ, we find $c_3 = 0$. Solving (i) for ρ, we get

$$\rho = \frac{2b}{1 + \cos \theta}.$$

This is the equation of a parabola referred to the focus as pole and the axis as initial line.

PROBLEMS

1. A particle of weight w lb. moves in a straight line from a distance a toward a charged point which attracts with a force whose magnitude in pounds is equal numerically to $w/(2gr^2)$, r denoting the distance of the particle from the point. If the particle had an initial velocity toward the point of $1/\sqrt{a}$, how long will it take to traverse half the distance to the point?   Use (7) of §53.

2. A particle moves in a straight line from rest at a distance a toward a center of attraction, the attraction varying inversely as the cube of the distance.   How long will it take the particle to reach the center?   Use (7) §53.

3. The areal velocity of a moving particle P with respect to a fixed point A is the rate at which the line AP generates area.   If A is the pole and (ρ, θ), with θ in radians, the polar coordinates of P, then the areal velocity is $\frac{1}{2}\rho^2 \, d\theta/dt$.   Prove that a particle moving in a plane through a point A under the action of a force always directed toward point A has a constant areal velocity with respect to A. *Hint:* First show that a_θ in equation (20) of this section is zero.

4. A particle moves so that its radial acceleration is always 1 ft./sec.^{2} and the angular velocity of its radius vector is always 2 radians/sec.   If $\rho = \frac{3}{4}$, $\theta = 0$, and $\dot\rho = 6$ when $t = 0$, find ρ and θ in terms of t.   Also find a_θ in terms of t.

5. A particle moves so that its radial velocity $\dot\rho$ is always 1 ft./sec., and the force on the particle is directed along the radius vector.   If initially $\rho = 1$, $\theta = 0$, $\dot\theta = 2$, when $t = 0$, find ρ, θ, and the magnitude of the force in terms of t.

6. Prove that a particle moving with constant speed under the action of a force always directed toward a fixed point A in its plane of motion must move in a circle with A as center or move in a straight line.

7. A particle of mass m at point P situated b units from a fixed point A is moving at right angles to AP with velocity v_0.   Taking AP as initial line and A as pole, find the equation of the path of the particle if it is acted on by a force always directed toward point A and equal in magnitude to $nmb^2v_0^2/\rho^3$, where n is real and positive.   Discuss the curve (a) when $n = 1$ and (b) when $n = 2$.

8. If, in problem 7, the magnitude of the force is $nmbv_0^2/\rho^2$, find the equation of the path of the particle.

9. A particle moves in a plane under the action of a force always directed toward a fixed point A in its plane; its velocity is $k\rho^n$, where ρ is its distance from A and the values of k* and n are constant.   Find the equation of its path.   Tell the nature of its path when (a) $n = 0$, (b) $n = -2$, (c) $n = 1$, (d) $n = -3$.

10. Prove that the force in problem 9 is $k^2nm\rho^{2n-1}$, where m is the mass of the particle.

11. An airplane flying 105 mi./hr. at a height of 2000 ft. lets fall a dummy weighing 180 lb.   If v_x and v_y are, respectively, the horizontal component and the vertical component of the velocity, in feet per second, and if air resistance in pounds has a vertical component equal numerically to $0.006v_y^2$ and a horizontal component of $0.006v_x^2$, find (a) the equation of the path; (b) the time of descent; (c) the horizontal distance traveled while coming down.

* The dimensions of k are $L^{1-n}t^{-1}$.

CHAPTER X

DIFFERENTIAL EQUATIONS IN MORE THAN TWO VARIABLES. EXISTENCE THEOREMS

73. Foreword

Most of the theory used in the preceding chapters relates to the solution of special types of differential equations in two unknowns. This chapter will give a broad view of general equations, discuss the nature of their solutions, consider existence theorems relating to solutions of them, and suggest some general plans for seeking solutions. This will give deeper insight into the general methods set forth in the next chapter.

74. Differential equations of the first order and first degree in three unknowns

Consider the equations

$$\begin{aligned} P_1 \, dx + Q_1 \, dy + R_1 \, dz = 0, \\ P_2 \, dx + Q_2 \, dy + R_2 \, dz = 0, \end{aligned} \tag{1}$$

in which the P's, Q's, and R's represent functions of x, y, and z. A solution consists of two non-differential equations in x, y, and z which satisfy both equations. *The main method of solution consists in (a) combining the given equations and others derived from them so as to obtain an equation in two unknowns, or an equation which is the result of equating to zero the total derivative of some expression involving the variables; (b) integrating the equations thus obtained and combining the results with the given differential equations to obtain other relations among the variables.*

Dividing equations (1) by dz and solving the results for dx/dz and dy/dz, we obtain

$$\frac{dx}{dz} = \frac{P}{R}, \frac{dy}{dz} = \frac{Q}{R}, \quad \text{or} \quad \frac{dx}{P} = \frac{dy}{Q} = \frac{dz}{R}, \tag{2}$$

where

$$P:Q:R = \begin{vmatrix} Q_1 & R_1 \\ Q_2 & R_2 \end{vmatrix} : \begin{vmatrix} R_1 & P_1 \\ R_2 & P_2 \end{vmatrix} : \begin{vmatrix} P_1 & Q_1 \\ P_2 & Q_2 \end{vmatrix}. \tag{3}$$

From (2) we may write

$$\frac{l\,dx}{lP} = \frac{m\,dy}{mQ} = \frac{n\,dz}{nR},\tag{4}$$

and then apply the theorem that in a continued proportion the sum of the antecedents is to the sum of the consequents as any antecedent is to its consequent, to obtain

$$\frac{dx}{P} = \frac{dy}{Q} = \frac{dz}{R} = \frac{l\,dx + m\,dy + n\,dz}{lP + mQ + nR},\tag{5}$$

where l, m, and n are functions of x, y, and z at our disposal. (a) *It may happen that, by suitably choosing l, m, and n, we can find an equation in only two variables or an equation readily integrable.* In either case an integration gives us a required relation. (b) *Again we may be able to choose l, m, and n so that $lP + mQ + nR = 0$ and so that $l\,dx + m\,dy + n\,dz = du$, where u is some function of x, y, and z.* In this case, since $lP + mQ + nR = 0$ and since the last fraction in (5) is finite, it follows that $l\,dx + m\,dy + n\,dz = 0$; that is, $du = 0$, and $u = c$ (*constant*) *is a required relation.* The examples will illustrate these methods of procedure.

The method suggested in exercise 15 of this section is general and occasionally effective.

Example 1. Solve

$$\frac{dx}{xz} = \frac{dy}{yz} = \frac{2\,dz}{x+y}.\tag{a}$$

Solution. Integration of the equation of the first two ratios gives

$$y = c_1 x.\tag{b}$$

Writing equations (5) for (a) with $l = 1$, $m = 1$, $n = 0$, we obtain

$$\frac{2\,dz}{x+y} = \frac{dx+dy}{z(x+y)}.\tag{c}$$

Multiplying through by $z(x+y)$ and integrating, we have

$$x + y = z^2 + c_2.\tag{d}$$

Equations (b) and (d) constitute the solution.

It is instructive to note that, after finding equation (b), we could have substituted $c_1 x$ from (b) for y in $dx/xz = 2\,dz/(x+y)$ and integrated the resulting equation in x and z to obtain

$$x + c_1 x = z^2 + c, \quad\text{or}\quad x + y = z^2 + c.$$

Also we could have noticed that

$$P + Q - 2zR = xz + yz - xz - yz = 0,$$

and therefore that

$$l\,dx + m\,dy + n\,dz = dx + dy - 2z\,dz = 0.$$

Hence

$$x + y - z^2 = c.$$

Example 2. Solve

$$\frac{dx}{y - xz} = \frac{dy}{x + yz} = \frac{dz}{x^2 + y^2}. \tag{a}$$

Solution. Here, taking l, m, and n equal to y, x, and -1, respectively, we have

$$lP + mQ + nR = y^2 - xyz + x^2 + xyz - x^2 - y^2 = 0. \tag{b}$$

Therefore,

$$l\,dx + m\,dy + n\,dz = y\,dx + x\,dy - dz = 0. \tag{c}$$

Integration of (c) gives

$$\mathbf{xy - z = c_1}. \tag{d}$$

Clearing of fractions the equation of the first two ratios in (a) and replacing z in the result by its value $xy - c_1$ from (d), we obtain the exact differential equation,

$$[x + y(xy - c_1)]\,dx + [-y + x(xy - c_1)]\,dy = 0. \tag{e}$$

Integrating (e) by the method of §20 we find

$$x^2 + (xy - c_1)^2 - y^2 = c_2, \qquad \text{or} \qquad \mathbf{x^2 + z^2 - y^2 = c_2}. \tag{f}$$

Equations (d) and (f) constitute the solution.

Again it is instructive to observe that, by taking $l = x$, $m = -y$, and $n = z$, we obtain

$$lP + mQ + nR = xy - x^2z - xy - y^2z + x^2z + y^2z = 0.$$

Therefore

$$l\,dx + m\,dy + n\,dz = x\,dx - y\,dy + z\,dz = 0.$$

Hence,

$$x^2 - y^2 + z^2 = c$$

EXERCISES

1. $\dfrac{dx}{y} = \dfrac{dy}{x} = \dfrac{dz}{z}$

2. $\dfrac{dx}{ayz} = \dfrac{dy}{bzx} = \dfrac{dz}{cxy}$

3. $y\,dx + (y - 2x)\,dy + yz\,dz = 0,\ (x - y)\,dy - yz\,dz = 0$

4. $z\,dx + (y - x)\,dy + z\,dz = 0,\ 2z\,dx - (2x + y)\,dy - z\,dz = 0$

5. $(x + z)\,dx + (x - z)\,dy - (x + z)\,dz = 0,\ x(x + z)\,dx + y(z - x)\,dy - z(x + z)\,dz = 0$

6. $\dfrac{dx}{x} = \dfrac{dy}{y} = \dfrac{dz}{3x + 2y - z}$

7. $\dfrac{dx}{y} = \dfrac{dy}{x} = \dfrac{2\,dz}{1 - z^2}$

8. $\dfrac{dx}{x^2 - y^2 - z^2} = \dfrac{dy}{2xy} = \dfrac{dz}{2xz}$

9. $\dfrac{dx}{x(y - z)} = \dfrac{dy}{y(z - x)} = \dfrac{dz}{z(x - y)}$

10. $\dfrac{dx}{x^2 - y^2 - yz} = \dfrac{dy}{x^2 - y^2 - xz} = \dfrac{dz}{z(x - y)}$

11. $\dfrac{dx}{ny - mz} = \dfrac{dy}{lz - nx} = \dfrac{dz}{mx - ly}$

12. $\dfrac{dx}{-1 - xz^2} = \dfrac{dy}{1 + yz^2} = \dfrac{dz}{z^2(y - x)}$

13. $\dfrac{dx}{y} = \dfrac{dy}{x} = \dfrac{dz}{w} = \dfrac{dw}{z}$

14. $\dfrac{dx}{w - z} = \dfrac{dy}{w - z} = \dfrac{dz}{x + y - 2w} = \dfrac{dw}{2z - x - y}$

15. The solution of equations of the type indicated in equation (1) can often be obtained by eliminating one variable (say z), solving the result for y in terms of x, and then using this solution to find a relation involving z. For example, to solve

$$dx = \frac{dy}{-5x + 12y - 5z} = \frac{dz}{x + 2y + z}, \tag{I}$$

write

$$\frac{dy}{dx} = -5x + 12y - 5z, \qquad \frac{dz}{dx} = x + 2y + z. \tag{II}$$

Differentiate the first of (II) to obtain

$$\frac{d^2y}{dx^2} = -5 + 12\frac{dy}{dx} - 5\frac{dz}{dx}. \tag{III}$$

In (III) replace dz/dx by its value from the second equation of (II); in the result replace z by its value from the first of (II), and simplify to obtain

$$\frac{d^2y}{dx^2} - 13\frac{dy}{dx} + 22y = -5. \tag{IV}$$

Solve (IV) for y and substitute the result in the second of (II) to obtain, after slight simplification,

$$y = c_1 e^{2x} + c_2 e^{11x} - \tfrac{5}{22}, \tag{V}$$
$$5z = 10c_1 e^{2x} + c_2 e^{11x} - 5x - \tfrac{30}{11}.$$

Equations (V) constitute the solution of (I).

Using the method just illustrated, solve the following systems of equations:

(a) $dx = \dfrac{dy}{10x - y + 5z} = \dfrac{dz}{2x - y + z}$

(b) $dx = \dfrac{dy}{2e^x + y + z} = \dfrac{dz}{4e^x + y + z}$

(c) $dx = \dfrac{dy}{6x^2 - y + 3z} = \dfrac{dz}{2x^2 + y + z}$

(d) $dx = \dfrac{dy}{a \sin 2x + y + 2z} = \dfrac{dz}{-a \cos 2x - y - z}$

75. Total differential equations

The number of variables in a system of differential equations may exceed the number of equations by more than one. We shall consider here only the special case of one first-order, first-degree differential equation in three variables. Under certain conditions such an equation is integrable; for example, the solution of

$$2x\, dx + 2y\, dy + 2z\, dz = 0 \tag{6}$$

evidently is

$$x^2 + y^2 + z^2 = c, \tag{7}$$

and, in general, the solution of

$$\frac{\partial f(x,y,z)}{\partial x}\, dx + \frac{\partial f(x,y,z)}{\partial y}\, dy + \frac{\partial f(x,y,z)}{\partial z}\, dz = 0 \tag{8}$$

is

$$f(x,y,z) = c. \tag{9}$$

The object of this article is to arrive at the condition of integrability of an equation

$$P\, dx + Q\, dy + R\, dz = 0, \tag{10}$$

where P, Q, and R are continuous functions of x, y, and z, possessing continuous first partial derivatives with respect to x, y, and z.

If (10) is integrable, there exists a function $\mu(x,y,z)$ such that the expression

$$\mu P\, dx + \mu Q\, dy + \mu R\, dz \tag{11}$$

is exactly the derivative of some function, say $f(x,y,z)$. Hence, comparing the left-hand member of (8) with (11), we have

$$\frac{\partial f}{\partial x} = \mu P, \qquad \frac{\partial f}{\partial y} = \mu Q, \qquad \frac{\partial f}{\partial z} = \mu R. \tag{12}$$

Since $\partial^2 f/\partial x\, \partial y = \partial^2 f/\partial y\, \partial x$, we have, from (12),

$$\mu \frac{\partial P}{\partial y} + P \frac{\partial \mu}{\partial y} = \mu \frac{\partial Q}{\partial x} + Q \frac{\partial \mu}{\partial x}. \tag{13}$$

Similarly

$$\mu \frac{\partial Q}{\partial z} + Q \frac{\partial \mu}{\partial z} = \mu \frac{\partial R}{\partial y} + R \frac{\partial \mu}{\partial y}, \tag{14}$$

$$\mu \frac{\partial R}{\partial x} + R \frac{\partial \mu}{\partial x} = \mu \frac{\partial P}{\partial z} + P \frac{\partial \mu}{\partial z}. \tag{15}$$

Multiplying equation (13) by R, (14) by P, and (15) by Q, adding the results, and rearranging, we have

$$P \left(\frac{\partial Q}{\partial z} - \frac{\partial R}{\partial y} \right) + Q \left(\frac{\partial R}{\partial x} - \frac{\partial P}{\partial z} \right) + R \left(\frac{\partial P}{\partial y} - \frac{\partial Q}{\partial x} \right) = 0. \tag{16}$$

This equation states a necessary condition that (10) be integrable; we shall prove that it is also a sufficient one.

Since the equation $P \, dx + Q \, dy = 0$ is always integrable if z is considered constant, there will be no loss in generality in assuming that $P \, dx + Q \, dy$ is an exact differential with respect to x and y. The solution of

$$P \, dx + Q \, dy = 0, \tag{17}$$

considering z as constant, may now be written in the form

$$f(x,y,z) + \varphi(z) = 0, \tag{18}$$

where φ represents an arbitrary function of z. Since $P \, dx + Q \, dy$ has been assumed to be an exact differential, we may write

$$\frac{\partial P}{\partial y} = \frac{\partial Q}{\partial x}, \qquad P = \frac{\partial f}{\partial x}, \qquad Q = \frac{\partial f}{\partial y}. \tag{19}$$

Taking account of (19), we may write $P \, dx + Q \, dy + R \, dz = 0$ in the form

$$\frac{\partial f}{\partial x} \, dx + \frac{\partial f}{\partial y} \, dy + \frac{\partial f}{\partial z} \, dz + \left(R - \frac{\partial f}{\partial z} \right) dz = 0, \tag{20}$$

or

$$df + \left(R - \frac{\partial f}{\partial z} \right) dz = 0. \tag{21}$$

Equation (21) can be integrated if there exists a relation independent of x and y between $R - (\partial f / \partial z)$ and f; that is, if f and $R - (\partial f / \partial z)$ considered as functions of x and y (z constant) are dependent. Since the condition* that two functions of x and y, f_1 and f_2, be dependent is

$$\frac{\partial f_1}{\partial x} \frac{\partial f_2}{\partial y} - \frac{\partial f_1}{\partial y} \frac{\partial f_2}{\partial x} = 0, \tag{22}$$

* See SOKOLNIKOFF, I. S., "Advanced Calculus," p. 422.

the condition that $f_1 = f$ and $f_2 = R - (\partial f/\partial z)$ be dependent is

$$\frac{\partial f}{\partial x}\left(\frac{\partial R}{\partial y} - \frac{\partial^2 f}{\partial z\,\partial y}\right) - \frac{\partial f}{\partial y}\left(\frac{\partial R}{\partial x} - \frac{\partial^2 f}{\partial z\,\partial x}\right) = 0. \tag{23}$$

From (19),

$$\frac{\partial f}{\partial x} = P, \quad \frac{\partial f}{\partial y} = Q, \quad \frac{\partial^2 f}{\partial z\,\partial y} = \frac{\partial}{\partial z}\left(\frac{\partial f}{\partial y}\right) = \frac{\partial Q}{\partial z}, \quad \frac{\partial^2 f}{\partial z\,\partial x} = \frac{\partial}{\partial z}\left(\frac{\partial f}{\partial x}\right) = \frac{\partial P}{\partial z}.$$

Substituting these results in (23), we have

$$P\left(\frac{\partial R}{\partial y} - \frac{\partial Q}{\partial z}\right) - Q\left(\frac{\partial R}{\partial x} - \frac{\partial P}{\partial z}\right) = 0. \tag{24}$$

Since, from (19), $(\partial P/\partial y) - (\partial Q/\partial x) = 0$, it appears that (24) is the same as (16) with the signs changed. Hence, if (16) holds, (21) can be expressed in terms of the two variables f and z and solved. Since (21) and (10) are the same equation, this solution with f replaced by its value in terms of x and y will be the integral of (10).

The proof just given suggests the following rule—

RULE. *To integrate a total differential equation*

$$P\,dx + Q\,dy + R\,dz = 0 \tag{10}$$

which satisfies the condition (16), *first integrate the equation*

$$P\,dx + Q\,dy = 0$$

treating z as constant, to obtain

$$f(x,y,z) + \varphi(z) = 0, \tag{18}$$

$\varphi(z)$ *being an arbitrary function. Then differentiate this equation and determine the function φ by comparing the result of the differentiation with* (10).

If (10) is not integrable, we may assume any second relation

$$\varphi(x,y,z) = 0 \tag{25}$$

and solve it simultaneously with (10) to get a particular solution.

Example 1. Solve

$$yz^2\,dx - xz^2\,dy - (2xyz + x^2)\,dz = 0. \tag{a}$$

Solution. Substitution from (a) in (16) shows that (a) is integrable. The solution of

$$yz^2\,dx - xz^2\,dy = 0, \tag{b}$$

got by considering z as constant, is

$$\frac{y}{x} + \varphi(z) = 0. \tag{c}$$

Differentiating (c) and multiplying the result by $-x^2z^2$, we obtain

$$yz^2\, dx - xz^2\, dy - z^2x^2 \frac{d\varphi}{dz}\, dz = 0. \tag{d}$$

Comparing (d) with (a), we find

$$z^2 \frac{d\varphi}{dz} = 2z\frac{y}{x} + 1. \tag{e}$$

Replacing y/x in the right-hand member of (e) by its value $-\varphi(z)$ from (c), we obtain

$$z^2 \frac{d\varphi}{dz} = -2z\varphi + 1. \tag{f}$$

The solution of this equation by §22 is

$$\varphi = \frac{1}{z} + \frac{c}{z^2}. \tag{g}$$

Substituting φ from (g) in (c), we find

$$\frac{y}{x} + \frac{1}{z} + \frac{c}{z^2} = 0, \quad \text{or} \quad \mathbf{z^2 y = x(c_1 - z)}.$$

Example 2.   Prove that

$$dx + dy + y\, dz = 0 \tag{a}$$

is not integrable and then solve it simultaneously with

$$x - y + z = d. \tag{b}$$

Solution.   The equation (16) is not satisfied by (a).   The derivative of (b) is

$$dx - dy + dz = 0. \tag{c}$$

Solving (a) and (c) simultaneously for dx/dz and dy/dz, we find

$$\frac{dx}{y + 1} = \frac{dy}{y - 1} = \frac{dz}{-2}. \tag{d}$$

The solution of (d) is

$$x = y + 2 \log (y - 1) + c_1, \quad \mathbf{y = 1 + ce^{-z/2}}. \tag{e}$$

Equation (b) and either of the equations (e), considered simultaneously, constitute a solution.

76. Geometrical interpretation

It is proved in calculus that the normal to a surface $f(x,y,z) = 0$ at a point (x,y,z) on the surface has as direction numbers $\partial f/\partial x$, $\partial f/\partial y$, $\partial f/\partial z$ evaluated at (x,y,z). Hence if $f(x,y,z) = 0$ is a solution of equation (10) of §75, equation (12) shows that a line through (x,y,z) having direction numbers P,Q,R meets $f(x,y,z) = 0$ in (x,y,z) at right angles. Now the curves having tangents with direction numbers P,Q,R are defined by

$$\frac{dx}{P} = \frac{dy}{Q} = \frac{dz}{R}. \tag{26}$$

Hence *the curves defined by* (26) *meet at right angles the surfaces defined by the solution of an integrable equation* (10).

Example. Find the equation of a set of curves cutting the ellipsoids $2x^2 + 2y^2 + z^2 = c$ at right angles.

Solution. The differential equation of the ellipsoids is

$$2x\, dx + 2y\, dy + z\, dz = 0.$$

Hence the required curves are defined by

$$\frac{dx}{2x} = \frac{dy}{2y} = \frac{dz}{z}.$$

The solution of this equation is

$$\mathbf{x = c_1 y}, \qquad \mathbf{x = c_2 z^2}.$$

EXERCISES

Apply the condition of integrability and find the integrals of the differential equations numbered 1 to 11:

1. $x\, dy - y\, dx - 2x^2 z\, dz = 0$
2. $(y - z)\, dx + dy - dz = 0$
3. $(a - z)(y\, dx + x\, dy) + xy\, dz = 0$
4. $2x\, dx + 2y\, dy + (x^2 + y^2 + e^{-z})\, dz = 0$
5. $2zxy^2\, dx + (2x^2 yz + 1)\, dy + x^2 y^2\, dz = 0$
6. $y^2 z\, dx + 2xyz\, dy + (z^2 - xy^2)\, dz = 0$
7. $z\, dx + (x + a)^2\, dy - (x + a)\, dz = 0$
8. $dz = (3x^2 + y^2)\, dx + (2xy + 3y^2)\, dy$
9. $dz = \dfrac{2x - z}{x + y}\, dx + \dfrac{2y - z}{x + y}\, dy$
10. $(ay - bz)\, dx + (cz - ax)\, dy + (bx - cy)\, dz = 0$
11. $yz\, dx - (xz + x^2)\, dy - (xy + x^2)\, dz = 0$
12. Find the condition that $dz = M\, dx + N\, dy$ be integrable (*a*) if M and N represent functions of x, y, and z; (*b*) if M and N are functions of x and y only.

13. Solve simultaneously
$$z \, dx + x \, dy + y \, dz = 0,$$
$$ax + 2by - (a + 2b)z = c.$$

14. Find the equations of a set of curves cutting at right angles the family of surfaces:

(a) $x^2 + y^2 + z^2 = c^2$ (b) $x^2 + 3y^2 - z^2 = c^2$

(c) $2x^2 - 3y^2 - 4z^2 = c^2$ (d) $xyz = c$

15. Find the equations of the family of surfaces orthogonal to the curves defined by

(a) $\dfrac{dx}{2x + y} = \dfrac{dy}{x + z} = \dfrac{dz}{y}$ (b) $\dfrac{dx}{y} = \dfrac{dy}{-x} = \dfrac{dz}{2x^2 z}$

(c) $x \, dx = y \, dy = (3 - z) \, dz$

16. Find the equation of the surfaces orthogonal to the system of curves defined by

(a) $z \, dx + x \, dz = 0,\ yz \, dx + z^2 \, dy + y(x + z) \, dz = 0$

(b) $x^2 + 2y^2 + 3z^2 = a^2,\ z = b$

77. Replacement of differential equations by a system of the first order and the first degree

The solution of each set of equations in §74 consisted of as many non-differential relations as there were differential equations in the set. Also, the number of constants of integration was the same as the number of given equations. In general, it can be proved that *the general solution of a set of n first-order and first-degree differential equations in n + 1 variables consists of n non-differential relations among these variables and n constants of integration.*

In this article, we shall indicate how the problem of finding the solution of n differential equations in $n + 1$ unknowns can be reduced to that of solving a set of differential equations of the first order and the first degree.

To get an idea of the method of procedure, consider the special system

$$\frac{d^3y}{dx^3} = x + \frac{d^2y}{dx^2}\frac{dz}{dx}, \qquad \frac{d^2z}{dx^2} = zy + \frac{dy}{dx}\frac{dz}{dx}. \tag{27}$$

Making the substitutions $dy/dx = y_1$, $dz/dx = z_1$, $dy_1/dx = y_2$ in (27), we obtain the system of the first order and the first degree:

$$\frac{dy}{dx} = y_1, \qquad \frac{dz}{dx} = z_1, \qquad \frac{dy_1}{dx} = y_2,$$

$$\frac{dy_2}{dx} = x + y_2 z_1, \qquad \frac{dz_1}{dx} = zy + y_1 z_1. \tag{28}$$

Solving equations (28) and eliminating y_1, z_1, and y_2 from the resulting five equations, we obtain two equations in x, y, z, and the five constants of integration. These two equations constitute the general solution of equations (27).

Now consider a set of n independent differential equations in n dependent variables and an independent variable. Substitute a new variable for each derivative of a dependent variable, up to the next to the highest-ordered one, and solve the resulting system of the first order for the derivatives contained in it. This set of equations, together with the substitution set, constitutes a system of differential equations of the first order and first degree which is equivalent to the original system.

EXERCISES

1. Replace, in accordance with the principle stated above, each of the following sets of differential equations by an equivalent set of the first order and the first degree:

(a) $\dfrac{d^2y}{dx^2} + x^2\dfrac{dy}{dx} + x^3y = 0$ (b) $\dfrac{d^2y}{dx^2} + P(x)\dfrac{dy}{dx} + Q(x)y = 0$

(c) $\dfrac{d^3y}{dt^3} = 3y + \dfrac{d^2y}{dt^2} + \dfrac{d^2x}{dt^2},\ \dfrac{d^3y}{dt^3} = 3x - \dfrac{d^2y}{dt^2}$

2. Solve $-dz/y = dy/z = dx/1$, and write from your result the solution of $(d^2y/dx^2) + y = 0$.

3. Solve by the method of this article and check:

(a) $x^2\dfrac{d^2y}{dx^2} - x\dfrac{dy}{dx} + y = 0$ (b) $\dfrac{d^2y}{dx^2} + x\dfrac{dy}{dx} + y = 0$

4. Write a system of equations of the first order and first degree, equivalent to a linear nth-order differential equation in two variables. How many constants of integration would appear in the solution of this system?

78. Existence theorems

Existence theorem II stated below, but not proved, gives conditions under which solutions of differential equations exist, and indicates the nature of the solutions. Theorem I of §5 is the special case of theorem II obtained by taking $n = 1$. Theorem II is especially enlightening in the study of the general methods of the next chapter.

THEOREM II. *For a system of differential equations*

$$\frac{dy_i}{dx} = f_i(x, y_1, y_2, \ldots, y_n) \qquad (i = 1, 2, \ldots, n), \qquad (29)$$

there exists a unique set of continuous solutions $y_1(x)$, $y_2(x)$, $\ldots$, $y_n(x)$

of the given equations which take on the values y_1^0, y_2^0, . . . , y_n^0 when $x = x_0$, provided that the functions

$$f_1, f_2, \ldots, f_n, \quad \frac{\partial f_i}{\partial y_1}, \ldots, \frac{\partial f_i}{\partial y_n}, \quad i = 1, 2, \ldots, n, \quad (30)$$

are continuous, and single-valued in the regions defined by

$$|x - x_0| \leqq a, |y_1 - y_1^0| \leqq b_1, \ldots, |y_n - y_n^0| \leqq b_n, \quad (31)$$

where the values of a and the b's are all greater than zero.

Observe that the theorem states sufficient conditions for the existence of solutions, but not necessary conditions.

Theorem II used in connection with the method of §77 may be applied to a set of differential equations of order higher than the first. Thus, to discuss the existence of a solution of any system of n equations in $n + 1$ unknowns, we would first find in accordance with §77 a related set having the form (29) and then apply theorem II. Thus the equation

$$\frac{d^3y}{dx^3} = f\left(x, y, \frac{dy}{dx}, \frac{d^2y}{dx^2}\right) \quad (32)$$

is related to the set of equations

$$\frac{dy}{dx} = y_1, \quad \frac{dy_1}{dx} = y_2, \quad \frac{dy_2}{dx} = f(x, y, y_1, y_2). \quad (33)$$

Applying theorem II to the set (33), we conclude that there exists a unique solution $y = \psi(x)$ of (32) which satisfies the initial conditions

$$y = y_0, \quad \frac{dy}{dx} - y_{10}, \quad \frac{d^2y}{dx^2} = y_{20}, \quad \text{when } x = x_0,$$

provided that $f(x, y, y_1, y_2)$ satisfies the conditions of theorem II. Here y_0, y_{10}, and y_{20} may be thought of as three constants of integration.

In dealing with a system of m consistent and independent equations in $n + 1$ variables, it is possible to replace $n - m$ variables by arbitrary functions of the remaining $m + 1$ unknowns and then apply theorem II to the result. A single total differential equation in three variables is a case in point. As in the case of total differential equations, a number of equations connecting the variables may often be found by solving exact equations or integrable equations derived from the given set.

EXERCISES

1. State theorem II for $n = 1$, and observe that the result is theorem I of §5.

2. Is a unique solution of $x \, dy/dx - y = 0$, satisfying the condition $y = 2$ when $x = 0$, to be expected? Why?

3. For $dy/dx = y^{\frac{4}{3}}$, the conditions of theorem II with $n = 1$ are satisfied in the whole XY-plane. What solution passes through $(0,0)$?

4. What condition of theorem II with $n = 1$ is not satisfied by $dy/dx = 3y/x$ at $(0,0)$? $y = y_0(x/x_0)^3$ satisfies $dy/dx = 3y/x$ if $x_0 \neq 0$. Does $y = cx^3$ have at $(0,0)$ the slope given by $dy/dx = 3y/x$?

5. Does theorem II show that the graph of the solution of

$$\frac{dy}{dx} = 2, \qquad \frac{dz}{dx} = x + y + z$$

consists of a unique curve through every point of space? Solve the equations and find the solution for which $y = 5$, $z = -10$, when $x = 0$.

6. Show that the solution of

$$x^2 \frac{d^2y}{dx^2} - 2x \frac{dy}{dx} + 2y = 2x^3$$

could be obtained from the solution of

$$\frac{dy}{dx} = z, \qquad \frac{dz}{dx} = \frac{2xz - 2y}{x^2} + 2x.$$

In accordance with theorem II would you expect a unique solution of the pair of equations for which $y = 0$, $z = 1$, when $x = 0$?

Show that the general solution of the pair of equations is $y = c_1x^2 + c_2x + x^3$, $z = 2c_1x + c_2 + 3x^2$ and that an infinite number of solutions $y = c_1x^2 + x + x^3$, $z = 2c_1x + 1 + 3x^2$ satisfy the conditions $y = 0$, $z = 1$, when $x = 0$.

7. Discuss the existence of solutions of

$$\frac{d^2y}{dx^2} + P(x) \frac{dy}{dx} + Q(x)y = 0$$

by using theorem II and the facts stated in §77.

8. Read exercise 6 and then discuss the existence of solutions of

$$\frac{d^ny}{dx^n} + A_1 \frac{d^{n-1}y}{dx^{n-1}} + \cdots + A_ny = 0,$$

where the A's are functions of x.

9. Use theorem II and §77 to find the values of a at which irregularities are to be expected in the solution of

$$x(x - 1) \frac{d^2y}{dx^2} + (4x - 2) \frac{dy}{dx} + 2y = 0$$

subject to the condition $y = 0$, $dy/dx = 1$, when $x = a$. Does the general solution $y = (c_1/x) + c_2/(x - 1)$ bear out your answer?

10. Irregularities in the solution of $x(x - 1)(d^2y/dx^2) - 2x(dy/dx) + 2y = 0$ are to be expected when $x = 0$ or $x = 1$ is involved in the initial conditions. Show that the general solution $y = c(x^2 - 1 - 2x \log x) + c_2x$ bears out this expectation.

CHAPTER XI

SOLUTION BY SERIES AND BY METHODS INVOLVING SUCCESSIVE APPROXIMATIONS

79. Introduction

The preceding chapters have been concerned mainly with solving special types of differential equations. This chapter is concerned with general methods. The two methods to be considered, *integration in series* and methods using *successive approximations*, may be applied to solve a large variety of differential equations. The method called *integration in series* is comparatively short and generally gives the complete solution. There are many methods of successive approximations; their range of application is very wide, but they involve much computation and give only a particular solution.

80. Integration in series

When an equation cannot be solved by any of the methods already discussed, we may try to find a convergent series which will express the value of the dependent variable in terms of the independent variable to any required degree of accuracy. We shall solve two problems to illustrate a method of finding such a series.

Example 1. Solve the following differential equation for y as a power series in x:

$$\frac{d^2y}{dx^2} - xy = 0. \qquad (a)$$

Solution. Assume that the solution has the form

$$y = c_0 + c_1x + c_2x^2 + \cdots + c_nx^n + \cdots, \qquad (b)$$

or, using the summation notation,

$$y = \sum_{n=0}^{\infty} c_nx^n, \qquad (c)$$

where the c's are constants to be determined. Substitute y from (b) in (a) to obtain

$$2c_2 + 2 \cdot 3c_3x + 3 \cdot 4c_4x^2 + \cdots + n(n-1)c_nx^{n-2} + \cdots$$
$$- c_0x - c_1x^2 - \cdots - c_{n-3}x^{n-2} - \cdots = 0. \quad (d)$$

Since (b) is a solution of (a), equation (d) is an identity. Hence, equating the coefficients of x to zero, obtain

$$2c_2 = 0, \quad 3 \cdot 2c_3 - c_0 = 0, \quad 4 \cdot 3c_4 - c_1 = 0, \ldots, n(n-1)c_n$$
$$- c_{n-3} = 0. \quad (e)$$

Solving equations (e) for $c_2, c_3, \ldots$ in terms of c_0 and c_1, we find

$$c_2 = 0, \quad c_3 = \frac{c_0}{2 \cdot 3}, \quad c_4 = \frac{c_1}{3 \cdot 4}, \quad c_5 = 0, \quad c_6 = \frac{c_3}{5 \cdot 6}$$
$$= \frac{c_0}{2 \cdot 3 \cdot 5 \cdot 6}, \quad c_7 = \frac{c_4}{6 \cdot 7} = \frac{c_1}{3 \cdot 4 \cdot 6 \cdot 7}, \cdots, c_n = \frac{c_{n-3}}{n(n-1)} \quad (f)$$

We may write the first six terms of the solution by substituting the values from (f) in (b) to obtain

$$y = c_0 + c_1x + \frac{c_0}{2 \cdot 3} x^3 + \frac{c_1}{3 \cdot 4} x^4 + \frac{c_0}{2 \cdot 3 \cdot 5 \cdot 6} x^6$$
$$+ \frac{c_1}{3 \cdot 4 \cdot 6 \cdot 7} x^7 + \cdots. \quad (g)$$

This is the important part of the solution for values of x near zero.

However, a law for writing any number of terms is desired. By rearranging the values for the c's found in (f) and by using the last equation of (f) successively for different values of n, we find

$$c_0 = c_0, \quad c_1 = c_1, \quad c_2 = 0, \quad c_3 = \frac{c_0}{2 \cdot 3}, \quad c_4 = \frac{c_1}{3 \cdot 4},$$
$$c_5 = 0, \quad c_6 = \frac{1 \cdot 4c_0}{6!}, \quad c_7 = \frac{2 \cdot 5c_1}{7!}, \quad c_8 = 0, \quad (h)$$
$$c_{3n} = \frac{1 \cdot 4 \cdot 7 \cdots (3n-2)c_0}{(3n)!}, \quad c_{3n+1} = \frac{2 \cdot 5 \cdot 8 \cdots (3n-1)c_1}{(3n+1)!},$$
$$c_{3n+2} = 0.$$

Substituting the values of the c's from (h) in (b), obtain

$$y = c_0 \left[1 + \frac{x^3}{3!} + \cdots + \frac{1 \cdot 4 \cdot 7 \cdots (3n-2)}{(3n)!} x^{3n} + \cdots \right]$$
$$+ c_1 \left[x + \frac{2x^4}{4!} + \cdots + \frac{2 \cdot 5 \cdot 8 \cdots (3n-1)x^{3n+1}}{(3n+1)!} + \cdots \right], \quad (i)$$

or, using the summation notation,

$$y = c_0 + c_1 x + c_0 \sum_{n=1}^{\infty} \frac{1 \cdot 4 \cdot 7 \cdots (3n-2)}{(3n)!} x^{3n}$$

$$+ c_1 \sum_{n=1}^{\infty} \frac{2 \cdot 5 \cdot 8 \cdots (3n-1)x^{3n+1}}{(3n+1)!}. \qquad (j)$$

Equation (j) is the required solution. Since it is absolutely convergent* for all values of x and since it contains two independent arbitrary constants, it is the general solution of the given differential equation.

Example 2.   Find the first six terms in the solution of

$$\frac{d^2y}{dx^2} + (1 + x^3)\frac{dy}{dx} + (1 + 2x^2)y = 0. \qquad (a)$$

Solution.   Substituting y from (b) Example 1 in (a), obtain

$$2c_2 + 6c_3x + 12c_4x^2 + 20c_5x^3 + \cdots$$
$$c_1 + 2c_2x + 3c_3x^2 + 4c_4x^3 + \cdots$$
$$+ c_1x^3 + \cdots$$
$$c_0 + c_1x + c_2x^2 + c_3x^3 + \cdots$$
$$+ 2c_0x^2 + 2c_1x^3 + \cdots = 0. \qquad (b)$$

Equating the constant term and the coefficients of x to zero, solving the results for c_2, c_3, c_4, c_5, and c_6 in terms of c_0 and c_1, and substituting the results in (b) of Example 1 obtain

$$y = c_0 + c_1 x - \frac{(c_0 + c_1)x^2}{2!} + \frac{c_0 x^3}{3!} - \frac{(4c_0 - c_1)x^4}{4!} + \frac{(3c_0 - 19c_1)x^5}{5!}$$
$$+ \cdots .$$

* The interval of convergence for a series solution obtained as above may be found by using the Cauchy ratio test or any other well-known method. Also the following statement may be used:
   Consider the differential equation

$$D^m y + \sum_{j=1}^{m} A_j(x) D^{m-j}y = 0, \qquad (a)$$

where the functions $A_j(z)$, z complex, are continuous except for values $a_k + ib_k$, $i = \sqrt{-1}$ and k finite, at which one or more of them have ordinary poles or, roughly speaking, become infinite. Then the interval of convergence for a series solution $y = a_0 + a_1(x - a) + a_2(x - a)^2 + \cdots$ of equation (a) is $|x - a| < r$, where r is the least of the quantities $\sqrt{(a - a_k^2) + b_k^2}$. Thus if the A_j are polynomials in x, the series solutions converge for all values of x, whereas a series solution of $D^2y + y/[(x^2 + 9)(x - 5)] = 0$ in powers of x converges if $|x| < 3$.

EXERCISES

Solve differential equations 1 to 6 by using infinite series of form (b) of Example 1. D means d/dx.

1. $Dy - y = 0$ **2.** $Dy - 2xy = 0$
3. $D^2y - x^2y = 0$ **4.** $(x^2 + 1)D^2y + 6x\,Dy + 6y = 0$
5. $(x^2 - 1)\,D^2y - 6y = 0$ **6.** $x^2\,D^2y - 4x\,Dy + 6y = 0$

7. Find a solution of $(x^2 - 2x)\,D^2y + 6(x - 1)\,Dy + 6y = 0$ in series having the form

$$y = c_0 + c_1(x - 1)^1 + c_2(x - 1)^2 + \cdots + c_n(x - 1)^n + \cdots .$$

8. Find a solution of $(x^2 + 2x)\,D^2y + 8(x + 1)\,Dy + 12y = 0$ in a series having the form

$$y = c_0 + c_1(x + 1) + c_2(x + 1) + \cdots + c_n(x + 1)^n + \cdots .$$

Using series of type (b) of Example 1, find the first five terms in the solutions of equations 9 and 10:

9. $(x - 1)\,D^2y + y = 0$ **10.** $(x^2 + 1)\,D^2y + x\,Dy + xy = 0$

11. Find a particular solution of $x^2(dy/dx) - y = 5x^{-3} + 3x^{-2}$ by series. If $y = c_3x^{-3} + c_4x^{-4} + \cdots + c_nx^{-n} + \cdots$, show that $c_3 = -1$, that $c_4 = -1$, $c_5 = \frac{1}{5}$, etc.

★12. The theory of the oscillator in quantum mechanics uses those solutions of the equation

$$-\frac{d^2u}{dx^2} + x^2u = (2n + 1)u, \qquad n \text{ constant}, \tag{a}$$

that remain finite as x increases without limit. Find these solutions.

First show that $u = e^{-\frac{1}{2}x^2}$ satisfies (a) when $n = 0$. Then let

$$u = ve^{-\frac{1}{2}x^2}$$

in (a) and deduce the equation

$$\frac{d^2v}{dx^2} - 2x\frac{dv}{dx} + 2nv = 0. \tag{b}$$

Next solve (b) to obtain the solutions v_1 and v_2 as infinite series. Now show that the solutions of (a)

$$u = v_1e^{-\frac{1}{2}x^2}, \qquad u = v_2e^{-\frac{1}{2}x^2} \tag{c}$$

satisfy the required condition when and only when n is zero or a positive integer. Write the solutions (c) when $n = 0$, $n = 2$, and $n = 3$.

13. Find a particular solution of $D^2y + x\,Dy + 2y = x^3$. *Hint:* Use a series of the form $y = x^k(a_0 + a_1x + a_2x^2 + \cdots)$.

81. Solution involving a more general type of series

A function $f(x)$ is analytic at a value a of x if it can be expanded in an infinite series having the form

$$f(x) = a_0 + a_1(x - a) + a_2(x - a)^2 + \cdots + a_n(x - a)^n + \cdots \tag{1}$$

and converging in an interval $a - r < x - a < a + s$, where $r > 0$ and $s > 0$.

Series solutions in powers of $x - a$ of a differential equation

$$D^2 y + p(x)\, Dy + q(x)y = 0 \tag{2}$$

exist if D means d/dx and $p(x)$ and $q(x)$ are analytic at $x = a$. They can be found by the method used in §80.

This section and the next will deal mainly with differential equations having the form

$$D^2 y + \frac{p(x)}{x}\, Dy + \frac{q(x)}{x^2}\, y = 0, \tag{3}$$

where at least one of the functions $p(x)/x$, $q(x)/x^2$ is not analytic at $x = 0$. In this section we shall deal mainly with solutions made up of series having the form

$$y = x^m (c_0 + c_1 x + c_2 x^2 + \cdots + c_n x^n + \cdots), \tag{4}$$

where m is a real number. The next section will deal with special cases of (3) in which series of form (4) play a prominent role.

If y in (3), *cleared of fractions, is replaced by* x^m, *the equation obtained by equating to zero the coefficient of the lowest (or highest, in case a series of descending powers is used) power of x in the result is called the* **indicial equation.**

Example. Solve $2x^2\, D^2 y + 3x\, Dy - (x^2 + 1)y = 0$.

Solution. Substituting y from (4) in the given equation, obtain after some simplification

$$c_0[2m(m - 1) + 3m - 1] + c_1[2(m + 1)m + 3(m + 1) - 1]x +$$

$$\sum_{n=2}^{\infty} \{[2(n + m)(n + m - 1) + 3(n - m) - 1]c_n - c_{n-2}\}x^n = 0. \quad (a)$$

To dispose of the first term, assume that the indicial equation $2m(m - 1) + 3m - 1 = 0$ holds. This is satisfied if

$$(m + 1)(2m - 1) = 0, \qquad m = -1, \qquad m = \tfrac{1}{2}. \tag{b}$$

To dispose of the second term of (a), take $c_1 = 0$. From the third part of (a) obtain

$$c_n = \frac{c_{n-2}}{(n + m + 1)[2(n + m) - 1]}. \tag{c}$$

Substituting -1 from (b) for m in (c), obtain

$$c_n = \frac{c_{n-2}}{n(2n-3)}. \tag{d}$$

Now using in (4), $m = -1$, $c_0 = c_0$, $c_1 = 0$, and (d) with $n = 2, 4,$ $6, \ldots$, we get

$$y_1 = c_0 x^{-1}\left(1 + \frac{x^2}{2 \cdot 1} + \frac{x^4}{2 \cdot 4 \cdot 1 \cdot 5} + \frac{x^6}{2 \cdot 4 \cdot 6 \cdot 1 \cdot 5 \cdot 9} + \cdots\right). \tag{e}$$

Now substituting $\frac{1}{2}$ from (b) for m in (c), obtain

$$c_n = \frac{c_{n-2}}{(2n+3)n}. \tag{f}$$

Then using in (4) $m = \frac{1}{2}$, $c_0 = b$, $c_1 = 0$, and (f) with $n = 2, 4, 6, \ldots$, we get

$$y_2 = bx^{\frac{1}{2}}\left[1 + \frac{x^2}{2 \cdot 7} + \frac{x^4}{2 \cdot 4 \cdot 7 \cdot 11} + \frac{x^6}{2 \cdot 4 \cdot 6 \cdot 7 \cdot 11 \cdot 15}\right.$$
$$\left. + \cdots\right]. \tag{g}$$

The general solution is

$$y = y_1 + y_2. \tag{h}$$

When the degree in m of the indicial equation is less than the order of the equation to be solved, a solution may be found by using a series of descending powers of x, having the form

$$y = x^m(c_0 + c_1 x^{-1} + c_2 x^{-2} + \cdots).$$

The procedure in this case is the same as when equation (1) is used. Exercises 9 to 11 below involve this type of expansion.

EXERCISES

1. $2x\,D^2y + Dy - 2y = 0$

2. $(x^3 - x)\,D^2y + (8x^2 - 2)\,Dy + 12xy = 0$

3. $x\,D^2y + 3\,Dy - x^2y = 0$

4. $x^2\,D^2y + (x + 2x^2)\,Dy - 4y = 0$

5. Show that the regular procedure gives as the solution of $x^2\,D^2y - x^2\,Dy + (x - 2)y = 0$

$$y = c_0 x^2\left(1 + \frac{1}{4}x + \frac{1}{4 \cdot 5}x^2 + \cdots\right) + c_1 x^{-1}\left(1 + x + \frac{1}{2!}x^2 + \frac{1}{3!}x^3 + \cdots\right).$$

Then show that this can be written

$$y = c_1\left(x^{-1} + 1 + \frac{1}{2}x\right) + cx^2\left(1 + \frac{1}{4}x + \frac{1}{4 \cdot 5}x^2 + \cdots\right),$$

where $c = c_0 + \frac{1}{6}c_1$.

6. $(x^3 - x) D^2y + (4x^2 - 2) Dy + 2xy = 0$

7. $(x - x^2) D^2y - (x + 1) Dy + y = 0$

8. $x^4 D^2y + x Dy + y = 0$.   *Hint:* Let $y = x^m(c_0 + c_1x^{-1} + c_2x^{-2} + \cdots)$

9. Show that the solution of $(x^4 - x^2) D^2y + 2x Dy - (2 + 2x^2)y = 0$ is

$$y = Ax^2 + Bx(1 - x^2 - \tfrac{1}{3}x^4 - \tfrac{1}{5}x^6 - \tfrac{1}{7}x^8 - \cdots).$$

Show that

$$y = cx^{-1}(1 + \tfrac{3}{5}x^{-2} + \tfrac{3}{7}x^{-4} + \tfrac{3}{9}x^{-6} + \cdots)$$

is also a solution which converges when $|x| > 1$. Note that the series in the first solution converges when $|x| < 1$ and that y does not exist for either solution when $x = 1$. It is interesting to observe that the conditions of theorem II in §78 for the system

$$\frac{dy}{dx} = y_1, \qquad \frac{dy_1}{dx} = \frac{(2 + 2x^2)y - 2xy_1}{x^4 - x^2}$$

are not satisfied for a region in which x may be zero or 1.

10. To solve $x^4 D^2y + x Dy - 2y = 0$, let $y = x^m(c_0 + c_1x + c_2x^2 + \cdots)$ to obtain the solution $y = cx^2(1 - x^2 + 3x^4 - 3 \cdot 5x^6 + \cdots)$, and show that this series diverges for all values of x except zero. Solve the differential equation by using $y = x^m(c_0 + c_1x^{-1} + c_2x^{-2} + \cdots)$, and show that the series thus obtained converges for all values of x except zero.

11. Show that a solution of

$$(x^4 - x^2) D^2y - (2x^3 - 3x) Dy + (2x^2 - 3)y = 0$$

is

$$y = c_0x + c_1x^3 \left(1 + \frac{1}{4}x^2 + \frac{1 \cdot 3}{4 \cdot 6}x^4 + \frac{1 \cdot 3 \cdot 5}{4 \cdot 6 \cdot 8}x^6 + \cdots\right).$$

Also derive the solution

$$y = cx^2 \left[1 + \frac{(-1)}{2}x^{-2} + \frac{(-1)(1)}{2 \cdot 4}x^{-4} + \frac{(-1)(1)(3)}{2 \cdot 4 \cdot 6}x^{-6} + \cdots\right].$$

★12. $x^3 D^3y + 6x^2 D^2y + 6x Dy + a^3x^3y = 0$

★13. Find a particular solution of $x^2 D^2y + x Dy - (1 + x^2)y = x^{\frac{3}{2}}$.

★14. Show that the solution of $x^2 D^2y + y = 0$ is

$$y = x^{\frac{1}{2}}[c_1 \cos (\tfrac{1}{2}\sqrt{3}\log x) + c_2 \sin (\tfrac{1}{2}\sqrt{3}\log x)].$$

Hint: With $i = \sqrt{-1}$, use $x^{ai} = e^{ia\log x} = \cos (a\log x) + i \sin (a\log x)$.

82. Solutions of $D^2y + (P/x) Dy + (Q/x^2)y = 0$ valid near $x = 0$

While the statements made below refer to second-order equations at $x = 0$, they may easily be extended to apply for linear equations of any order at $x = a$.

When two roots of the indicial equation for an equation of type (3) of §81 are equal, the process of §81 fails to give the general solution at $x = 0$, and the same thing may be true when two roots differ by an integer. The following example will illustrate the procedure to be used in solving such equations.

Example.   Solve

$$x^2\, D^2 y + 2x\, Dy - xy = 0. \tag{a}$$

Solution.   In the given equation substitute

$$y = x^m(c_0 + c_1 x + c_2 x^2 + \cdots + c_n x^n + \cdots). \tag{b}$$

Collect the coefficients of like terms and simplify to obtain

$$c_0(m^2 + m) + \sum_{n=1}^{\infty} [c_n(n + m)(n + m + 1) - c_{n-1}]x^n = 0. \tag{c}$$

Solving the indicial equation for m, we get

$$c_0(m^2 + m) = 0, \qquad m = 0,\, -1. \tag{d}$$

Equating the coefficient of x^n to 0 in (c) and solving for c_n, obtain

$$c_n = \frac{c_{n-1}}{(m + n)(m + n + 1)}. \tag{e}$$

Solve (e) for the c's in terms of c_0 and substitute the results in (b) to obtain

$$Y = c_0 x^m \left[m + 1 + \frac{x(m + 1)}{(m + 1)(m + 2)} + \frac{x^2}{(m + 2)^2(m + 3)} \right.$$
$$\left. + \frac{x^3}{(m + 2)^2(m + 3)^2(m + 4)} + \cdots \right], \tag{f}$$

where we have replaced c_0 by $c_0(m + 1)$ to avoid a zero in denominators when $m = -1$ from (d).   Substituting $m = 0$ from (d) in (f), we obtain one solution of (a):

$$y_1 = c_0 \left(1 + \frac{x}{1 \cdot 2} + \frac{x^2}{2^2 \cdot 3} + \frac{x^3}{2^2 \cdot 3^2 \cdot 4} + \cdots \right). \tag{g}$$

If we replace m in (f) by -1, we duplicate (g) and must seek further. Replacing y in the left member of (a) by Y from (f), obtain

$$x^2\, D^2 Y + 2x\, DY - xY = c_0(m + 1)(m + 1)m, \tag{h}$$

no matter what value m may have.   Now taking the derivative of (h) partially with respect to m, and noting that $\partial(D^k Y)/\partial m = D^k\, \partial Y/\partial m$, obtain

$$x^2\, D^2 \left(\frac{\partial Y}{\partial m} \right) + 2x\, D \left(\frac{\partial Y}{\partial m} \right) - x\, \frac{\partial Y}{\partial m} = c_0(m + 1)(3m + 1). \tag{i}$$

Since, when $m = -1$, the right member of (i) is zero, we see that

$$y_2 = \left(\frac{\partial Y}{\partial m}\right)_{m=-1} \tag{j}$$

is a solution of (a). The general solution of (a) then is

$$y = A y_1 + B y_2. \tag{k}$$

In finding $\partial Y/\partial m$, formula (5) below, got by logarithmic differentiation, is useful. If

$$f(m) = \frac{(m - a_1)(m - a_2) \cdots (m - a_n)}{(m - b_1)(m - b_2) \cdots (m - b_t)} \tag{5}$$

then

$$\frac{\partial f(m)}{\partial m} = f(m) \left(\sum_{k=1}^{n} \frac{1}{m - a_k} - \sum_{k=1}^{t} \frac{1}{m - b_k} \right).$$

From (f) we get

$$
\begin{aligned}
\frac{\partial Y}{\partial m} = Y \log x + c_0 x^m \Bigg[&1 - \frac{x}{(m + 2)^2} \\
&+ x^2 \frac{-2/(m + 2) - 1/(m + 3)}{(m + 2)^2(m + 3)} \\
&+ x^3 \frac{-2/(m + 2) - 2/(m + 3) - 1/(m + 4)}{(m + 2)^2(m + 3)^2(m + 4)} + \cdots \Bigg].
\end{aligned} \tag{l}
$$

By finding a few terms from (g) and from (l) with $m = -1$, we can indicate the answer in the form

$$
\begin{aligned}
y = c_0 &\left(1 + \frac{x}{1!2!} + \frac{x^2}{2!3!} + \frac{x^3}{3!4!} + \qquad \right) \\
&+ c_1 x^{-1} \log x \left(x + \frac{x^2}{1!2!} + \frac{x^3}{2!3!} + \cdots \right) \\
&+ c_1 x^{-1} \left[1 - x + \frac{x^2}{1!2!}\left(-\frac{2}{1} - \frac{1}{2}\right) + \cdots \right]. \tag{m}
\end{aligned}
$$

Observing that the second parenthesized expression in (m) is x times the quantity in the first parenthesis, and generalizing, we can write (m) in the form

$$
\begin{aligned}
y = (c_0 + c_1 \log x) &\sum_{n=0}^{\infty} \frac{x^n}{n!(n + 1)!} \\
&+ c_1 x^{-1} \left[1 - x - \sum_{n=2}^{\infty} \frac{x^n}{(n - 1)!n!} \left(\frac{1}{n} + \sum_{k=1}^{n-1} \frac{2}{k} \right) \right]. \tag{n}
\end{aligned}
$$

Remarks. To deal with an equation of type (3) §81 for which the method of §81 fails, let α and β, where $\beta \leq \alpha$, be the roots of the indicial equation. Using a general series of type (b), write the general equation corresponding to (f) with constant term $c(m - \beta)$, and then use the formula

$$y = A(Y)_{m=\alpha} + B\left(\frac{\partial Y}{\partial m}\right)_{m=\beta}. \tag{6}$$

A similar kind of procedure is effective for many differential equations of higher order.

EXERCISES

1. Using the regular procedure for $(x^2 - x) D^2y + x Dy - y = 0$, obtain

$$Y = c_0 x^m \left(1 + \frac{m-1}{m} x + \frac{m-1}{m+1} x^2 + \cdots + \frac{m-1}{m+n-1} x^n + \cdots\right). \tag{a}$$

Show that the roots of the indicial equation are 0,1. Get one solution by substituting 1 for m in (a). Replace c_0 in (a) by $c_0 m$ and use $y_2 = (\partial Y/\partial m)_{m=0}$ on the result to get a second solution.

2. For the equation $(x^3 + x^2) D^2y + x Dy - 2xy = 0$ obtain

$$Y = c_0 x^m \left[1 - \frac{m-2}{m+1} x + \frac{(m-2)(m-1)}{(m+1)(m+2)} x^2 \right.$$
$$\left. + \sum_{n=3}^{\infty} \frac{(-1)^n (m-2)(m-1) m x^n}{(m+n-2)(m+n-1)(m+n)}\right].$$

Show that the roots of the indicial equation are 0,0. Now find the solution by using $y = Y_{m=0} + (\partial Y/\partial m)_{m=0}$.

3. $x D^2y + Dy - xy = 0$ **4.** $x D^2y - y = 0$

5. $x D^2y + Dy + y = 0$ **6.** $x D^2y + Dy - x^2y = 0$

7. $x D^2y + 3 Dy + xy = 0$

★8. $x^3 D^2y - y = 0$. Use a series having the form $y = x^m(c_0 + c_1 x^{-1} + c_2 x^{-2} + \cdots)$.

★9. $x^2 D^4y + 6x D^3y + 6 D^2y - y = 0$. Show that the roots of the indicial equation are 1, 0, 0, −1. Write an equation for Y in terms of m with $c_0(m + 1)$ taken as constant. The four parts of the solution are $Y_{m=1}$, $Y_{m=0}$, $(\partial Y/\partial m)_{m=0}$, $(\partial Y/\partial m)_{m=-1}$.

83. Important equations

A number of differential equations have great importance because they arise frequently in physical theory. We shall consider four of them associated with the names of Legendre, Bessel, Laguerre, and Hermite. All these equations are used in the theory of quantum mechanics relating to the structure of the atom.

84. Legendre's equation

The Legendre equation having the form

$$(1 - x^2) D^2y - 2x\, Dy + k(k + 1)y = 0 \tag{7}$$

is named after the famous French mathematician Adrien Marie Legendre. The solution of (7) is generally obtained in a series having the form

$$y = c_0x^m + c_1x^{m-1} + c_2x^{m-2} + \cdots + c_nx^{m-n} + \cdots. \tag{8}$$

To get the indicial equation, set $y = x^m$ in (7) and equate to zero the coefficient of x^m to get

$$-m^2 - m + k(k + 1) = 0, \qquad \text{or} \qquad m = k,\ -k - 1. \tag{9}$$

Next substitute y from (8) in (7), equate to zero the coefficient of x^{m-n}, and solve for c_n to get

$$c_n = \frac{(m - n + 2)(m - n + 1)}{(m - n - k)(m - n + k + 1)}\, c_{n-2}. \tag{10}$$

Using (10) first with $m = k$, and then with $m = -k - 1$, obtain in the usual way

$$y_k = x^k\left[1 - \frac{k(k - 1)}{2(2k - 1)}\, x^{-2} + \frac{k(k - 1)(k - 2)(k - 3)}{2 \cdot 4(2k - 1)(2k - 3)}\, x^{-4} \right.$$
$$\left. - \cdots \right], \tag{11}$$

$$y_{-k-1} = x^{-k-1}\left[1 + \frac{(k + 1)(k + 2)}{2(2k + 3)}\, x^{-2} \right.$$
$$\left. + \frac{(k + 1)(k + 2)(k + 3)(k + 4)}{2 \cdot 4(2k + 3)(2k + 5)}\, x^{-4} + \cdots \right]. \tag{12}$$

The general solution is

$$y = c_1y_k + c_2y_{-k-1},$$

and this series converges for all values of x satisfying $|x| > 1$.

If k is zero or a positive integer, the series (11) for y_k will terminate. The polynomials $P_k(x)$ defined by

$$P_k(x) = \frac{(2k)!}{2^k(k!)^2}\, y_k, \tag{13}$$

where y_k is defined by (11), are called **Legendre polynomials.** The coefficient $(2k)!/[2^k(k!)^2]$ was chosen so that

$$P_k(1) = 1. \tag{14}$$

From (11) and (13) we easily obtain

$$P_0(x) = 1, \quad P_1(x) = x, \quad P_2(x) = \tfrac{1}{2}(3x^2 - 1), \quad P_3(x) = \tfrac{1}{2}(5x^3 - 3x),$$

$$P_4(x) = \frac{5 \cdot 7}{2 \cdot 4} x^4 - 2 \frac{3 \cdot 5}{2 \cdot 4} x^2 + \frac{1 \cdot 3}{2 \cdot 4}, \text{ etc.} \tag{15}$$

Another important property, permitting the expression of any function in Legendre polynomials, will now be considered.

A set of functions $f_r(x)$ continuous in the interval $a \leqq x \leqq b$ and having the property

$$\int_a^b f_r(x)f_s(x)\, dx = 0, \qquad r \neq s,$$

is called an **orthogonal set**. The trignometric functions $\sin nx$ and $\cos nx$ constitute an orthogonal set with $a = -\pi$ and $b = \pi$.

The following proof shows that the Legendre polynomials constitute an orthogonal set in the interval $-1 \leqq x \leqq 1$ by demonstrating that

$$\int_{-1}^1 \mathbf{P}_r(\mathbf{x})\mathbf{P}_k(\mathbf{x})\, \mathbf{dx} = \mathbf{0}, \qquad \mathbf{r \neq k.} \tag{16}$$

Equation (7) may be written

$$\frac{d}{dx}[(1 - x^2)y'] + k(k + 1)y = 0.$$

In this replace y by the solution $P_k(x)$, multiply through by $P_r(x)$, and integrate to obtain

$$\int_{-1}^1 P_r(x) \frac{d}{dx}[(1 - x^2)P_k'(x)]\, dx + k(k + 1) \int_{-1}^1 P_k(x)P_r(x)\, dx = 0.$$

Apply integration by parts to the first integral to get

$$[(1 - x^2)P_k'(x)P_r(x)]_{-1}^1 - \int_{-1}^1 (1 - x^2)P_r'P_k'\, dx$$
$$+ k(k + 1) \int_{-1}^1 P_k P_r\, dx = 0. \tag{17}$$

The first term of this vanishes. Now write (17) with r and k interchanged to obtain

$$- \int_{-1}^1 (1 - x^2)P_k'P_r'\, dx + r(r + 1) \int_{-1}^1 P_r P_k\, dx = 0.$$

Subtract this from (17), member by member, to get

$$(k - r)(k + r + 1) \int_{-1}^1 P_r P_k\, dx = 0.$$

This shows that (16) holds true.

Also it can be proved that

$$\int_{-1}^{1} P_k^2(x) \, dx = \frac{2}{2k + 1}. \tag{18}$$

Exercise (3) below indicates the method of expanding functions in a series of Legendre polynomials by using (16) and (18).

EXERCISES

1. Using the functions (15) show that (a) $P_0(1) = P_1(1) = P_2(1) = P_3(1) = 1$;
(b) $\int_{-1}^{1} P_1(x)P_2(x) \, dx = \int_{-1}^{1} P_2(x)P_3(x) \, dx = 0$; (c) $\int_{-1}^{1} P_2^2(x) \, dx = [2/(2k + 1)]_{k=2} = 2/5$.

2. Find $P_6(x)$ by using (13) and show that $P_6(1) = 1$.

3. Assuming that there are constants a_i such that

$$f(x) = a_0 P_0(x) + a_1 P_1(x) + \cdots + a_n P_n(x) + \cdots, \tag{a}$$

and that the series obtained by multiplying the right-hand member by $P_n(x)$ can be integrated, term by term, multiply both sides of (a) by $P_n(x)$, consider the integrals of all terms between the limits -1 and $+1$, and, remembering (16) and (18), obtain

$$a_n = \frac{2n + 1}{2} \int_{-1}^{1} f(x) P_n(x) \, dx.$$

4. Using a method suggested by exercise 3, expand x^4 in Legendre polynomials.

5. Find the first four terms of the expansion of e^x in Legendre polynomials.

85. The Bessel equation.

The Bessel equation, named after the German mathematician Friedrich Wilhelm Bessel, has the form

$$x^2 \, D^2 y + x \, Dy + (x^2 - k^2)y = 0. \tag{19}$$

The theory developed in §§80 to 82 may be used to solve it. First get the indicial equation by substituting x^m for y in (19) and equating the coefficient of x^m to zero. This gives

$$m(m - 1) + m - k^2 = 0, \qquad \text{or} \qquad m = \pm k. \tag{20}$$

Next substitute $\sum_{r=0}^{\infty} c_r x^{m+r}$ for y in (19), equate the coefficient of x^{m+n} to zero, and solve for c_n to obtain

$$c_n = \frac{-c_{n-2}}{(m + n + k)(m + n - k)}. \tag{21}$$

Using this with $m = k$, we obtain as a solution of (19)

$$y_1 = x^k \left[1 - \frac{(x/2)^2}{1(1 + k)} + \frac{(x/2)^4}{1 \cdot 2(1 + k)(2 + k)} - \cdots \right.$$
$$\left. + \frac{(-1)^r (k!)(x/2)^{2r}}{r!(r + k)!} + \cdots \right]. \quad (22)$$

Similarly, if k is not an integer, we obtain from (21), with $m = -k$,

$$y_2 = x^{-k} \left[1 - \frac{(x/2)^2}{1(1 - k)} + \frac{(x/2)^4}{1 \cdot 2(1 - k)(2 - k)} - \cdots \right.$$
$$\left. + \frac{(-1)^r (x/2)^{2r}}{r!(1 - k)(2 - k) \cdots (r - k)} + \cdots \right]. \quad (23)$$

In this case, the solution is

$$y = c_1 y_1 + c_2 y_2. \quad (24)$$

If k is an integer, (23) fails to give a solution, and the method of §82 may be applied. Write

$$y_m = x^m \left[m + k + \sum_{r=1}^{\infty} \frac{(-1)^r (m + k) x^{2r}}{\prod_{n=1}^{r} (m + 2n + k)(m + 2n - k)} \right], \quad (25)$$

where the sign II indicates the product of the $2r$ factors obtained by replacing n in the denominator of (25) by the numbers $1, 2, \ldots, r$ in succession. Observe that, when $r \geqq k$, the factor $m + k$ cancels. Hence, taking the partial derivative of (25) with respect to m, replacing m by $-k$ in the result, multiplying by $(k - 1)!$, and simplifying, we get

$$Y = \left(\frac{\partial Y_m}{\partial m} \right)_{m=-k} = x^{-k} \log x \sum_{r=k}^{\infty} \frac{2(-1)^{r+k-1}(x/2)^{2r}}{r!(r - k)!}$$
$$+ x^{-k} \sum_{r=0}^{k-1} \frac{(k - r - 1)!(x/2)^{2r}}{r!}$$
$$+ x^{-k} \sum_{r=k}^{\infty} \left\{ \frac{2(-1)^{r+k}(x/2)^{2r}}{r!(r - k)!} \sum_{n=1}^{r} \left[\frac{1}{2n} + \frac{1}{2(n - k)} \right] \right\}, \quad (26)$$

where the n in $n - k$ takes on all integral values from 1 to r except k, and $0! = 1$. The solution for the case when $k = 0$ cannot be obtained from (26) by replacing k by zero. This case will be considered in exercise 2.   The general solution of (19), when k is any integer not zero, is

$$y = c_1 y_1 + c_2 Y. \tag{27}$$

EXERCISES

1. Write the solution of (19) when (a) $k = \frac{1}{2}$; (b) $k = 3$.

2. Find the general solution of (19) when $k = 0$.

3. If $J_k(x)$, $k = 0$ or a positive integer, is defined by

$$J_k(x) = \frac{1}{2^k k!} y_1(x) = \frac{x^k}{2^k k!} \sum_{r=0}^{\infty} \frac{(-1)^r k! (x/2)^{2r}}{r!(r+k)!},$$

show that the part of (26) represented by the first sum may be written in the form $-[(\log x)/2^{k-1}]J_k(x)$. *Hint:* Replace r by $R + k$ in the first sum of (26) and observe that the numbers on the summation sign will then be $R = 0$ to $R = \infty$.

4. Using the definition $J_k(x)$ from exercise 3, show that (a) $J_0(x) + J_2(x) = (2/x)J_1(x)$; (b) $d[J_0(x)]/dx = J_1(x)$.

86. Laguerre polynomials and Hermite polynomials

The polynomial solutions of

$$\mathbf{x D^2 L}_q + (1 - x)\, \mathbf{D L}_q + q \mathbf{L}_q = 0, \tag{28}$$

where $q = 0$ or an integer, are called **Laguerre polynomials.** The polynomial solutions of

$$\mathbf{D^2 H}_q - 2\mathbf{x\, D H}_q + 2q \mathbf{H}_q = 0, \tag{29}$$

where $q = 0$ or an integer, are called **Hermite polynomials.**

EXERCISES

1. Derive the following solutions of Laguerre's equation (28):

$$
\begin{aligned}
L_0 &= c, & L_2 &= c(2 - 4x + x^2) \\
L_1 &= c(1 - x), & L_3 &= c(6 - 18x + 9x^2 - x^3).
\end{aligned}
$$

2. Derive the following solutions of Hermite's equations (29):

$$
\begin{aligned}
H_0 &= c(1), & H_3 &= c(-12x + 8x^3), \\
H_1 &= c(2x), & H_4 &= c(12 - 48x^2 + 16x^4), \\
H_2 &= c(-2 + 4x^2), & H_5 &= c(120x - 160x^3 + 32x^5).
\end{aligned}
$$

3. Hermite polynomials $H_q(x)$ are often defined by the results of equating coefficients of like powers of s in the equation

$$\left(1 - \frac{s^2}{1!} + \frac{s^4}{2!} - \frac{s^6}{3!} + \cdots\right)\left[1 + \frac{(2sx)^1}{1!} + \frac{(2sx)^2}{2!} + \cdots\right]$$

$$= H_0 + \frac{H_1}{1!}s + \frac{H_2}{2!}s^2 + \cdots.$$

The function on the left is called the generating function of $H_q(x)$. Use this equation to check the equations of exercise 2 and to find H_6.

4. Laguerre polynomials are often defined by the results of equating coefficients of like powers of s in the equation

$$f(s) - \frac{xsf'(s)}{(1!)^2} + \frac{x^2s^2f''(s)}{(2!)^2} - \cdots = L_0 + \frac{L_1}{1!}s + \frac{L_2}{2!}s^2 + \cdots ,$$

where $f(s) = 1 + s + s^2 + \cdots + s^n + \cdots$ and the primes denote derivatives with respect to s. Use this formula to check the equations of exercise 1 and to find the terms of L_q of degree in x less than 4.

5. The functions $H_q e^{-\frac{1}{2}x^2}$, where H_q is the Hermite polynomial defined by (29), are orthogonal functions. Prove that

$$\int_{-\infty}^{\infty} H_1 H_2 e^{-x^2}\, dx = 0.$$

87. Approximate integration of differential equations

There are many methods* of finding a result which approximates to any required degree of accuracy a solution of a given differential equation. The method is generally a step-by-step procedure which uses in each stage one or more of the results obtained in previous stages. Although the method usually requires a large amount of computation to obtain a particular result, it can often be applied when other methods fail, and the result is given in considerable detail. It was formerly used extensively to compute the trajectories described by shells in long-range gunfire, requiring high angles of elevation. Two methods of obtaining approximations to a solution of a differential equation are considered in §§88 and 89.

88. Method of successive approximations

We shall illustrate the method by applying it to solve two examples.

Example 1. Find approximately the solution of

$$\frac{dy}{dx} = xy \qquad\qquad (a)$$

which satisfies the initial conditions

$$y = 1, \qquad \text{when } x = 0. \qquad\qquad (b)$$

Solution. Taking $y = 1$ as a first approximation, substitute 1 for y in the right-hand member of (a) to obtain

$$\frac{dy}{dx} = x. \qquad\qquad (c)$$

---

* J. B. Scarborough, in his "Numerical Mathematical Analysis" (2d ed., pp. 235–307, 1950), considers four methods.

Integrating (c) and using initial conditions (b), we find, as a second approximation,

$$y = 1 + \frac{x^2}{2}. \tag{d}$$

Substituting y from (d) in the right-hand member of (a), integrating, and using the initial conditions (b), we obtain, as a third approximation,

$$y = 1 + \frac{x^2}{2} + \frac{x^4}{2^2 \cdot 2!}. \tag{e}$$

By continuing this step-by-step process, we could obtain, as the $(n + 1)$th approximation,

$$y = 1 + \frac{x^2}{2} + \frac{x^4}{2^2 \cdot 2!} + \cdots + \frac{x^{2n}}{2^n n!}. \tag{f}$$

These happen to be the first $(n + 1)$ terms of the series solution satisfying conditions (b).   Hence it appears that *the limit of the nth approximation, as n becomes infinite, is the exact solution.*

Example 2. Find approximately the solution of $(d^2y/dx^2) - 2x(dy/dx) = 2x$ which satisfies the initial conditions $y = 1, dy/dx = 0$, when $x = 0$.

Solution. Writing $D = d/dx$, $z = dy/dx$, $Dz = d^2y/dx^2$ in the statement of the problem, we have the system

$$Dy = z, \qquad Dz = 2x + 2xz \tag{a}$$

and the initial conditions

$$y = 1, z = 0, \qquad \text{when } x = 0. \tag{b}$$

The process to be performed repeatedly consists in substituting the approximations for y and z in terms of x in the right-hand members of (a), integrating the results, and determining the constants of integration by using (b).

Substituting the first approximation $y = 1, z = 0$ in the right-hand member of (a), we get

$$Dy = 0, \qquad Dz = 2x. \tag{c}$$

Integrating these equations and determining the constants of integration by using (b), we get

$$y = 1, \qquad z = x^2 \tag{d}$$

as the second approximation. Substituting these values in the right-hand member of (a), integrating, and determining the constants, we get the third approximation,

$$y = 1 + \frac{x^3}{3}, \qquad z = x^2 + \frac{x^4}{2}. \qquad (e)$$

The fourth approximation is

$$y = 1 + \frac{x^3}{3} + \frac{x^5}{5 \cdot 2!}, \qquad z = x^2 + \frac{x^4}{2} + \frac{x^6}{3!}, \qquad (f)$$

and the $(n + 2)$nd $(n > 1)$ approximation for y is found to be

$$\mathbf{y = 1 + \frac{x^3}{3} + \frac{x^5}{5 \cdot 2!} + \cdots + \frac{x^{2n+1}}{(2n+1)n!}}. \qquad (g)$$

Here again the limit approached by the nth approximation, as n becomes infinite, is the series solution which satisfies the given initial conditions.

In general, the method applied to the system (a) of Example 2 may be applied to approximate a solution of any system of n first-order equations in $n + 1$ unknowns, provided the conditions of theorem II of §78 are satisfied for the system.*

EXERCISES

Solve each of the following differential equations by the method of this article and compare the results with the solution found by some other method:

1. $\dfrac{dy}{dx} = y + x$; $y = 1$, when $x = 0$

2. $\dfrac{dy}{dx} = xy + 1$; $y = 1$, when $x = 0$

3. $\dfrac{dx}{dt} = y$, $\dfrac{dy}{dt} = x + t$; $x = 1$, $y = -1$, when $t = 0$

4. $\dfrac{d^2y}{dx^2} = xy$; $y = 1$, $y' = 0$, when $x = 0$.   *Hint:* Solve $\dfrac{dy}{dx} = z$, $\dfrac{dz}{dx} = xy$

5. Find a five-term approximation of y if

$$\frac{d^2y}{dx^2} + 3x \frac{dy}{dx} - 6y = 0$$

and if $y = 1$, $dy/dx = 1$, when $x = 0$.

89. The Runge-Kutta method

The method set forth in this article was devised by C. Runge about 1894 and extended by W. Kutta a few years later.   It will serve as an illustration of a method based mainly on computation.

* See INCE, E. L., "Ordinary Differential Equations," pp. 63–74.

Let x_0 and y_0 be initial values of the variables x and y for a solution of the equation

$$\frac{dy}{dx} = f(x,y). \tag{30}$$

A change h is made in x, and the corresponding change Δy in y is found by computing in order k_1, k_2, k_3, k_4, and Δy by means of the following formulas:

$$\begin{aligned}
k_1 &= f(x_0,y_0)h, \\
k_2 &= f\left(x_0 + \frac{h}{2}, \, y_0 + \frac{k_1}{2}\right) h, \\
k_3 &= f\left(x_0 + \frac{h}{2}, \, y_0 + \frac{k_2}{2}\right) h, \\
k_4 &= f(x_0 + h, \, y_0 + k_3)h, \\
\Delta y &= \tfrac{1}{6}(k_1 + 2k_2 + 2k_3 + k_4).
\end{aligned} \tag{31}$$

This gives the values $x_1 = x_0 + h$, $y_1 = y_0 + \Delta y$. To find a third pair of values, use the same formulas (31) with x_1 and y_1 taking the place of x_0 and y_0, respectively. When x_2 and y_2 are found, use (31) with x_0 and y_0 replaced by x_2 and y_2, etc.

The error in the Runge-Kutta method is not easy to estimate. Roughly it is of the order of h^5. If $h = 0.1$, we expect an error in Δy affecting the fifth decimal place.*

The following example will illustrate the procedure.

Example. Find three pairs of values of x and y for the solution of $dy/dx = -x + y$ by means of formulas (31) if the initial values of the variables are $x = 0$, $y = 2$.

Solution. The first value pair is $x = 0$, $y = 2$. Take $h = 0.1$, $x_0 = 0$, $y_0 = 2$ in (31), keep five decimal places during the computation, but round off the value of Δy to four decimal places. This gives

$$\begin{aligned}
k_1 &= (-0 + 2)0.1 = 0.2, \\
k_2 &= \left(-0 - \frac{0.1}{2} + 2 + \frac{0.2}{2}\right)0.1 = 0.205, \\
k_3 &= \left(-0 - \frac{0.1}{2} + 2 + \frac{0.205}{2}\right)0.1 = 0.20525, \\
k_4 &= (-0 - 0.1 + 2 + 0.20525)0.1 = 0.21053, \\
\Delta y &= \tfrac{1}{6}[0.2 + 2(0.205) + 2(0.20525) + 0.21053] = 0.2052.
\end{aligned}$$

* See WILLERS, F. A., "Numerische Integration," pp. 91–92. Also consult "Numerical Solutions" by H. Levy and E. A. Baggott, Dover Publications, Inc.

Hence
$$\mathbf{x_1 = 0.1,} \qquad \mathbf{y_1 = 2.2052.}$$

Substituting these values of x_1 and y_1 for x_0 and y_0 and 0.1 for h in (31), we obtain $k_1 = 0.21052$, $k_2 = 0.21605$, $k_3 = 0.21632$, $k_4 = 0.22215$, and $\Delta y = \frac{1}{6}(k_1 + 2k_2 + 2k_3 + k_4) = 0.21624$. Hence the third pair of values of x and y is

$$\mathbf{x_2 = 0.2,} \qquad \mathbf{y_2 = 2.4214.}$$

The next pair of values could be computed by using x_2 and y_2 for x_0 and y_0 in (31).

EXERCISES

1. Check the values for x_2 and y_2 in the solution just given. Then compute $x_3 = 0.3$, $y_3 = 2.6499$ by using (31) with $x_0 = x_2$, $y_0 = y_2$, and $h = 0.1$. Finally compute y when $x = 0.4$.

2. Find three value pairs of x and y by using (31) for the solution of $dy/dx = xy + 1$ in which $y = 1$ when $x = 0$. Use $h = 0.1$.

3. The Runge-Kutta equations for solving two simultaneous equations of the type

$$\frac{dx}{dt} = f(t,x,y), \qquad \frac{dy}{dt} = F(t,x,y)$$

are

$$k_1 = f(t_0,x_0,y_0)\,\Delta t,$$
$$l_1 = F(t_0,x_0,y_0)\,\Delta t,$$
$$k_2 = f\left(t_0 + \frac{\Delta t}{2},\, x_0 + \frac{k_1}{2},\, y_0 + \frac{l_1}{2}\right)\Delta t,$$
$$l_2 = F\left(t_0 + \frac{\Delta t}{2},\, x_0 + \frac{k_1}{2},\, y_0 + \frac{l_1}{2}\right)\Delta t,$$
$$k_3 = f\left(t_0 + \frac{\Delta t}{2},\, x_0 + \frac{k_2}{2},\, y_0 + \frac{l_2}{2}\right)\Delta t,$$
$$l_3 = F\left(t_0 + \frac{\Delta t}{2},\, x_0 + \frac{k_2}{2},\, y_0 + \frac{l_2}{2}\right)\Delta t,$$
$$k_4 = f(t_0 + \Delta t,\, x_0 + k_3,\, y_0 + l_3)\,\Delta t,$$
$$l_4 = F(t_0 + \Delta t,\, x_0 + k_3,\, y_0 + l_3)\,\Delta t,$$
$$\Delta x = \tfrac{1}{6}(k_1 + 2k_2 + 2k_3 + k_4),$$
$$\Delta y = \tfrac{1}{6}(l_1 + 2l_2 + 2l_3 + l_4).$$

In using these equations, first find k_1 and l_1, then k_2 and l_2, then k_3 and l_3, then k_4 and l_4, and finally Δx and Δy. Apply these equations to solve

$$\frac{dx}{dt} = y - t, \qquad \frac{dy}{dt} = x + t$$

for the value sets x, y, t having $t = 0.1$, 0.2, and 0.3 if $x = 1$, $y = 1$, when $t = 0$.

CHAPTER XII

PARTIAL DIFFERENTIAL EQUATIONS OF THE FIRST ORDER

90. Solution of a partial differential equation

This chapter is concerned with partial differential equations, that is, equations containing partial derivatives. A solution or integral of such an equation is a relation among the variables involved that satisfies the equation. It is concerned with two or more independent variables and may or may not involve arbitrary constants and arbitrary functions. The following examples and exercises will illustrate these facts.

Example 1. Prove that

$$z = ax + a^2y^2 + b \qquad (a)$$

is a solution of

$$\frac{\partial z}{\partial y} = 2y \left(\frac{\partial z}{\partial x} \right)^2. \qquad (b)$$

Solution. Differentiating (a) partially with respect to x and with respect to y, we obtain

$$\frac{\partial z}{\partial x} = a, \qquad \frac{\partial z}{\partial y} = 2a^2y. \qquad (c)$$

Substitution from (c) in (b) gives the identity

$$2a^2y = 2ya^2.$$

Example 2. Prove that

$$y = \varphi(ct - x) + \psi(ct + x), \qquad (a)$$

where φ and ψ are arbitrary functions,* is a solution of

$$\frac{\partial^2 y}{\partial t^2} = c^2 \frac{\partial^2 y}{\partial x^2}.\dagger \qquad (b)$$

---

* Throughout the chapters on partial differential equations, we shall assume that the arbitrary functions are continuous and possess such continuous partial derivatives as we may wish to use.

† Equation (a) in Example 2 represents a motion compounded of two wave motions having equal wavelengths and periods but opposite directions. Because

183

Solution. It will be convenient to use the notation

$$\frac{d\varphi}{d(ct - x)} = \varphi', \qquad \frac{d^2\varphi}{[d(ct - x)]^2} = \varphi'',$$

$$\frac{d\psi}{d(ct + x)} = \psi', \qquad \frac{d^2\psi}{[d(ct + x)]^2} = \psi''.$$

Partial differentiation of (*a*) gives

$$\frac{\partial y}{\partial t} = c\varphi' + c\psi', \qquad \frac{\partial y}{\partial x} = -\varphi' + \psi',$$

$$\frac{\partial^2 y}{\partial t^2} = c^2\varphi'' + c^2\psi'', \qquad \frac{\partial^2 y}{\partial x^2} = \varphi'' + \psi''. \qquad (c)$$

Substituting from (*c*) in (*b*), we obtain the identity

$$c^2\varphi'' + c^2\psi'' = c^2\varphi'' + c^2\psi''.$$

Note: Throughout the chapters on partial differential equations, we shall use the notation

$$p = \frac{\partial z}{\partial x}, \; q = \frac{\partial z}{\partial y}, \; r = \frac{\partial^2 z}{\partial x^2}, \; s = \frac{\partial^2 z}{\partial x \, \partial y}, \; t = \frac{\partial^2 z}{\partial y^2}. \qquad (1)$$

EXERCISES

In the following exercises, φ and ψ represent arbitrary functions of the indicated variables.   Verify the fact that each equation on the left is a solution of the partial differential equation written opposite it:

1. $az = a^2x + y + b$ $pq = 1$
2. $2z = 2axe^y + a^2e^{2y} + b$ $q = xp + p^2$
3. $yz = ax + 2\sqrt{ay} + b$ $p = (yq + z)^2$
4. $6az = x^3y + x\varphi(y) + \psi(y)$ $ar = xy$
5. $z = x^n\varphi(y) + \psi(y)$ $xr = (n - 1)p$
6. $\varphi(x^2 - z^2, \; x^3 - y^3) = 0$ $y^2zp + x^2zq = xy^2$

Hint: Let $u = x^2 - z^2$, $v = x^3 - y^3$. Then $(\partial\varphi/\partial x) = (\partial\varphi/\partial u)(2x - 2zp) + (\partial\varphi/\partial v)3x^2 = 0$, etc.

7. $z = e^{y/a}\varphi(x - y)$ $z = a(p + q)$
8. $z^2 = x^3y^2 + x\varphi(y) + \psi(y)$ $zr + p^2 = 3xy^2$
9. $x = \varphi(z) + \psi(y)$ $ps - qr = 0$
10. $2z = x^2y - 2xy + \varphi(y) + e^{-x}\psi(y)$ $p + r = xy$
11. $z = \varphi\left(\dfrac{y}{x}\right) + \psi(xy)$ $x^2r - y^2t = qy - px$
12. $z = \varphi(x + iy) + \psi(x - iy), \; i = \sqrt{-1}$ $r + t = 0$

of this fact, equation (*b*) of Example 2 plays a very important role in mathematical physics, especially in the theory of sound and the theory of electricity and magnetism.

91. Partial differential equation from integral

In the case of ordinary differential equations, we were able to find a differential equation when its general solution was given (see §4, Chapter I). The same method will operate to find a partial differential equation satisfied by a given integral. The following examples will illustrate the process as well as the type of result to be expected.

Example 1. Find a partial differential equation whose integral is

$$z = ax + (a^2 + 3)y + b, \tag{a}$$

if a and b are arbitrary constants.

Solution. Differentiating (a) partially with respect to x and y, we find

$$p = a, \qquad q = a^2 + 3. \tag{b}$$

Elimination of a from equations (b) gives

$$\mathbf{q = p^2 + 3}.$$

Example 2. Find a partial differential equation whose integral is

$$z = ax^2 + by^2 + c, \tag{a}$$

where a, b, and c are arbitrary constants.

Solution. Taking first and second partial derivatives of (a), we find

$$p = 2ax, \qquad q = 2by, \qquad r = 2a, \qquad s = 0, \qquad t = 2b. \tag{b}$$

Here are six equations from which to eliminate three unknowns. Hence we obtain the three solutions

$$\mathbf{s = 0}, \qquad \mathbf{p = rx}, \qquad \mathbf{q = ty}, \tag{c}$$

all satisfied by (a).

Example 3. Find a partial differential equation satisfied by the equation of all spheres with centers in the XY-plane and radius 1.

Solution. The equation of the spheres is

$$(x - h)^2 + (y - k)^2 + z^2 = 1. \tag{a}$$

Differentiating this partially with respect to x and to y, we get

$$2(x - h) + 2zp = 0, \qquad 2(y - k) + 2z(q) = 0. \tag{b}$$

Eliminating h and k between (a) and (b), we obtain

$$\mathbf{z^2(p^2 + q^2 + 1) = 1}. \tag{c}$$

Example 4.   Find a partial differential equation whose integral is

$$\varphi(x^2 + y^2, \; x^2 - z^2) = 0, \tag{a}$$

where φ represents an arbitrary function.

Solution. Let $u = x^2 + y^2$ and $v = x^2 - z^2$. Partial differentiation of (a) gives

$$\frac{\partial\varphi}{\partial u}\frac{\partial u}{\partial x} + \frac{\partial\varphi}{\partial v}\frac{\partial v}{\partial x} = 2x\frac{\partial\varphi}{\partial u} + (2x - 2zp)\frac{\partial\varphi}{\partial v} = 0,$$

$$\frac{\partial\varphi}{\partial u}\frac{\partial u}{\partial y} + \frac{\partial\varphi}{\partial v}\frac{\partial v}{\partial y} = 2y\frac{\partial\varphi}{\partial u} - 2zq\frac{\partial\varphi}{\partial v} = 0. \tag{b}$$

Eliminating $(\partial\varphi/\partial v) \div (\partial\varphi/\partial u)$ from (b), we find

$$\frac{-\mathbf{x}}{\mathbf{x} - \mathbf{zp}} = \frac{\mathbf{y}}{\mathbf{zq}}, \quad \text{or} \quad \mathbf{z(yp - xq) = xy}.$$

EXERCISES

1. Find the partial differential equations of which the following are solutions:

(a) $z = ax + by$ (b) $z = a^2x - ay + b$

(c) $z^2 = ax^2 + by^2$ (d) $z = ax + f(a)y + b$

2. Find the partial differential equation of

(a) All planes through the origin not containing the Z-axis.

(b) All planes having the sum of their intercepts on the coordinate axes unity.

(c) All spheres with centers in the XZ-plane and radius 1.

(d) All spheres with centers on the line $x = y = z$.

(e) All right circular cones having the Z-axis as axis.

(f) All spheres passing through the origin and having centers in the XY-plane.

3. Find the partial differential equations of which the following equations are solutions:

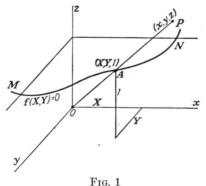

(a) $z = \varphi(x + y)$

(b) $z = x\varphi(x + y)$

(c) $y = z\varphi(x + y)$

(d) $y = \psi(z) + \varphi(x)$

(e) $z = \varphi(x) + \psi(y)$

(f) $y = \varphi(x + y) + \psi(z)$

(g) $z = \varphi(x + 2y) + \psi(x - y)$

(h) $z = \varphi(y/x) + \psi(xy)$

4. Show that, for all cylindrical surfaces $\varphi(x,z) = 0$ having their elements parallel to the Y-axis, $q = 0$.

5. Find the partial differential equation of all conical surfaces with vertex at

FIG. 1

$(0,0,0)$.   *Hint:* In Fig. 1, P represents any point on a conical surface, A the point where OP cuts plane $z = 1$, and curve MAN, having equations $f(X,Y) = 0$, $z = 1$, the trace of the conical surface on plane $z = 1$.   From Fig. 1

$$\frac{x - X}{X} = \frac{y - Y}{Y} = \frac{z - 1}{1}.$$

Solve these equations for X and Y and substitute in $f(X,Y) = 0$.

6. Show that the equation of all surfaces of revolution about the Z-axis may be written

$$f(z, \sqrt{x^2 + y^2}) = 0, \quad \text{or} \quad z = \varphi(x^2 + y^2),$$

and find the partial differential equation of these surfaces.

92. Equations easily integrable

Some partial differential equations may be solved by inspection. Thus, the equation

$$\frac{\partial z}{\partial x} = x^2 + y \tag{2}$$

evidently has as a solution

$$z = \frac{x^3}{3} + xy + \varphi(y), \tag{3}$$

where φ represents an arbitrary function.   Since only differentiation with respect to x was indicated in (2), we got (3) from it by integrating with respect to x while treating y as a constant.

Again consider the equation

$$ys + p = 4xy, \tag{4}$$

where s and p have the meanings defined in (1) of §90.   Writing this in the form

$$y \frac{\partial p}{\partial y} + p = 4xy, \tag{5}$$

we see that it is an ordinary linear equation of the first degree in p and y if x is considered constant.   Hence its solution is

$$py = 2xy^2 + \varphi(x). \tag{6}$$

Observe that the arbitrary function $\varphi(x)$ plays the role of a constant, since x was considered constant for the integration.   In (6) replace p by its equal $\partial z/\partial x$ and integrate again, considering y as a constant, to obtain

$$z = \int \left[2xy + \frac{1}{y} \varphi(x) \right] dx \qquad (y \text{ constant}),$$

or

$$z = x^2 y + \frac{1}{y}\,\varphi_1(x) + \psi(y).$$

Here $\varphi_1(x)$ $[= \int \varphi(x)\,dx]$ and $\psi(y)$ are arbitrary functions.

These illustrations indicate how a large class of partial differential equations may be integrated by using the methods of solving ordinary differential equations. It is worthy of note that *the constant of integration consists of an arbitrary function of the variable considered constant during the integration.*

EXERCISES

1. $\dfrac{\partial z}{\partial x} = 3x^2 + y^2$ **2.** $y\,\dfrac{\partial z}{\partial y} + z = x^2$

3. $y\,\dfrac{\partial p}{\partial y} + p = 2x$ **4.** $r = f(x,y)$

5. $ys = x + ay$ **6.** $t - q = e^x + e^y$
7. $p + r = xy$ **8.** $xr + p = xy$
9. $r + p^2 = y^2$ **10.** $zp + z^2 = xy^2$

11. $pr + p^2 = a$ **12.** $\dfrac{\partial r}{\partial y} + \dfrac{\partial p}{\partial x} = 12$

13. $yt + 2q = 12x^2 y^2$

93. Linear equations of the first order

The general linear partial differential equation of the first order in x, y, and z has the form

$$Pp + Qq = R, \tag{7}$$

where P, Q, and R represent functions of x, y, and z, and p and q are defined in equation (1). The following method of solving this type of equation is due to the great French mathematician Lagrange; it is often referred to as *Lagrange's method.*

Let $u(x,y,z) = a$ be a solution of (7). Then

$$\frac{\partial u}{\partial x} + p\,\frac{\partial u}{\partial z} = 0, \qquad \frac{\partial u}{\partial y} + q\,\frac{\partial u}{\partial z} = 0, \tag{8}$$

or, assuming that $\partial u / \partial z \neq 0$,

$$p = -\frac{\partial u}{\partial x}\Big/\frac{\partial u}{\partial z}, \qquad q = -\frac{\partial u}{\partial y}\Big/\frac{\partial u}{\partial z}. \tag{9}$$

Substituting p and q from (9) in (7), we have, after slight simplification,

$$P\,\frac{\partial u}{\partial x} + Q\,\frac{\partial u}{\partial y} + R\,\frac{\partial u}{\partial z} = 0. \tag{10}$$

Hence any solution of (7) is also a solution of (10).

Again let $u(x,y,z) = a$ be any solution of (10).   Then

$$\frac{\partial u}{\partial x} = -\frac{\partial u}{\partial z}\, p, \qquad \frac{\partial u}{\partial y} = -\frac{\partial u}{\partial z}\, q. \tag{11}$$

Substituting $\partial u/\partial x$ and $\partial u/\partial y$ from (11) in (10), we obtain, after slight simplification,

$$Pp + Qq = R. \tag{7}$$

Hence any solution of (10) is also a solution of (7).
Now consider the so-called subsidiary equations

$$\frac{dx}{P} = \frac{dy}{Q} = \frac{dz}{R} = \lambda, \tag{12}$$

where λ is the value of the equal ratios.   From (12) get

$$dx = P\lambda, \qquad dy = Q\lambda, \qquad dz = R\lambda, \tag{13}$$

multiply equations (13) by $\partial u/\partial x$, $\partial u/\partial y$, $\partial u/\partial z$, respectively, and add the results to obtain

$$\frac{\partial u}{\partial x}\, dx + \frac{\partial u}{\partial y}\, dy + \frac{\partial u}{\partial z}\, dz = \lambda\left(P\,\frac{\partial u}{\partial x} + Q\,\frac{\partial u}{\partial y} + R\,\frac{\partial u}{\partial z}\right). \tag{14}$$

Now if $\partial u/\partial z \neq 0$ and $u = c$ is an integral* of (12), the left member of (14) is zero, and therefore the right member is zero also; then (10) holds true, and therefore (7) also.   *Hence an integral of (12) is a solution of (10) and of (7).*
    If $P = 0$, then, from (13), $x = c$ is an integral of (12).   If $P = 0$ in (7), it becomes $qQ = R$ and may be integrated by treating x as a constant and using a function of x as constant of integration.   Similarly $y = c$ is an integral of (12) if $Q = 0$.   If $R = 0$, then $z = c$ is an integral of (12).
    Also if u_1 and u_2 are integrals of (12) then $\psi(u_1,u_2) = 0$, where ψ is an arbitrary function, is an integral of (7) provided $\partial\psi(u_1,u_2)/\partial z \neq 0$.   For

$$d\psi(u_1,u_2) = \frac{\partial\psi}{\partial u_1}\left(\frac{\partial u_1}{\partial x}\, dx + \frac{\partial u_1}{\partial y}\, dy + \frac{\partial u_1}{\partial z}\, dz\right)$$
$$+ \frac{\partial\psi}{\partial u_2}\left(\frac{\partial u_2}{\partial x}\, dx + \frac{\partial u_2}{\partial y}\, dy + \frac{\partial u_2}{\partial z}\, dz\right) = 0 \tag{15}$$

holds true.   Since (13) holds for each of the parentheses of (15), it holds for (15).   Replacing dx, dy, and dz in (15) by their values from

---

* If $u(x,y,z) = c$, a constant, satisfies (12), then $u(x,y,z)$ is called an integral of (12).

(13), canceling λ from the result, and letting $u = \psi_1(u_1, u_2)$, obtain (10) and therefore (7).

Evidently the solution $\psi(u_1, u_2) = 0$ could be written in the form $u_1 = \varphi(u_2)$.

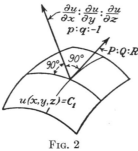

Since $\partial u/\partial x$, $\partial u/\partial y$, $\partial u/\partial z$ are direction numbers of a normal to surface $u(x,y,z) = c$ at (x,y,z), equation (9) shows that *a line with direction numbers $p,q,-1$ is normal to a surface represented by an integral $u(x,y,z) = c$ of (7)*, and (12) shows that *the surface is tangent at (x,y,z) to a line passing through (x,y,z) and having direction numbers P,Q,R.* Figure 2 is suggestive.

Fig. 2

In summary, if $u_1(x,y,z) = a$ and $u_2(x,y,z) = b$ are two independent integrals of the ordinary differential equations

$$\frac{dx}{P(x,y,z)} = \frac{dy}{Q(x,y,z)} = \frac{dz}{R(x,y,z)}, \tag{12}*$$

then either

$$\varphi(u_1, u_2) = 0, \quad \text{or} \quad u_2 = \psi(u_1) \tag{16}$$

as a general solution of

$$Pp + Qq = R. \tag{7}$$

The same line of reasoning shows that

$$\varphi(u_1, u_2, \ldots, u_n) = 0 \tag{17}$$

is the general solution of

$$P_1 \frac{\partial z}{\partial x_1} + P_2 \frac{\partial z}{\partial x_2} + \cdots + P_n \frac{\partial z}{\partial x_n} = R, \tag{18}$$

provided that

$$u_i(x_1, x_2, \ldots, x_n, z) = a_i \quad (i = 1, 2, \ldots, n)$$

are independent integrals of the differential equations

$$\frac{dx_1}{P_1} = \frac{dx_2}{P_2} = \cdots = \frac{dx_n}{P_n} = \frac{dz}{R}. \tag{19}$$

Example 1. Solve $(y + z)p + (x + z)q = x + y$.

Solution. The first step is to find two integrals of

$$\frac{dx}{y + z} = \frac{dy}{x + z} = \frac{dz}{x + y}. \tag{a}$$

* The theory of §74 applies to solve equations of type (12).

By the theory of proportion, we find from (a)

$$\frac{dx + dy + dz}{2x + 2y + 2z} = \frac{dx - dy}{-(x - y)} = \frac{dx - dz}{-(x - z)}. \qquad (b)$$

Two integrals of (b) evidently are

$$\log (x + y + z) + 2 \log (x - y) = C_1, \qquad \text{or}$$
$$(x + y + z)(x - y)^2 = c_1, \qquad (c)$$

and

$$\log (x - y) - \log (x - z) = C_2, \qquad \text{or} \qquad x - y = c_2(x - z). \qquad (d)$$

Hence the solution required is

$$\varphi\left[(x + y + z)(x - y)^2, \frac{x - y}{x - z} \right] = 0,$$

or it may be written

$$\mathbf{x} - \mathbf{y} = (\mathbf{x} - \mathbf{z})\varphi[(\mathbf{x} + \mathbf{y} + \mathbf{z})(\mathbf{x} - \mathbf{y})^2].$$

Example 2. Show how to use the method of this article to find an integrating factor of

$$M(x,y)\, dx + N(x,y)\, dy = 0. \qquad (a)$$

Solution. If $\mu(x,y)$ is an integrating factor of the given equation, then

$$\mu M\, dx + \mu N\, dy = 0 \qquad (b)$$

is exact. Hence, applying test (22) of §20, we have

$$\frac{\partial(\mu M)}{\partial y} = \frac{\partial(\mu N)}{\partial x}. \qquad (c)$$

Performing the indicated differentiation and rearranging terms, we obtain

$$M \frac{\partial \mu}{\partial y} - N \frac{\partial \mu}{\partial x} = \mu \left(\frac{\partial N}{\partial x} - \frac{\partial M}{\partial y} \right). \qquad (d)$$

Hence, any particular solution involving μ of

$$\frac{dx}{-N} = \frac{dy}{M} = \frac{d\mu}{\mu[(\partial N/\partial x) - (\partial M/\partial y)]} \qquad (e)$$

gives an integrating factor.

EXERCISES

1. $p + q = z$
2. $xp + yq = 2z$
3. $xp + zq = y$
4. $ap + bq = c$
5. $xp + zq + y = 0$
6. $xyq - x^2p = y^2$
7. $x^2p + y^2q = axy$
8. $yzp + xzq + 2xy = 0$
9. $xy^2p - y^3q + axz = 0$
10. $(x + y)(p - q) = z$

11. $xp + yq = 0$. *Hint:* $z = a$ is one required integral.
12. $zq = y$. *Hint:* $x = a$ is one required integral.
13. $(x + y)p = x - z$
14. $(x + y)p + (x - y)q = 0$
15. $yp + xq = x^2 - y^2 - z$.

16. $y \dfrac{\partial^2 z}{\partial x\, \partial y} + \dfrac{\partial^2 z}{\partial x^2} = 4x$. *Hint:* First integrate with respect to x, treating y as constant. Observe that $\displaystyle\int^x \psi_1(ye^{-x})\, dx = \int^x \psi'(ye^{-x})\ (-ye^{-x}\, dx) = \psi(ye^{-x}) + \varphi(y)$.

17. $x \dfrac{\partial^2 z}{\partial x^2} + y \dfrac{\partial^2 z}{\partial x\, \partial y} + \dfrac{\partial z}{\partial x} = 2x + y$

18. If u and v are functions of x, y, and z, and φ is an arbitrary function, prove that $\varphi(u,v) = 0$ satisfies a differential equation of the first order and first degree.

19. The solution of

$$py - qx = y \qquad\qquad (a)$$

is

$$\varphi(x^2 + y^2, z - x) = 0. \qquad\qquad (b)$$

Prove that any surface represented by (b) contains the curve

$$x^2 + y^2 = a^2 + b^2, \qquad z - x = c - a, \qquad\qquad (c)$$

if (a,b,c) is a point on the surface. How many curves defined by equations got by assigning various values to a, b, and c lie on each surface defined by (b)?

20. Determine the equations of the surfaces that cut orthogonally the system of ellipsoids $\frac{1}{2}x^2 + \frac{1}{3}y^2 + z^2 = c^2$. *Hint:* $P = \frac{2}{3}x$, $Q = \frac{2}{3}y$, $R = 2z$.

21. Find the equation of all surfaces whose normals intersect the line $x = y$, $z = 0$. *Hint:* $p/(x - a) = q/(y - a) = -1/z$. Eliminate a.

22. Using formula (e) of Example 2, find an integrating factor of

$$(y + y^2)\, dx - (x + y^2 + 2xy)\, dy = 0.$$

23. Use formula (e) of Example 2 to find an integrating factor of $M\, dx + N\, dy = 0$ if $(\partial N/\partial x) - (\partial M/\partial y)$ is equal to

(a) $Mf(y)$ (b) $Nf(x)$ (c) $\dfrac{k(xM - yN)}{xy}$

(d) $\dfrac{2(Nx - My)}{x^2 + y^2}$ (e) $\dfrac{axM - byN}{xy}$

24. Use formula (e) of Example 2 to find an integrating factor of

$$[ay^n + by^m + Q(x)y]\, dx + [a(n - 1)y^{n-1} + b(m - 1)y^{m-1}]\, dy = 0.$$

94. Determination of arbitrary function by means of initial conditions

In the treatment of ordinary differential equations the arbitrary functions were determined by initial conditions consisting of corresponding particular values of the variables and their derivatives. The arbitrary functions in the solutions of partial differential equations are often determined by given functional relations among the variables and their derivatives. For example, the arbitrary function of a solution representing surfaces in space by means of a relation involving only one arbitrary function, might be determined by specifying that the surface contain a particular curve in the XZ-plane. The equations of the curve would be the determining functional relations. The following example will serve to introduce the subject of boundary conditions, and applications later in the book will throw more light on the processes involving them.

Example. Find the solution of

$$yp + xq = z$$

representing a surface passing through the curve:

$$z = e^{x^2}, \qquad y = 2. \tag{I}$$

$$x + y + z = 3, \qquad z^2(x - y) = 2. \tag{II}$$

Solution. (I) The general solution of the equation, in accordance with §93, may be written

$$\varphi\left[\frac{z}{x + y}, \; z(x - y)\right] = 0. \tag{a}$$

Let

$$\frac{z}{x + y} = u, \qquad z(x - y) = v. \tag{b}$$

In (b) replace y by 2 and solve for x and z in terms of u and v to obtain

$$x = \pm \sqrt{4 + \frac{v}{u}}, \qquad z = 2u \pm u \sqrt{4 + \frac{v}{u}}. \tag{c}$$

Now substitute these values for x and z in $z - e^{x^2} = 0$ to get

$$u\left(2 \pm \sqrt{4 + \frac{v}{u}}\right) - e^{4 + v/u} = 0.$$

In this, replace u and v by their values from (b) to get

$$\left(\frac{z}{x + y}\right)(2 \pm \sqrt{4 + x^2 - y^2}) - e^{4 + x^2 - y^2} = 0. \tag{d}$$

Observe from (c) that the sign before the radical is that of x. This result (d) is a solution since it is a special case of (a) and $z - e^{x^2} = 0$ is obtained from it by replacing y by 2.

Remarks. Note that *we first obtain an equation in u and v by eliminating x, y, and z, from two equations expressing initial conditions and* $I_1 = u$, $I_2 = v$, *where* I_1 *and* I_2 *are two integrals; finally we replace u and v in this eliminant by their values* I_1 *and* I_2.

(II) According to the plan just outlined, eliminate x, y, and z from (b) and $x + y + z = 3$, $z^2(x - y) = 2$. Since $z(x - y) = v$ and $z^2(x - y) = 2$, we get

$$z = \frac{2}{v}. \tag{e}$$

From (b) and (e)

$$x + y = \frac{z}{u} = \frac{2}{uv}. \tag{f}$$

Replacing $x + y$ by $2/(uv)$ and z by $2/v$ in $x + y + z = 3$, obtain

$$\frac{2}{uv} + \frac{2}{v} = 3. \tag{g}$$

Replacing u and v in (g) by their values from (b) and simplifying, obtain

$$\mathbf{2x + 2y + 2z = 3z^2(x - y).} \tag{h}$$

EXERCISES

1. Solve the example of this article without reference to the given solution.

2. Find the solution of $xp - yq = 0$ which represents a surface through the curve (a) $xy^2 = z$, $y + z = 10$; (b) $x^2y = z$, $xy + xz = 2y$; (c) $xz = 1$, $xy + 1 = 2y$.

3. Find the solution of $xp + yq = z$ which represents a surface through the curve (a) $x + y = 1$, $x^2 + y^2 + z^2 = 25$; (b) $x - z = 1$, $x^2 + z^2 = 25$; (c) $xy = 2$, $z = y(1 + x^2 + x^4)$.

4. Find a solution of $p + q = z$ which represents a surface passing through the curve (a) $z = \sin x$, $y = 0$; (b) $z = y^2$, $x = a$; (c) $x^2 + z^2 = a^2$, $y = 0$.

5. Find the equation of all surfaces having tangent planes with x-intercept 1. Also find the equation of the particular surface passing through the circle $x = 0$, $y^2 + z^2 = 25$.

6. Find the equation of a surface for which

$$xyq - x^2p = y^2$$

and satisfying the condition $p = q$ when $x = 1$.

7. Find the equation of a surface satisfying the condition $\partial^2 z/\partial x^2 = 0$, cutting the YZ-plane in $z = y^2$, $x = 0$, and passing through curve $z = x$, $xy = 10$.

95. General, complete, singular solution

Consider the general partial differential equation of the first order represented by

$$f(x,y,z,p,q) = 0. \tag{20}$$

A solution of (20) involving an arbitrary function will be referred to as a *general solution;* a solution

$$\varphi(x,y,z,a,b) = 0, \tag{21}$$

where a and b are two arbitrary constants, will be called a *complete solution.*

The next article outlines the method of Lagrange and Charpit for finding a complete solution of a partial differential equation of the first order, and this article considers methods of finding the singular solution and a general solution from a complete solution.

Consider equation (21) as a known complete solution of (20). Then since z is a function of x and y, we have

$$dz = p\,dx + q\,dy, \tag{22}$$

where p and q are defined by

$$\frac{\partial\varphi}{\partial x} + \frac{\partial\varphi}{\partial z}p = 0, \qquad \frac{\partial\varphi}{\partial y} + \frac{\partial\varphi}{\partial z}q = 0. \tag{23}$$

From (21) other solutions of (20) may be obtained by treating a and b in (21) as functions of x and y. The following equations then take the place of (21):

$$\frac{\partial\varphi}{\partial x} + \frac{\partial\varphi}{\partial z}p + \frac{\partial\varphi}{\partial a}\frac{\partial a}{\partial x} + \frac{\partial\varphi}{\partial b}\frac{\partial b}{\partial x} = 0,$$
$$\frac{\partial\varphi}{\partial y} + \frac{\partial\varphi}{\partial z}q + \frac{\partial\varphi}{\partial a}\frac{\partial a}{\partial y} + \frac{\partial\varphi}{\partial b}\frac{\partial b}{\partial y} = 0. \tag{24}$$

Comparing (24) and (23), we see that p and q will take values at any point (x,y,z) that will satisfy (20), if

$$\frac{\partial\varphi}{\partial a}\frac{\partial a}{\partial x} + \frac{\partial\varphi}{\partial b}\frac{\partial b}{\partial x} = 0,$$
$$\frac{\partial\varphi}{\partial a}\frac{\partial a}{\partial y} + \frac{\partial\varphi}{\partial b}\frac{\partial b}{\partial y} = 0. \tag{25}$$

Equations (25) will be satisfied, if

$$\frac{\partial\varphi}{\partial a} = 0, \qquad \frac{\partial\varphi}{\partial b} = 0. \tag{26}$$

Elimination of a and b between (26) and (21) gives the equation of the envelope of the surfaces represented by (21). The equation of this envelope is called the **singular solution.** *

The condition that equations (25) be consistent is

$$
\begin{vmatrix} \dfrac{\partial a}{\partial x} & \dfrac{\partial b}{\partial x} \\[2mm] \dfrac{\partial a}{\partial y} & \dfrac{\partial b}{\partial y} \end{vmatrix} = 0, \tag{27}
$$

and this is also the condition that b be a function of a,

$$
b = \psi(a), \tag{28}
$$

where ψ represents an arbitrary function. If (28) holds, we have, from (25),

$$
\frac{\partial \varphi}{\partial a} + \frac{\partial \varphi}{\partial b}\frac{d\psi}{da} = 0, \tag{29}
$$

and the result of eliminating a and b from (21), (28), and (29) is a solution. This last solution is the *general solution*, since it involves an arbitrary function. For each particular function $\psi_1(a)$, equations (21), (28), and (29) represent the envelope of $\varphi[x,y,z,a,\psi_1(a)] = 0$, and the general solution represents the total system of such envelopes.†

It now appears that, if we can find a complete solution

$$
\varphi(x,y,z,a,b) = 0 \tag{21}
$$

of a partial differential equation

$$
f(x,y,z,p,q) = 0, \tag{20}
$$

then any singular solution that may exist can be found by eliminating a and b from

$$
\varphi = 0, \qquad \frac{\partial \varphi}{\partial a} = 0, \qquad \frac{\partial \varphi}{\partial b} = 0, \tag{30}
$$

---

* The equation of the envelope of a two-parameter family of surfaces $\varphi(x,y,z,a,b)$ $= 0$, if there is one, is found generally by eliminating the parameters a and b from

$$
\varphi(x,y,z,a,b) = 0, \qquad \frac{\partial \varphi}{\partial a} = 0, \qquad \frac{\partial \varphi}{\partial b} = 0.
$$

Any factor of the eliminant used as a solution of a given differential equation should be tested by substitution in the equation.

† If the one-parameter family of surfaces represented by $\varphi(x,y,z,a) = 0$ has an envelope, it is generally found by eliminating the parameter a between $\varphi(x,y,z,a)$ $= 0$, $\partial\varphi/\partial a = 0$.

and the general solution is represented by

$$\varphi_1(x,y,z,a) = \varphi[x,y,z,a,\psi(a)] = 0, \qquad \frac{\partial \varphi_1}{\partial a} = 0, \qquad (31)$$

where ψ represents an arbitrary function.

Example. Discuss the solutions of

$$z^2(p^2 + q^2 + 1) = 1. \qquad (a)$$

Solution. By substitution it is easy to show that

$$(x - a)^2 + (y - b)^2 + z^2 = 1 \qquad (b)$$

is a complete solution of (a). Equating to zero the partial derivatives of (b) with respect to a and to b, we obtain

$$x - a = 0, \qquad y - b = 0. \qquad (c)$$

Eliminating a and b from (b) and (c), we get

$$\mathbf{z = \pm 1,}$$

as the singular solution of (b). It is the envelope of the spheres represented by (b). Obviously the spheres (b) have their centers in the XY-plane and, having 1 as radius, are tangent to the planes $z = \pm 1$. The general solution, in accordance with (31), is represented by

$$\begin{aligned}(x - a)^2 + [y - \psi(a)]^2 + z^2 &= 1, \\ x - a + [y - \psi(a)]\psi'(a) &= 0.\end{aligned} \qquad (d)$$

Observe that it represents the envelope of the spheres having centers on curve $x = a$, $y = \psi(a)$, $z = 0$, and radius 1. To each function $\psi(a)$ there is associated an envelope, and the totality of the envelopes is represented by the general solution (d). To illustrate one of these envelopes, take $\psi(a) = 3$ in (d) to get $(x - a)^2 + (y - 3)^2 + z^2 = 1$, $x - a = 0$, that is,

$$(y - 3)^2 + z^2 = 1, \qquad (e)$$

a right circular cylinder of radius 1 and axis through $(0,3,0)$ parallel to the X-axis.

EXERCISES

1. Show that, if $\psi(a) = a$ in equation (d) of this section, the particular solution represented is the right circular cylinder $(x - y)^2 + 2z^2 = 2$.

2. Verify that the partial differential equation

$$z = px + qy + pq \qquad (a)$$

has $z = ax + by + ab$ as a complete solution. Show that the singular solution of (a) is $z = -xy$, and write the general solution in the form indicated by (31). Also find the particular solution corresponding to $\psi(a) = a$.

3. Show that $z = ax + by$, representing planes through (0,0,0), is a complete solution of $z = px + qy$. Find the general solution in the form indicated by (31). Note that a is an arbitrary function of y/x and therefore that $z/x = a + \psi(a)(y/x) = \varphi(y/x)$.

4. Show that $2(x - a)^2 + 2(y - b)^2 + 2z^2 = a^2 + b^2$ is a complete solution of

$$z^2(p^2 + q^2 + 2) = x^2 + y^2 + 2z(px + qy).$$

Show that the singular solution is the cone $z^2 = x^2 + y^2$. Find the general solution in form (31), and find the particular solution corresponding to $\psi(a) = a$. Give a complete geometric interpretation.

5. Find a partial differential equation whose complete solution is $4(x - a)^2 + 4(y - b)^2 + z^2 = (b - a)^2$. Find its singular solution and its general solution. Give a complete geometric interpretation of the solutions.

96. General equation of the first order

The object of this article is to explain the method, developed by Lagrange and Charpit, of solving an equation of the form

$$F(x,y,z,p,q) = 0. \tag{32}$$

The variables p, q, and z are functions of x and y connected by the equations

$$p = \frac{\partial z}{\partial x}, \qquad q = \frac{\partial z}{\partial y}, \qquad \frac{\partial p}{\partial y} = \frac{\partial q}{\partial x}, \tag{33}$$

and

$$dz = p \, dx + q \, dy. \tag{34}$$

The third equation of (33) is evidently the condition that (34) be integrable. It holds true whenever its members are continuous functions of x, y, and z.

The general method of solving (32) consists in deriving another equation

$$\varphi(x,y,z,p,q) = 0, \tag{35}$$

*solving it simultaneously with (32) for p and q, substituting the values thus found in (34), and integrating the resulting equation.**

---

* The equations represented by (32) and (35) can be solved for p and q in terms of x, y, and z provided that

$$\begin{vmatrix} \dfrac{\partial F}{\partial p} & \dfrac{\partial F}{\partial q} \\[2mm] \dfrac{\partial \varphi}{\partial p} & \dfrac{\partial \varphi}{\partial q} \end{vmatrix}$$

is not identically zero.

It is important then to find a method of obtaining a relation having the form (35). By differentiating each of the equations (32) and (35) partially with respect to x and with respect to y, we obtain

$$\frac{\partial F}{\partial x} + \frac{\partial F}{\partial z} p + \frac{\partial F}{\partial p} \frac{\partial p}{\partial x} + \frac{\partial F}{\partial q} \frac{\partial q}{\partial x} = 0,$$

$$\frac{\partial F}{\partial y} + \frac{\partial F}{\partial z} q + \frac{\partial F}{\partial p} \frac{\partial p}{\partial y} + \frac{\partial F}{\partial q} \frac{\partial q}{\partial y} = 0,$$

$$\frac{\partial \varphi}{\partial x} + \frac{\partial \varphi}{\partial z} p + \frac{\partial \varphi}{\partial p} \frac{\partial p}{\partial x} + \frac{\partial \varphi}{\partial q} \frac{\partial q}{\partial x} = 0,$$

$$\frac{\partial \varphi}{\partial y} + \frac{\partial \varphi}{\partial z} q + \frac{\partial \varphi}{\partial p} \frac{\partial p}{\partial y} + \frac{\partial \varphi}{\partial q} \frac{\partial q}{\partial y} = 0.$$

$$(36)$$

From these four equations we may eliminate the three quantities $\partial p/\partial x$, $\partial q/\partial y$, and $\partial p/\partial y = \partial q/\partial x$. Multiply the first equation by $-\partial\varphi/\partial p$, the second by $-\partial\varphi/\partial q$, the third by $\partial F/\partial p$, and the fourth by $\partial F/\partial q$, add the four results, and rearrange terms to obtain

$$\frac{\partial F}{\partial p} \frac{\partial \varphi}{\partial x} + \frac{\partial F}{\partial q} \frac{\partial \varphi}{\partial y} - \left(\frac{\partial F}{\partial x} + p \frac{\partial F}{\partial z}\right) \frac{\partial \varphi}{\partial p} - \left(\frac{\partial F}{\partial y} + q \frac{\partial F}{\partial z}\right) \frac{\partial \varphi}{\partial q}$$

$$+ \left(p \frac{\partial F}{\partial p} + q \frac{\partial F}{\partial q}\right) \frac{\partial \varphi}{\partial z} = 0. \quad (37)$$

This is an equation of the first order connecting the variables x, y, z, p, q, and φ. Consequently it may be solved by equating to zero an arbitrary function of integrals of

$$\frac{dp}{-\left(\dfrac{\partial F}{\partial x} + p \dfrac{\partial F}{\partial z}\right)} = \frac{dq}{-\left(\dfrac{\partial F}{\partial y} + q \dfrac{\partial F}{\partial z}\right)} = \frac{dx}{\dfrac{\partial F}{\partial p}} = \frac{dy}{\dfrac{\partial F}{\partial q}} = \frac{dz}{p \dfrac{\partial F}{\partial p} + q \dfrac{\partial F}{\partial q}}. \quad (38)$$

Since any integral of (38) will be sufficient for our purposes, we choose the simplest one involving p, q, or both, and an arbitrary constant.

Example. Solve

$$pq = z. \tag{a}$$

Solution. Equation (38) for this case is

$$\frac{dx}{q} = \frac{dy}{p} = \frac{dp}{p} = \frac{dq}{q} = \frac{dz}{2pq}. \tag{b}$$

From the equality of the second and third fractions we find the integral

$$p = y + a. \tag{c}$$

Solving (a) and (c) for p and q, we have

$$p = y + a, \qquad q = \frac{z}{y + a}. \tag{d}$$

Substitution of p and q from (d) in (34) gives

$$dz = (y + a)\, dx + \frac{z}{y + a}\, dy. \tag{e}$$

The solution of (e) is the complete integral*

$$\mathbf{z = (x + b)(y + a)}.$$

There is no singular solution, and the general solution is represented by

$$\mathbf{z = (y + a)[x + \varphi(a)], \qquad x + (y + a)\frac{d\varphi}{da} + \varphi(a) = 0,}$$

where φ represents an arbitrary function of a.

EXERCISES

1. To find a complete integral of $z = p + q$, use the first two ratios of (38) to get

$$\frac{dp}{-p} = \frac{dq}{-q}, \qquad \text{or} \qquad p = aq.$$

Now substitute this value of p in $z = p + q$ and solve to find $q = z/(1 + a)$. Hence $p = az/(1 + a)$.   Hence solve

$$dz = p\, dx + q\, dy = \frac{az}{1 + a}\, dx + \frac{z}{1 + a}\, dy$$

to get the complete solution $(1 + a) \log z = ax + y + b$.

2. Find a complete solution of (a) $z = 5p + 6q$; (b) $z = pq$.

3. Find a complete solution of $2xz = p + q$.   *Hint:* Use the second and third ratios of (38).   To integrate

$$dz = (2xz - ae^{z^2})\, dx + ae^{z^2}\, dy,$$

write it in the form

$$e^{-z^2}(dz - 2xz\, dx) = -a\, dx + a\, dy.$$

4. Find a complete solution of $px + qy = 0$.   *Hint:* Use the first and third ratios of (38).

5. Using the first and second ratios of (38), show that $p = aq$ may be used in solving $f(z,p,q) = 0$.   Find a complete solution of

(a) $z^2 = p + q$

(c) $z^2(p^2 + q^2 + 1) = c^2$

(b) $p^2 + q^2 = z$

(d) $z^{2n-2}(p^2z^n + pq) = R^2$

---

* See §75.

6. $z = px + qy + f(p,q)$ is analogous to Clairaut's equation of §37. Show by direct substitution that $z = ax + by + f(a,b)$ is a solution of it. Find a complete solution of

(a) $z = px + qy + pq$

(b) $z = px + qy - np^{1/n}q^{1/n}$

(c) $z = px + qy$

(d) $f(z - px - qy, p, q) = 0$

7. In solving a partial differential equation having the form $f(x,p) = \varphi(y,q)$, show that $f(x,p) = a$, $\varphi(y,q) = a$ may be used. Solve:

(a) $p + x = q - y$

(b) $p^2 - q^2 = x - y$

(c) $p^2y = q^2x$

(d) $p - \dfrac{df(x)}{dx} = q + \dfrac{dF(y)}{dy}$

8. Prove that $z = ax + by + c$ is a solution of $F(p,q) = 0$, provided that $F(a,b) = 0$. Solve:

(a) $pq = 1$

(b) $3p^2 - 2q^2 = pq$

(c) $p - e^q$

(d) $p + q^2 + 5q = 6$

9. Find a complete solution of

(a) $p = 2xq^2$

(b) $(p^2 + q^2)x = pz$

(c) $(p^2 + q^2)y = z$

(d) $z(p^2 - q^2) = x - y$

(e) $(2x - y)q^2 - p = 0$

(f) $z = 2x^3q^2 - px$

CHAPTER XIII

PARTIAL DIFFERENTIAL EQUATIONS OF ORDER HIGHER THAN THE FIRST

97. Definitions

Since the equation

$$\sum_{i=0,j=0}^{n,n} A_{ij} \frac{\partial^{i+j}z}{\partial x^i\, \partial y^j} = f(x,y), \qquad i + j \leqq n, \qquad \frac{\partial^0 z}{\partial x^0\, \partial y^0} = z, \qquad (1)$$

where the quantities A_{ij} are functions of x and y or constants, is linear in the dependent variable z and its derivatives, it is referred to as the *general linear partial differential equation*. If $i + j$ for every term in the left-hand member is equal to a constant n and if $f(x,y) = 0$, the equation is called *homogeneous*.

In this chapter, we shall consider methods of solving equation (1) in case the A_{ij} are constant and also in case the equation is of the second order, with the A_{ij} functions of x, y, z, p, and q.

98. Notation. Operators

As methods of procedure in solving linear partial equations are similar in many respects to those used in the case of ordinary linear differential equations, we shall use similar notation. Writing

$$D \text{ for } \frac{\partial}{\partial x}, \qquad D' \text{ for } \frac{\partial}{\partial y}, \qquad (2)$$

we define $F(D,D')z$ by the equation

$$\sum_{i=1,j=1}^{m,n} A_{ij} \frac{\partial^{i+j}z}{\partial x^i\, \partial y^j} + A_{00}z = \sum_{i=1,j=1}^{m,n} A_{ij}D^i D'^j z + A_{00}z = F(D,D')z, \quad (3)$$

where the A_{ij} are constants and i and j are positive integers. Equation (1) may now be written

$$F(D,D')z = f(x,y), \qquad (4)$$

202

provided that the A_{ij} are constants. The student can show by the methods used in the case of operators for ordinary differential equations that

$$F(D,D')(z_1 + z_2 + \cdots) = F(D,D')z_1 + F(D,D')z_2 + \cdots, \quad (5)$$

and that

$$F(D,D')G(D,D')z = G(D,D')F(D,D')z. \quad (6)$$

From (5) it appears that, when $z = z_1(x,y)$, $z = z_2(x,y)$, . . . are solutions of $F(D,D')z = 0$, then

$$z = z_1 + z_2 + \cdots \quad (7)$$

is also a solution; that is, *the sum of any number of solutions of $F(D,D')z = 0$ is also a solution.* Equation (6) indicates that, when $F(D,D')$ is factored, any order of the factors may be used.

It is easy to verify that

$$(D - mD')[\varphi(y + mx)\psi(x)] = \varphi(y + mx)\frac{d\psi}{dx}, \quad (8)$$

and, by applying (8) k times, in succession, that

$$(D - mD')^k[\varphi(y + mx)\psi(x)] = \varphi(y + mx)\frac{d^k\psi}{dx^k}. \quad (9)$$

Similarly, the student may verify that

$$(D - mD' - n)[e^{nx}\varphi(y + mx)\psi(x)] = e^{nx}\varphi(y + mx)\frac{d\psi}{dx}, \quad (10)$$

and then apply (10) repeatedly to obtain

$$(D - mD' - n)^k[e^{nx}\varphi(y + mx)\psi(x)] = e^{nx}\varphi(y + mx)\frac{d^k\psi}{dx^k}. \quad (11)$$

99. Homogeneous partial differential equation

The general solution of the simplest type of homogeneous equation $A_1(\partial z/\partial x) + A_2(\partial z/\partial y) = 0$, according to §93, is $z = \varphi[y - (A_2x/A_1)]$, where φ represents an arbitrary function. This suggests that the more general equation

$$F(D,D')z = A_0\frac{\partial^n z}{\partial x^n} + A_1\frac{\partial^n z}{\partial x^{n-1}\partial y} + \cdots + A_n\frac{\partial^n z}{\partial y^n} = 0, \quad (12)$$

where the A's are constants, may have a solution of the form

$$z = \varphi(y + mx). \quad (13)$$

Substituting z from (13) in (12), we obtain

$$\varphi^{(n)}(A_0 m^n + A_1 m^{n-1} + \cdots + A_n) = 0, \tag{14}$$

where $\varphi^{(n)}$ is the nth derivative of $\varphi(y + mx)$ with respect to $y + mx$. If $\varphi^{(n)}$ is deleted from equation (14), the result is called the *auxiliary equation*. If m is a root of (14), evidently (13) is a solution of (12). Hence, if $m_1, m_2, \ldots, m_n$ are n distinct roots of

$$F(m,1) = 0, \tag{15}$$

it appears that

$$z_1 = \varphi_1(y + m_1 x), \qquad z_2 = \varphi_2(y + m_2 x), \; \ldots \tag{16}$$

are solutions of (12) and therefore that

$$z = \varphi_1(y + m_1 x) + \varphi_2(y + m_2 x) + \cdots + \varphi_n(y + m_n x) \tag{17}$$

is the general solution of (12).

Similarly, by substituting $z = \varphi(x + ky)$ in (12), we get

$$\varphi^{(n)}(A_0 + A_1 k^1 + \cdots + A_{n-1} k^{n-1} + A_n k^n) = 0, \tag{18}$$

and, just as before, obtain the roots $k_1, k_2, \ldots, k_n$ and the corresponding solution

$$z = \psi_1(x + k_1 y) + \psi_2(x + k_2 y) + \cdots + \psi_n(x + k_n y). \tag{19}$$

The result of deleting $\varphi^{(n)}$ from (14) or (18) is referred to as an *auxiliary equation*.

The roots $k_1, k_2, \ldots$ of (18) are, as a whole, the reciprocals of the roots $m_1, m_2, \ldots$ of (14).* The arbitrary functions indicated by (17) or (19) may be used in a solution to correspond with non-zero roots of an auxiliary equation; but to a root $m = 0$ of (14) corresponds $\varphi(y)$, and to a root $k = 0$ of (18) corresponds $\psi(x)$, where φ and ψ represent arbitrary functions.

For example, to solve

$$\frac{\partial^2 z}{\partial x^2} + \frac{\partial^2 z}{\partial x \, \partial y} - 2 \frac{\partial^2 z}{\partial y^2} = 0, \tag{20}$$

write

$$m^2 + m - 2 = 0, \qquad \text{or} \qquad m = -2, 1,$$

and as the corresponding solution

$$z = \varphi_1(y - 2x) + \varphi_2(y + x);$$

* If a root m of (14) is zero, the corresponding root k of (18) does not exist; conversely, if a root k is zero, the corresponding root m does not exist.

or write
$$1 + k - 2k^2 = 0, \qquad k = -\tfrac{1}{2}, 1$$

and, as the corresponding solution,
$$z = \psi_1(x - \tfrac{1}{2}y) + \psi_2(x + y).$$

In solving the equation
$$(D^2D' + DD'^2 - 6D'^3)z = 0,$$

we get, as the roots of the auxiliary equation,
$$m_1 = 2, \; m_2 = -3, \qquad k_1 = \tfrac{1}{2}, k_2 = -\tfrac{1}{3}, k_3 = 0,$$

and write the solution in the form
$$z = \varphi_1(y + 2x) + \varphi_2(y - 3x) + \psi(x).$$

The first two functions could have been written in the form $\psi_1(x + \tfrac{1}{2}y)$ $+ \psi_2(x - \tfrac{1}{3}y)$, but the last had to be an arbitrary function of x.

100. Auxiliary equation has multiple roots

If a root of (15) is multiple, the sum of several of the arbitrary functions of (17) could be replaced by a single function, and the solution would involve a smaller number of arbitrary functions than n.   Suppose that m is a p-fold multiple root of (15).   The corresponding case of ordinary differential equations suggests that

$$z_p = \varphi_0(y + mx) + x\varphi_1(y + mx) + \cdots + x^{p-1}\varphi_{p-1}(y + mx) \quad (21)$$

may be a solution.   Substituting z from (21) in (12) and taking account of (9), we have

$$F(D,D')z_p = \psi(D,D')[(D - mD')^p \sum_{k=0}^{p-1} x^k \varphi_k(y + mx)]$$
$$= \psi(D,D')(0) = 0; \quad (22)$$

that is, (21) is the part of the general solution of (12) corresponding to a p-fold root of (15).

Similarly, if the auxiliary equation $F(1,k) = 0$ has a root k repeated p times, the corresponding part of the solution may be written

$$z_p = \psi_0(x + ky) + y\psi_1(x + ky) + \cdots + y^{p-1}\psi_{p-1}(x + ky). \quad (23)$$

For example, an auxiliary equation of $(D - aD') D'^3z = 0$ is

$$(1 - ak)k^3 = 0, \qquad \text{or} \qquad k = \frac{1}{a}, 0, 0, 0,$$

and the solution of $(D - aD') D'^3z = 0$ is

$$z = \psi_1\left(x + \frac{y}{a}\right) + \psi_2(x) + y\psi_3(x) + y^2\psi_4(x).$$

101. Auxiliary equation has imaginary roots

The part of a solution corresponding to a pair $a \pm ib$ ($i = \sqrt{-1}$) of imaginary roots is

$$\varphi[y + (a + ib)x] + \psi[y + (a - ib)x]. \tag{24}$$

This is generally not convenient to use. Therefore another form will be derived. Special cases of (24) are

$$a_n[e^{ny+n(a+ib)x} + e^{ny+n(a-ib)x}] = 2a_n e^{n(y+ax)} \cos nbx, \tag{25}$$

$$\frac{1}{i} b_n[e^{ny+n(a+ib)x} - e^{ny+n(a-ib)x}] = 2b_n e^{n(y+ax)} \sin nbx, \tag{26}$$

where a_n and b_n are arbitrary constants. The sum of the terms in (25) and (26) constitutes the solution

$$z_n = e^{n(y+ax)}(a_n \cos nbx + b_n \sin nbx). \tag{27}$$

Also the sum of solutions (27) for various values of n,

$$z = \sum^n e^{n(y+ax)}(a_n \cos nbx + b_n \sin nbx), \tag{28}$$

is a solution. Here n may take on all values in any finite set of numbers. Also n may take on the series of integers $1, 2, \ldots$, provided the corresponding infinite series has a suitable region of convergence.

In summary, the general solution of the homogeneous partial differential equation with constant coefficients $F(D,D')z = 0$ is written

$$z = z_d + z_m + z_c, \tag{29}$$

where z_d for distinct roots, z_m for multiple roots, and z_c for complex roots represent sums of expressions having the forms indicated in (16), (21), and (28), respectively.

By way of illustration, it appears that the auxiliary equation of $(D^5 - D^4D' + D^3D'^2 - D^2D'^3)z = 0$ has the roots $0, 0, 1, \pm i$. Hence the general solution is

$$z = \varphi_1(y) + x\varphi_2(y) + \varphi_3(y + x) + \sum^n e^{ny}(a_n \cos nx + b_n \sin nx).$$

EXERCISES

1. $D(D^2 - DD' - 2D'^2)z = 0$ **2.** $(D^4 + D'D^3)z = 0$

3. $D'^2(D - 2D')z = 0$ **4.** $D^2D'^2z = 0$

5. $(D^2 - 4DD' + 13D'^2)z = 0$ **6.** $(D^2 + a^2D'^2)z = 0$

7. $(D^2 - a^2D'^2)z = 0$ **8.** $(D^4 - a^4D'^4)z = 0$

9. $(D^3 - 8D'^3)z = 0$ **10.** $D^n z = 0$

11. Find the solution of $(D^2 - D'^2)z = 0$ for which $z = 6x^2$, and $\partial z/\partial y = 6x^2 + 6$ when $y = 0$. *Hint:* Show that $z = \varphi(x + y) + \psi(x - y)$, $z_{y=c} = \varphi(x) + \psi(x) = 6x^2$, $(\partial z/\partial x)_{y=0} = [\partial\varphi(x)/\partial x] + [\partial\psi(x)/\partial x] = 12x$.

12. Find the solution of $D(D^2 - 4D'^2)z = 0$ for which $z = 8y^2$, $\partial z/\partial x = 0$, $\partial^2 z/\partial x^2 = 16$ when $x = 0$.

102. Linear equation with constant coefficients

In this article, we shall deal with the general equation

$$F(D,D')z = \sum_{i=0,j=0}^{n,n} A_{ij}\frac{\partial^{i+j}z}{\partial x^i\,\partial y^j} = 0 \qquad (i + j \leq n), \tag{30}$$

where the A_{ij} are constants. To solve this, make the substitution

$$z = ce^{hx+ky} \tag{31}$$

and, since $D^iD'^ie^{hx+ky} = h^ik^ie^{hx+ky}$, obtain

$$F(h,k)ce^{hx+ky} = 0.$$

In order that (31) be a solution, $F(h,k)$ must vanish. Represent any linear factor of $F(h,k)$ by

$$h - mk - n. \tag{32}$$

$F(h,k)$ will vanish if any one of its factors vanishes, that is, if $h = mk + n$. Substitution of this value of h in (31) gives the solution

$$z = ce^{nx}e^{k(y+mx)}.$$

The numbers k and c are arbitrary, and, in accordance with (7), we can add together any number of terms like the right-hand member, to obtain

$$z = e^{nx}\sum^{k} c_k e^{k(y+mx)}, \tag{33}$$

where c_k is an arbitrary constant and the sum extends over any group of numbers for k. Equation (33) suggests that

$$z = e^{nx}\varphi(y + mx), \tag{34}$$

where φ represents an arbitrary function, may be a solution of (30). Since $F(D,D') = F_1(D,D')(D - mD' - n)$, we have

$$F_1(D,D')\{(D - mD' - n)[e^{nx}\varphi(y + mx)]\} = F_1(D,D')(0) = 0;$$

that is, (34) is a solution of (30).   Since there are n factors of the form (32), there will be n terms like (34), and the general solution will be

$$z = \sum_{j=1}^{n} e^{n_j x}\varphi_j(y + m_j x), \tag{35}$$

where $h - m_j k - n_j$, $j = 1, 2, \ldots, n$ are the factors of $F(h,k)$.

If $(h - mk - n)^p$ is a factor of $F(h,k)$, the corresponding part of the general solution may be shown, by using (11), to be

$$e^{nx}[\varphi_0(y + mx) + x\varphi_1(y + mx) + \cdots + x^{p-1}\varphi_{p-1}(y + mx)]. \tag{36}$$

For a factor of $F(h,k)$ having the form $k - Mh - N$, $F(h,k)$ would be zero when $k = Mh + N$; the corresponding solution would be

$$z = ce^{hx+(Mh+N)y} = ce^{Ny}e^{h(x+My)}, \tag{37}$$

and, just as before, we would derive the solution

$$z = e^{Ny}\psi(x + My) \tag{38}$$

and then find the general solution in the form

$$z = \sum_{j=1}^{n} e^{N_j y}\psi_j(x + M_j y). \tag{39}$$

If m_i or M_i for the factor of $F(h,k)$ is not zero, the corresponding term of the solution may be written in the form (34) or the form (38).   But, corresponding to a factor having the form $h - n$, the form $e^{nx}\varphi(y)$ must be used in the solution, and corresponding to a factor $k - N$, the form $e^{Ny}\psi(x)$ must be used.

Example 1.   Solve $(D + D' - 3)(D - 2)(D' + 4)z = 0$.

Solution.   In this case

$$F(h,k) = (h + k - 3)(h - 2)(k + 4) = 0.$$

In the first factor $m = -1, n = 3$, and the corresponding part of the solution, by (34), is $e^{3x}\varphi_1(y - x)$.   In the second factor $m = 0, n = 2$, and the corresponding part of the solution, by (34), is $e^{2x}\varphi_2(y)$.   In the third factor $M = 0, N = -4$, and the corresponding part of the solution, by (38), is $e^{-4y}\psi(x)$.   Hence the required solution is

$$\mathbf{z = e^{3x}\varphi_1(y - x) + e^{2x}\varphi_2(y) + e^{-4y}\psi(x).}$$

Example 2. Solve $(D + D' + 2)^2(D - D')z = 0$.

Solution. In this case

$$F(h,k) = (h + k + 2)^2(h - k) = 0.$$

For the first factor $m = -1$, $n = -2$, and since the factor is repeated, the corresponding part of the solution is

$$e^{-2x}[\varphi_1(y - x) + x\varphi_2(y - x)].$$

Corresponding to the second factor we have $e^{0x}\varphi_3(y + x)$, and the required solution is

$$\mathbf{z = e^{-2x}[\varphi_1(y - x) + x\varphi_2(y - x)] + \varphi_3 (y + x)}.$$

103. $F(h,k)$ cannot be reduced to a product of linear factors

When $F(h,k)$ for an equation of type (30) is not reducible to factors linear in h and k, the solution can be expressed as sums of powers of e. For example, consider

$$(D^3 - D')(D + D'^2 + 1)z = 0. \tag{40}$$

Substitute ce^{hx+ky} for z in this to obtain

$$c(h^3 - k)(h + k^2 + 1)e^{hx+ky} = 0.$$

It now appears that ce^{hx+ky} will be a solution of (40) if $k = h^3$ or if $h = -k^2 - 1$. Also a sum of such terms will satisfy (40). Accordingly, a solution may be written

$$z = \sum^h c_h e^{hx+h^3y} + \sum^k c_k e^{-(k^2+1)x+ky},$$

where c_h and c_k represent arbitrary constants and h and k may assume the values in any sequence of numbers. This solution represents a general process to be used when convenient. The next section presents another procedure which is often effective.

EXERCISES

1. By using (11) prove that the expression (36), when substituted for z in $F(D,D')z = 0$, will satisfy it provided that $(h - mk - n)^p$ is a factor of $F(h,k)$.

Solve the following equations:

2. $(D + D' + 3)(D - D')z = 0$ **3.** $(D + 2)(D - D' - 3)z = 0$

4. $(2D + 3D' - 3)(D' + 4)z = 0$ **5.** $(D + D' + 1)^3z = 0$

6. $D(D' + 2D - 3)^2z = 0$ **7.** $(D' + D + 1)(D' - 4)z = 0$

8. $(D' - 4)(D' + 4)z = 0$ **9.** $(D + a)(D'^2 - a^2)z = 0$

10. $(D^3 + D')z = 0$ **11.** $(D^3 + D')(D + D'^2)z = 0$

12. $(D^2 - DD' + D' - 1)z = 0$.   **13.** $(DD' + aD + bD' + ab)z = 0$

14. $(D'^2 + DD' + D - 1)z = 0$ **15.** $(D'^2 - 3DD' + 2D^2 + D' - D)z = 0$

16. Show that the solution of $(D^2 + D'^2 + 1)z = 0$ may be written in the form

$$z = \sum^k e^{ky}(A_k \cos \sqrt{k^2 + 1}\, x + B_k \sin \sqrt{k^2 + 1}\, x).$$

17. Prove that a solution of $[(D + aD' + m)^2 + b^2D'^2]z = 0$ may be written in the form

$$z = e^{-mx} \sum^k (A_k \sin bkx + B_k \cos bkx)e^{k(y-ax)}.$$

18. $[(D + aD' + m)^2 + n^2]z = 0$
19. $(D^2 + 2DD' + D'^2 + 4D + 4D' + 4)z = 0$
20. $(D^2 + 2DD' + D'^2 + 1)z = 0$
21. $(D^3 - 8D'^2)z = 0$

104. Separation of variables

A process often used in the investigations of physical science is called separation of variables. An illustration will exhibit the process, will show the nature of answers obtained, and will indicate the reason for the name.

Example. Solve

$$(D^2 + 4D'^2)z = 0. \tag{a}$$

Solution. Assume a solution having the form

$$z = XY, \tag{b}$$

where X is a function of x only and Y a function of y only. Using dots to denote derivatives, we have

$$\frac{dX}{dx} = \dot{X}, \qquad \frac{d^2X}{dx^2} = \ddot{X}, \qquad \frac{dY}{dy} = \dot{Y}, \text{ etc.} \tag{c}$$

Substituting z from (b) in (a), obtain

$$\ddot{X}Y + 4\ddot{Y}X = 0. \tag{d}$$

Dividing this by XY, obtain

$$\frac{\ddot{X}}{X} + \frac{4\ddot{Y}}{Y} = 0. \tag{e}$$

If k represents any constant, this will be satisfied provided that

$$\frac{\ddot{X}}{X} = k, \qquad \frac{4\ddot{Y}}{Y} = -k. \tag{f}$$

The solutions of this for k positive are

$$X = a_1 e^{\sqrt{k}x} + a_2 e^{-\sqrt{k}x}, \qquad Y = a_3 \sin \left(\tfrac{1}{2}\sqrt{k}\, y\right) + a_4 \cos \left(\tfrac{1}{2}\sqrt{k}\, y\right). \tag{g}$$

Now z defined by (b) and (g) satisfies (a) for k any value. Hence, in accordance with the principle of adding solutions of linear equations, we may write as a solution of (a)

$$z = \sum^k X_k Y_k = \sum^k \{e^{\sqrt{k}x}[a_k \sin\,(\tfrac{1}{2}\sqrt{k}\,y) + b_k \cos\,(\tfrac{1}{2}\sqrt{k}\,y)]$$

$$+\, e^{-\sqrt{k}x}[c_k \sin\,(\tfrac{1}{2}\sqrt{k}\,y) + d_k \cos\,(\tfrac{1}{2}\sqrt{k}\,y)]\}, \quad (h)$$

where k may take in succession the values in any finite set of positive numbers. If k takes the values 1, 2, 3, . . . , then equation (h), an infinite series, is a valid solution within its region of convergence.

If k is negative, the sine-cosine part of the solution would go with X and the power part with Y. If $k = 0$, we would have

$$X = c_1 x + c_2, \qquad Y = c_3 y + c_4. \tag{i}$$

Thus it appears that the solution is made up of three types. For any application, appropriate types are used.

EXERCISES

Use the method of *separation of variables* to find the various types of solutions of equations 1 to 4:

1. $(D^2 + D'^2)z = 0$ **2.** $(D^2 - D')z = 0$
3. $(D + D')z = 0$ **4.** $(D + D' - 3)z = 0$

5. Solve $(D^2 + D'^2 + 1)z = 0$ assuming that $\ddot{X}/X = k - 1$, where $k > 1$. What values of k will involve other types of solutions?

6. If, in solving $(D^2 + D'^2 + D + 2D')z = 0$, we use $\ddot{X}/X + \dot{X}/X = k$, state the ranges of k associated with oscillation of (a) the x-factor; (b) the y-factor; (c) neither factor.

★**7.** For Laplace's equation* $(\partial^2 u/\partial x^2) + (\partial^2 u/\partial y^2) + (\partial^2 u/\partial^2 z) = 0$, assume that $u = XYZ$ and obtain $\ddot{X}/X + \ddot{Y}/Y + \ddot{Z}/Z = 0$. This will be satisfied if

$$\frac{\ddot{X}}{X} = l, \qquad \frac{\ddot{Y}}{Y} = m, \qquad \frac{\ddot{Z}}{Z} = n, \qquad l + m + n = 0.$$

Find a solution, assuming that $l > 0$, $m > 0$, $n = -l - m$. How many different types of solutions, each associated with a set of values for l, m, and n, exist?

★**8.** Laplace's equation for two dimensions and polar coordinates is

$$\frac{\partial^2 u}{\partial \rho^2} + \frac{1}{\rho}\frac{\partial u}{\partial \rho} + \frac{1}{\rho^2}\frac{\partial^2 u}{\partial \theta^2} = 0.$$

---

* This equation, called Laplace's equation, is of basic importance because it must hold for a flow of substance, such as heat, air, or water, if the quantity entering a region is equal to the quantity leaving (see §112). Exercise 1 relates to Laplace's equation for two dimensions.

Show that one solution has the form (h), of the illustrative example, with x replaced by θ and y by $\log \rho$.*

9. To solve $(D^2 + DD' + D'^2)z = 0$, let $z = XY$ and obtain

$$\frac{\ddot{X}}{X} + \frac{\dot{X}}{X}\frac{\dot{Y}}{Y} + \frac{\ddot{Y}}{Y} = 0.$$

Let $\dot{X}/X = k$ and solve for X; show that $\ddot{X}/X = k^2$; then solve for Y and write a solution of the given equation.

10. Laplace's equation for cylindrical coordinates in space is

$$\frac{\partial^2 u}{\partial \rho^2} + \frac{1}{\rho}\frac{\partial u}{\partial \rho} + \frac{1}{\rho^2}\frac{\partial^2 u}{\partial \theta^2} + \frac{\partial^2 u}{\partial z^2} = 0.$$

Show that a solution is $u = R\Theta Z$, where

$$\frac{\ddot{Z}}{Z} = k_1, \qquad \frac{\ddot{\Theta}}{\Theta} = k_2, \qquad \rho^2\ddot{R} + \rho R + (k_2 + k_1\rho^2)R = 0.$$

105. Right-hand member not zero

Consider the linear partial differential equation

$$F(D,D')z = f(x,y), \tag{41}$$

where the coefficients of the derivatives and z are constants. The solution of (41), $z = z_c + z_p$, consists of two parts: z_c, the integral of $F(D,D')z = 0$, and z_p, any particular integral of (41). In this section a few methods of finding a particular integral are suggested by examples. The following formulas, easily derived by modifying the arguments of §§38, 39, and 47, will be used. If $f(x,y)$ is a rational fraction and $P(x,y)$ a polynomial,

$$f(D,D')e^{hx+ky} = f(h,k)e^{hx+ky}, \tag{42}$$

$$f(D^2,DD',D'^2)\sin(hx + ky) = f(-h^2,-hk,-k^2)\sin(hx + ky),\dagger \tag{43}$$

$$e^{hx+ky}f(D,D')z = f(D - h, D' - k)ze^{hx+ky}, \tag{44}$$

$(aD + bD' + c)^{-1}P$

$$= \frac{1 - [bD'/(aD + c)]^1 + [bD'/(aD + c)]^2 + \cdots}{aD + c}P, \tag{45}$$

$$(aD^2 + bDD' + cD'^2)^{-1}P = \left[1 - \left(\frac{b}{a}\frac{D'}{D} + \frac{c}{a}\frac{D'^2}{D^2}\right)^1 + \cdots\right]\frac{1}{aD^2}P. \tag{46}$$

---

* The method of §65 is involved.

† In (43) sin may be replaced by cos.

Example 1.   Find a particular solution of $(D^2 - D'^2 + D - D')z = x - 2y$.

Solution.   The given equation can be written

$$(D + D' + 1)(D - D')z = (D + D' + 1)u = x - 2y, \qquad (a)$$

where $u = (D - D')z$.   Applying the method of §93 to solve equation (a), while taking zero as constant of integration, obtain

$$u = x - 2y + 1. \qquad (b)$$

Since $u = (D - D')z$, we have

$$(D - D')z = x - 2y + 1. \qquad (c)$$

Again applying the method of §93, we obtain from (c)

$$\mathbf{z = \tfrac{1}{2}y^2 - xy - y.} \qquad (d)$$

Example 2.   Find a particular solution of

$$(D^2 + DD' + 2D'^2)z = x^2y.$$

Solution.   Using (46) on the given equation, obtain

$$z = \left[1 - \left(\frac{D'}{D} + \frac{2D'^2}{D^2}\right)^1 + \cdots\right]\frac{x^2y}{D^2} = \frac{1}{12}x^4y - \frac{1}{60}x^5.$$

Example 3.   Find a particular solution of

$$(D^2 + D')z = \sin (2x + y)e^{x-y}. \qquad (a)$$

Solution.   Multiplying through by e^{-x+y} and using (44), obtain

$$[(D + 1)^2 + (D' - 1)]ze^{-x+y} = (D^2 + 2D + D')ze^{-x+y}$$
$$= \sin (2x + y). \quad (b)$$

Now let

$$ze^{-x+y} = A \sin (2x + y) + B \cos (2x + y) \qquad (c)$$

in (b), equate coefficients of $\sin (2x + y)$ and $\cos (2x + y)$ of the two members, and solve the resulting equations to get $A = -\tfrac{4}{41}$, $B = -\tfrac{5}{41}$.   Substituting these values in (c) and solving for z, obtain

$$\mathbf{z = -\tfrac{1}{41}[4 \sin (2x + y) + 5 \cos (2x + y)]e^{x-y}.} \qquad (d)$$

EXERCISES

Find particular solutions of the differential equations:

1. $(D^2 + D - 3D')z = 3e^{2x+3y}$.   Use (42).

2. $(2D^2 + DD' - D'^2)z = x + 2y$.   Use the method of Example 1.

3. $(2D^2 + DD' - D'^2)z = x + 2y.$ Use (46).
4. $(D + D')z = 6x + 2y.$ Use (45).
5. $(D^2 + D'^2)z = 40x^3y^2.$ Use (46).
6. $(D^2 + D'^2)z = \sin (2x - y) - 2 \cos (2x - y).$ Use (43).
7. $[(D - 2)^2 + (D' + 3)^2]z = 10e^{2x-3y} \cos (x + 3y).$ Use (44) and then (43).
8. $(D + D' - 2)z = 4xy.$ Solve by the method of §93 and also by using (45).
Note that $[1/(D - 2)]xy = -\frac{1}{2}(1 + \frac{1}{2}D)xy.$

9. $(D^2 + D')z = 120xy$ **10.** $(D^2 - D')z = 6xye^{x+y}$
11. $(D + D')(D + 4)z = 24xy$ **12.** $(D - D')(D - D' - 2)z = 4xe^{-2y}$

13. $D'(D - D')^2z = \dfrac{1}{x^2}$ **14.** $(D^2 + DD' + D'^2)z = 6x^2$

15. $(D^2 + 3DD' - D'^2)z = 2x + 6y$ **16.** $(D^2 + DD' - D'^2)z = 60x^2y$
17. $(D^2 + D'^2)z = 210x^4y^3$ **18.** $(D + D')^2z = 2e^{x-y}$
★19. $(D - 4D')^2z = e^{4x-y} \cos (4x - y)$ **20.** $(D^2 - 2D'^2)z = 143x^{10}y^2$

21. $(D^2 - 4D'^2 + 2D + 1)z = xy + 24e^{x-2y}.$

106. Special types of second-order equations*

In §92 partial differential equations that could be integrated by the methods of ordinary differential equations were considered. In the process only two quantities were considered as variables for a particular integration, and the constant of integration generally took the form of an arbitrary function of the variable treated as constant. In this article, the same method and also the method of Lagrange discussed in §93 will be used. The notation of equations (1) in §90 will be employed.

Evidently equations of the types

$$r = \varphi(x,y), \qquad s = \psi(x,y), \qquad t = \chi(x,y) \tag{47}$$

may be solved by two successive integrations. The student may review the process by solving the equation

$$s = \frac{\partial^2 z}{\partial x \, \partial y} = 12x^2 + y^{-\frac{1}{2}},$$

to get as a solution

$$z = 4x^3y + 2xy^{\frac{1}{2}} + \varphi(y) + \psi(x).$$

Methods of ordinary differential equations apply to solve equations having one of the forms

$$Rr + Pp + Zz = V, \qquad Tt + Qq + Zz = V, \tag{48}$$

* J. B. Scarborough, in his "Numerical Mathematical Analysis" (2d. ed., pp. 309–350, 1950), considers three methods of approximating solutions of partial differential equations.

where the capital letters represent functions of x and y. For example, to solve

$$t + 2q - 3z = 9x^2y, \tag{49}$$

write

$$\frac{\partial^2 z}{\partial y^2} - 2\frac{\partial z}{\partial y} - 3z = 9x^2y,$$

and, treating x as a constant and using functions of x as constants of integration, solve the equation as though it were an ordinary differential equation in z and y. The solution is

$$z = \varphi(x)e^{3y} + \psi(x)e^{-y} - 3x^2y + 2x^2. \tag{50}$$

Finally, consider the types of equations represented by

$$R_1r + S_1s = V_1, \qquad S_2s + T_2t = V_2, \tag{51}$$

where R_1, S_1, and V_1 are functions of x, y, and p, and S_2, T_2, and V_2 are functions of x, y, and q. To solve the first equation of (51), write it in the form

$$R_1\frac{\partial p}{\partial x} + S_1\frac{\partial p}{\partial y} = V_1 \tag{52}$$

and, using the method of Lagrange in §93, solve (52) for p in terms of x and y; then replace p by $\partial z/\partial x$ and complete the solution for z by an integration in which y is considered as constant. The following example will illustrate the method.

Example. Solve

$$2xr - ys + 2x + 2p = 0. \tag{a}$$

Solution. Equation (a) may be written

$$2x\frac{\partial p}{\partial x} - y\frac{\partial p}{\partial y} = -2x - 2p. \tag{b}$$

Then, applying Lagrange's method, write

$$\frac{dx}{2x} = \frac{dy}{-y} = \frac{dp}{-2x - 2p}; \tag{c}$$

find the integral $xy^2 = c_1$ from the first two ratios and $2px + x^2 = c_2$ from the first and third ratios; then derive from these integrals

$$p = -\frac{1}{2}x + \frac{1}{2x}c_2 = -\frac{1}{2}x + \frac{1}{2x}\varphi(xy^2). \tag{d}$$

Now observing that

$$\int \frac{1}{x}\varphi(xy^2)\,dx \text{ } (y,\text{ constant}) = \int \frac{1}{xy^2}\varphi(xy^2)y^2\,dx = \varphi_1(xy^2), \tag{e}$$

replace p in (d) by $\partial z/\partial x$ and, treating y as constant, derive

$$z = -\tfrac{1}{4}x^2 + \varphi_1(xy^2) + \psi(y).$$

EXERCISES

Solve the following partial differential equations:

1. (a) $t = 12xy$ (b) $s = 6xe^{-3y}$

2. (a) $r + p - 6z = 0$ (b) $t + q - 2z = 0$

    (c) $t + 4z = x^2$ (d) $r - yp - 2y^2z = 2xy^2$

3. (a) $xr - ys = 2y$ (b) $xr + ys = 0$

    (c) $xs - yt = 2x$ (d) $s = 6x + p$

    (e) $xs - yt + q = 12xy$ (f) $xs - 2x^2t = q$

4. (a) $pr = xy^2$ (b) $r - ys = 0$

    (c) $xr + 2ys = p + x$ (d) $2r + 3p - 5z = 25xy$

    (e) $xs - 2yt = 2q + x$ (f) $t - 2q = 3x^2$

    (g) $r + ys = p$ (h) $xr + s + p = 0$

    (i) $x^2r + xp + z = xy$ (j) $qs - pt = 0$

Hint to (i): Let $w = \log x$. Then $\dfrac{\partial z}{\partial x} = \dfrac{\partial z}{\partial w}\dfrac{\partial w}{\partial x} = \dfrac{\partial z}{\partial w}\dfrac{1}{x}$.

Hint to (j): Consider $\dfrac{\partial}{\partial y}\dfrac{p}{q}$.

107. Equation $Rr + Ss + Tt = V$

Gaspard Monge applied the method of this article to solve the equation

$$Rr + Ss + Tt = V, \tag{53}$$

where R, S, T, and V represent functions of p, q, x, y, and z, and r, s, and t have the usual meanings.

Since z, p, and q are functions of x and y, we have

$$dz = p\,dx + q\,dy, \tag{54}$$

$$dp = r\,dx + s\,dy, \tag{55}$$

$$dq = s\,dx + t\,dy. \tag{56}$$

Solving (55) and (56) for r and t, respectively, substituting the results in (53), and collecting the terms containing s in the left-hand member and the others in the right, we find

$$s\left(R\frac{dy}{dx} - S + T\frac{dx}{dy}\right) = R\frac{dp}{dx} + T\frac{dq}{dy} - V. \tag{57}$$

Evidently this equation will be satisfied if each member vanishes, that is, if

$$R\,dy^2 - S\,dx\,dy + T\,dx^2 = 0, \tag{58}$$

$$R\,dp\,dy + T\,dq\,dx - V\,dx\,dy = 0. \tag{59}$$

The equations (54), (58), and (59) are three total differential equations in five unknowns; ordinarily four equations are required for a determinate system. Hence integrals of (54), (58), and (59) can be found only when certain conditions are satisfied.

To solve an equation of type (53), form the corresponding equations (58) and (59); solve the first for dy/dx to obtain

$$\frac{dy}{dx} = \alpha, \qquad \frac{dy}{dx} = \beta; \tag{60}$$

use one of these equations with the corresponding (59), and sometimes (54), to obtain an equation

$$\varphi(x,y,p,q) = 0; \tag{61}$$

and then solve this equation to obtain a solution. When relation (61) is linear in p and q, Lagrange's method, considered in §93, may be used.

Another method is considered in exercise 8 below. Also other methods may be employed.*

Example. Solve

$$r - 2xs + x^2 t = q + 6x. \tag{a}$$

Solution. Equations (58) and (59) give in this case

$$dy^2 + 2x\, dx\, dy + x^2\, dx^2 = 0, \tag{b}$$

$$dp\, dy + x^2\, dq\, dx - (q + 6x)\, dx\, dy = 0. \tag{c}$$

One factor of (b) is $dy + x\, dx$. Hence

$$dy = -x\, dx, \qquad \text{or} \qquad 2y + x^2 = c, \tag{d}$$

Divide (c) by dy and use (d) to obtain

$$dp - (x\, dq + q\, dx) - 6x\, dx = 0,$$

or

$$p - qx = 3x^2 + \varphi(2y + x^2). \tag{e}$$

Note that, because of (d), the constant of integration could be taken in the form $\varphi(2y + x^2)$. Now, applying Lagrange's method of §93 to (e), write

$$\frac{dx}{1} = \frac{dy}{-x} = \frac{dz}{\varphi(2y + x^2) + 3x^2}. \tag{f}$$

From the first two fractions (f) deduce

$$2y + x^2 = c. \tag{g}$$

* See, for example, "Partial Differential Equations" by Frederic H. Miller, pp. 182–194.

Using (g) and the first and third ratios of (f), write

$$dz = [\varphi(c) + 3x^2]\, dx. \qquad (h)$$

Hence,

$$\mathbf{z} = \varphi(\mathbf{c})\mathbf{x} + \mathbf{x}^3 + \mathbf{c_1} = \mathbf{x}\varphi(2\mathbf{y} + \mathbf{x}^2) + \mathbf{x}^3 + \psi(2\mathbf{y} + \mathbf{x}^2). \qquad (i)$$

Remarks. Most problems in the exercises below can be solved by the method of the example using the equation from only one of the factors of (58). Observe that, in finding an integral from (59), *we may use (a) an equation $dy/dx = \alpha$ from* (58), *(b) the result of integrating $dy/dx = \alpha$, and (c) $dz = p\, dx + q\, dy$.* Thus if (58) and (59) for a special case are

$$dy^2 + 2y\, dy\, dx = 0, \qquad (62)$$

$$dp\, dy - (2p + ye^{2x})\, dy\, dx = \mathbf{0}, \qquad (63)$$

we obtain from (62)

$$dy + 2y\, dx = 0, \qquad ye^{2x} = c_1, \qquad (64)$$

and from (63) and (64)

$$-2y\, dp - 2p\, dy - ye^{2x}\, dy = -2\, d(yp) - c_1\, dy = \mathbf{0}. \qquad (65)$$

The integral obtained from (65) and (64) is

$$2py + c_1y = 2py + y^2e^{2x} = \varphi(ye^{2x}). \qquad (66)$$

Observe, however, that, in the integration of (66) by the method of §93 or other means, no use of (64) may be made.

Note that an arbitrary function may be chosen in a form suitable to our purpose. Thus we may write

$$\textstyle\int[2x + x^{-3}\varphi(cx^2)]\, dx = \int[2x + x^{-3}2c^2x^4\psi'(cx^2)]\, dx = x^2 + c\psi(cx^2),$$

where $\psi(cx^2) = 2c^2x^4\psi'(cx^2) = 2c^2x^4\, d\psi(cx^2)/d(cx^2)$ and ψ is an arbitrary function because φ is arbitrary.

EXERCISES

1. Solve $xr + 2xs + xt = p + q$. Follow the general plan used in the solution of Example 1.

2. $x^2r + 2xys + y^2t = 0$
3. $(y + 1)r - (y^2 - 1)s - y(y + 1)t = p + q$
4. $x(r - 2s + t) = p - q$
5. $x(x + y)r + (x^2 - y^2)s - (x + y)yt = (x - y)(p + q)$
6. $(x^2 - xy)r + (y^2 - x^2)s + (xy - y^2)t = (x + y)(p - q)$
7. $x^2r - y^2t = qy - px$

★**8.** To solve $r + ys - 2y^2t = 2yq$, use each factor of the corresponding (58) with (59) to find two integral relations. Solve these for p and q, substitute the results in (54), and integrate the resulting exact equation.

9. $r - 2ys = 2p + 4ye^{2x}$ **10.** $2xs - t = 2x(1 + 2xe^{2y})$

11. $q^2r - 2pqs + p^2t = pq^2z$.   *Hint:* $z = c$ is a solution of $p\,dx + q\,dy = 0$.
12. $q^2r - 2pqs + p^2t = 0$.   Read the hint to exercise 11.
13. $x^2r - xys + yq = 0$.   *Hint:* To get an integral from $-x\,dp + q\,dy = 0$, add to it the zero value $dz - p\,dx - q\,dy$ to obtain $-d(xp) + dz = 0$.

14. $y^2r - 2ys + t = 6y + p$ **15.** $ps - qr = 0$
16. *$r - 3sy + 2y^2t + 2qy = 0$ **17.** $r - y^2t - qy = 0$

18. $x^2r - 3xys + 2y^2t + xp + 2yq = 0$

* The method suggested in exercise 8 works well on exercises 16 to 18.

CHAPTER XIV

APPLICATIONS OF PARTIAL DIFFERENTIAL EQUATIONS

108. Fourier series

Because Fourier series play a very important role in many applications of partial differential equations, a brief discussion of them will be given.

A series having the form

$$a_0 + a_1 \cos x + a_2 \cos 2x + \cdots + a_n \cos nx + \cdots$$
$$+ b_1 \sin x + b_2 \sin 2x + \cdots + b_n \sin nx + \cdots \qquad (1)$$

is called a *Fourier series*. If there is a Fourier series that represents $f(x)$ in the interval $-\pi < x < \pi$ and if the term-by-term integration of this series used in the following development is permissible, then the values of the coefficients a_i and b_i are easily determined. Formulas for finding these constants will now be derived.

By direct evaluation of integrals, we get

$$\int_{-\pi}^{\pi} \sin mx \, dx = 0, \qquad \int_{-\pi}^{\pi} \cos mx \, dx = 0,$$
$$\int_{-\pi}^{\pi} \sin mx \cos nx \, dx = 0 \qquad (m \neq n), \qquad (2)$$

$$\int_{-\pi}^{\pi} \sin^2 mx \, dx = \int_{-\pi}^{\pi} \cos^2 mx \, dx = \pi, \qquad (3)$$

where m and n represent integers. Writing $f(x)$ equal to the series (1) obtain

$$f(x) = a_0 + a_1 \cos x + a_2 \cos 2x + \cdots$$
$$+ b_1 \sin x + b_2 \sin 2x + \cdots. \qquad (4)$$

Multiplying (4) through by dx, equating the definite integrals of the two members for the limits $-\pi$ and π, and taking account of (2) and (3), we get

$$\int_{-\pi}^{\pi} f(x) \, dx = 2\pi a_0, \qquad \text{or} \qquad a_0 = \frac{1}{2\pi} \int_{-\pi}^{\pi} f(x) \, dx. \qquad (5)$$

Next multiply both members of (4) by cos $mx\, dx$, equate the definite integrals of the two members for the limits $-\pi$ and π, and take account of (2) and (3) to obtain

$$\int_{-\pi}^{\pi} f(x)\, \cos\, mx\, dx = \int_{-\pi}^{\pi} a_m \cos^2 mx\, dx = \pi a_m,$$

or

$$a_m = \frac{1}{\pi} \int_{-\pi}^{\pi} f(x)\, \cos\, mx\, dx. \tag{6}$$

Similarly, by using (4) multiplied through by sin $mx\, dx$, obtain

$$b_m = \frac{1}{\pi} \int_{-\pi}^{\pi} f(x)\, \sin\, mx\, dx. \tag{7}$$

It has been proved* that, if $f(x)$ is single-valued and finite in the interval $-\pi < x < \pi$ and has only a finite number of discontinuities and of maxima and minima in this interval, then the Fourier series resulting from (4) by substituting in it from (5), (6), and (7)

$$\mathbf{a_0} = \frac{1}{2\pi} \int_{-\pi}^{\pi} \mathbf{f}(\alpha)\, \mathbf{d}\alpha, \qquad \mathbf{a_m} = \frac{1}{\pi} \int_{-\pi}^{\pi} \mathbf{f}(\alpha)\, \cos\, \mathbf{m}\alpha\, \mathbf{d}\alpha,$$

$$\mathbf{b_m} = \frac{1}{\pi} \int_{-\pi}^{\pi} \mathbf{f}(\alpha)\, \sin\, \mathbf{m}\alpha\, \mathbf{d}\alpha \qquad \mathbf{m} = \mathbf{1, 2, \ldots} \tag{8}$$

is equal to $f(x)$ for all values of x in the interval $-\pi < x < \pi$, excepting at points of discontinuity. At a point of discontinuity where $x = a$, the value of the series is

$$\tfrac{1}{2} \lim_{\epsilon \to 0} [f(a - \epsilon) + f(a + \epsilon)]. \tag{9}$$

When $x = -\pi$ and when $x = \pi$, the value of the series for $f(x)$ is

$$\tfrac{1}{2}[f(-\pi) + f(\pi)]. \tag{10}$$

Both sin mx and cos mx have the period 2π, since sin $m(x + 2k\pi) =$ sin mx and cos $m(x + 2k\pi) = $ cos mx, where m and k are integers. Hence the values assumed by series (1) in the interval $-\pi < x < \pi$ are assumed by it in any other interval $(2k - 1)\pi < x < (2k + 1)\pi$. Figure 1 indicates this situation by showing the graph of a function from $-\pi$ to π and repetitions of it.

* Expansion in Fourier series is explained in books on advanced calculus. Also consult:

BYERLY, W. E., "Fourier's Series and Spherical Harmonics."

CARSLAW, H. S., "Introduction to the Theory of Fourier's Series and Integrals."

The Fourier series representing ∫f(x) dx may be obtained by integrating, term by term, the Fourier series for f(x); but only under certain conditions* will the Fourier series for df(x)/dx be obtained by differentiating the Fourier series for f(x), term by term.

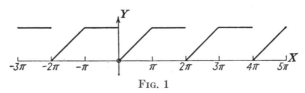

Fig. 1

Example.   Find a Fourier series equal to π for values of x between $-\pi$ and 0 and equal to x for values of x between 0 and π.

Solution.   Figure 1 represents the function.   Using formulas (8), we get

$$a_0 = \frac{1}{2\pi} \int_{-\pi}^{0} \pi \, dx + \frac{1}{2\pi} \int_{0}^{\pi} x \, dx = \frac{\pi}{2} + \frac{\pi^2}{4\pi} = \frac{3\pi}{4},$$

$$a_m = \frac{1}{\pi} \int_{-\pi}^{0} \pi \cos mx \, dx + \frac{1}{\pi} \int_{0}^{\pi} x \cos mx \, dx,$$

$$a_m = \frac{-2}{\pi m^2} \ (m, \text{ odd}), \qquad a_m = 0 \ (m, \text{ even}),$$

$$b_m = \frac{1}{\pi} \int_{-\pi}^{0} \pi \sin mx \, dx + \frac{1}{\pi} \int_{0}^{\pi} x \sin mx \, dx = \frac{-1}{m}.$$

Substituting these values in (4), we obtain

$$\mathbf{f(x)} = \frac{3\pi}{4} - \frac{2}{\pi} \left(\frac{\cos x}{1^2} + \frac{\cos 3x}{3^2} + \frac{\cos 5x}{5^2} + \cdots \right)$$
$$- \left(\sin x + \frac{\sin 2x}{2} + \frac{\sin 3x}{3} + \cdots \right) \quad \textbf{(11)}$$

A few observations may be of interest.

---

* From a theorem of calculus relating to the differentiation of series term by term, it follows that, if a series of the form (1) converges to $f(x)$ in the interval $a \leqq x \leqq b$ and if the series of derivatives obtained from (1)

$$\sum_{n=1}^{\infty} na_n \sin nx + \sum_{n=1}^{\infty} nb_n \cos nx$$

is uniformly convergent in $a \leqq x \leqq b$, then the series of derivatives converges to $f'(x)$.

When $x = 0$, the series (11), in accordance with (9), will take the value $\pi/2$. Hence,

$$\frac{\pi}{2} = \frac{3\pi}{4} - \frac{2}{\pi}\left(\frac{1}{1^2} + \frac{1}{3^2} + \frac{1}{5^2} + \cdots\right),$$

or

$$\frac{1}{1^2} + \frac{1}{3^2} + \frac{1}{5^2} + \cdots = \frac{\pi^2}{8}.$$

The term-by-term integral with limits $-\pi$ and x of the series (11) represents the area under the graph of $f(x)$, that is, $\pi(\pi + x)$ when $-\pi < x \leqq 0$ and $\pi^2 + \frac{1}{2}x^2$ when $0 < x \leqq \pi$.

EXERCISES

1. Assuming that a series of type (1) exists for the expansion of $f(x)$ and that term-by-term integration is permissible, derive formulas (8).

2. Expand $f(x) = x$ in a Fourier series by using (4) and (8). Replace x by $\pi/2$ in the result to show that $1 - \frac{1}{3} + \frac{1}{5} - \frac{1}{7} + \cdots = \pi/4$.

3. Find a Fourier series which will be equal to zero in the interval $-\pi < x < 0$, and equal to 1 in the interval $0 < x < \pi$. In the result let $x = \pi/2$ to check the sum of the series in exercise 2. Also check that the series has the sum zero when $x = -\pi/2$.

4. Find a Fourier series for $f(x)$ where $f(x) = \frac{1}{2}$ when $-\pi < x < 0$, and $f(x) = x/\pi$ when $0 < x < \pi$.

109. Cosine series.   Sine series

If a function $f(x)$ is even, that is, if $f(x) = f(-x)$, then b_m from (8) will be zero, since, in one kind of defining sum, each element

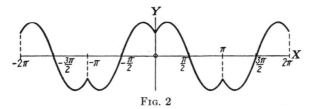

FIG. 2

$\sin mx_i f(x_i)\, \Delta x_i$ will cancel an element $\sin(-mx_i)f(-x_i)\, \Delta x_i = -\sin(mx_i)f(x_i)\, \Delta x_i$. Moreover a_n will be equal to twice the value of $(1/\pi)\int_0^\pi f(x)\cos mx\, dx$. Hence, an even function may be expanded by using (4) with

$$a_0 = \frac{1}{\pi}\int_0^\pi f(x)\, dx, \qquad a_m = \frac{2}{\pi}\int_0^\pi f(x)\cos mx\, dx, \qquad b_m = 0. \quad (12)$$

Figure 2 shows a function represented by a Fourier expansion from $-\pi$ to π by means of (4) and (12). Note that the graph is symmetrical to the Y-axis.

It also appears that any function $f(x)$ can generally be expanded by using (4) and (12); for expansion of a function $\varphi(x)$, where $\varphi(x) = f(x)$ in $0 < x < \pi$ and $\varphi(x) = f(|x|)$ in $-\pi < x < 0$, by means of (4) and (8) will give the same result as expansion by means of (4) and (12).

Similarly, if $f(x)$ is an odd function, that is, if $f(-x) = -f(x)$, it may be expanded by (4) with

$$\mathbf{a_0 = 0}, \qquad \mathbf{a_m = 0}, \qquad \mathbf{b_m = \frac{2}{\pi} \int_0^\pi f(x) \sin mx \, dx}. \qquad (13)$$

Figure 3 indicates the type of function represented by a Fourier sine series. Note that it is symmetrical with respect to the origin. In

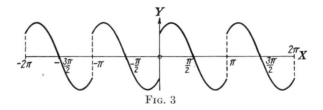

Fig. 3

general, formula (13) may be used to expand a function in the interval $0 < x < \pi$. Each of the expansions using (8), (12), and (13) will represent $f(x)$ between 0 and π but will generally represent different functions outside this interval.

A Fourier series representing $f(x)$ in the interval between $-c$ and c can be obtained by replacing x in $f(x)$ by cz/π,

$$x = \frac{cz}{\pi}, \qquad (14)$$

expanding $f(cz/\pi)$ by using (4) and (8), and then replacing z by $\pi x/c$ in the result. The substitution (14) may be employed in connection with (12) and (13) to obtain an expansion relating to the interval $0 < x < c$.

Example 1. Expand $f(x) = 1$ in a sine series by using (4) and (13).
Solution. Using (13), we get

$$a_0 = 0, \qquad a_m = 0, \qquad b_m = \frac{2}{\pi} \int_0^\pi \sin mx \, dx = \frac{2(1 - \cos m\pi)}{m\pi}.$$

Substituting these values in (4), we obtain

$$1 = \frac{4}{\pi}\left(\sin x + \frac{\sin 3x}{3} + \frac{\sin 5x}{5} + \cdots \right). \tag{15}$$

Example 2. By using (4) and (12) expand x in a cosine series valid for the interval $0 < x < c$.

Solution. Let $x = cz/\pi$ and apply (12) to obtain

$$a_0 = \frac{1}{\pi}\int_0^\pi \frac{c}{\pi} z \, dz = \frac{c}{2}, \qquad a_m = \frac{2}{\pi}\int_0^\pi \frac{cz}{\pi}\cos mz \, dz$$

$$= \frac{2c}{\pi^2 m^2}(\cos m\pi - 1), \qquad b_m = 0.$$

Substitute these values in (4) to get

$$\frac{cz}{\pi} = \frac{c}{2} + \frac{2c}{\pi^2}\left(\frac{-2\cos z}{1^2} - \frac{2\cos 3z}{3^2} - \frac{2\cos 5z}{5^2} - \cdots \right),$$

or, replacing z by $\pi x/c$ and simplifying slightly,

$$x = \frac{c}{2} - \frac{4c}{\pi^2}\left(\frac{1}{1^2}\cos\frac{\pi x}{c} + \frac{1}{3^2}\cos\frac{3\pi x}{c} + \cdots \right). \tag{16}$$

EXERCISES

1. (a) Use (4), (13), and (14) to expand x in a sine series valid for the interval from 0 to c. (b) Using integration with the result and the fact that $a_0 = (1/\pi)$ $\int_0^\pi (c^2 z^2/\pi^2)\, dz = c^2/3$, obtain an expansion of x^2 in a series of cosines. (c) In the result of part (b), set $x = c$ and then deduce that $1/1^2 + 1/2^2 + 1/3^2 + \cdots$ $= \pi^2/6$.

2. Using (4), (12), and (14), expand x^2 in a cosine series valid for the interval $0 < x < c$.

3. Integrate series (15) to obtain all terms except the constant term of (16) with $c = \pi$. Determine the constant term by using the value $\pi/2$ for x.

4. Show that, for the interval $0 < x < L$,

$$mx(L - x) = \frac{8L^2 m}{\pi^3}\left(\frac{1}{1^3}\sin\frac{\pi x}{L} + \frac{1}{3^3}\sin\frac{3\pi x}{L} + \frac{1}{5^3}\sin\frac{5\pi x}{L} + \cdots \right).$$

5. Expand x^2 in a sine series valid for the interval $0 < x < c$.

6. Expand $h + kx$ in a sine series valid for the interval $0 < x < c$.

110. Vibrations of a string

Figure 4 represents a string L units long fastened at A and D. Assume that the vibrations are so small that the tension T in the string may be considered constant, that the weight of the string is small in comparison with T, that the length of the string may be considered as a constant L for each of its positions, and that each point in the string moves parallel to the Y-axis. Consider the motion of a small piece PQ (see Fig. 4) of the string Δx units long. Two forces of magnitude T act at its ends, one inclined θ and the other $\theta + \Delta\theta$ to the

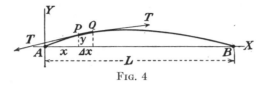

FIG. 4

X-axis. Since θ is small, $\sin \theta = \tan \theta = \partial y/\partial x$, approximately. Therefore, applying Newton's law parallel to the Y-axis, we get

$$T[\sin (\theta + \Delta\theta) - \sin \theta] = T\left[\frac{\partial y(x + \Delta x, t)}{\partial x} - \frac{\partial y(x,t)}{\partial x}\right]$$

$$= \frac{\rho \Delta x}{g} \frac{\partial^2 y}{\partial t^2}, \tag{17}$$

where ρ is the weight per unit length of the string. Dividing (17) through by $\rho \Delta x/g$ and equating the limits of its members, we have

$$\mathbf{a}^2 \frac{\partial^2 \mathbf{y(x,t)}}{\partial \mathbf{x}^2} = \frac{\partial^2 \mathbf{y}}{\partial \mathbf{t}^2}, \qquad \mathbf{a}^2 = \frac{\mathbf{Tg}}{\rho}. \tag{18}$$

Example. A string is stretched along the X-axis, to which it is attached at $x = 0$ and at $x = L$. Find y in terms of x and t, assuming that $y = mx(L - x)$ when $t = 0$.

Solution. Using the method of separation of variables, §104, substitute

$$y = X(x)T(t) \tag{a}$$

in (18) and divide the result by XT to obtain

$$\frac{a^2 \, d^2X/dx^2}{X} = \frac{d^2T/dt^2}{T}. \tag{b}$$

Equating each member of (b) to $-\omega^2$ and solving the resulting equations, obtain

$$X = c_1 \sin \frac{\omega x}{a} + c_2 \cos \frac{\omega x}{a}, \tag{c}$$

$$T = c_3 \sin \omega t + c_4 \cos \omega t. \tag{d}$$

It now appears from (a), (c), and (d) that solutions of (18) for y can consist of sums of terms having the forms

$$A \cos \frac{\omega}{a} x \cos \omega t, \qquad B \cos \frac{\omega}{a} x \sin \omega t,$$

$$C \sin \frac{\omega}{a} x \cos \omega t, \qquad F \sin \frac{\omega}{a} x \sin \omega t. \qquad (e)$$

The initial conditions are

$$y = 0, \text{ when } x = 0, \qquad \text{and} \qquad y = 0, \text{ when } x = L, \qquad (f)$$

$$y = mx(L - x) \text{ when } t = 0. \qquad (g)$$

Conditions (f) will be satisfied, provided we take

$$\omega = \frac{n\pi a}{L} \qquad (n, \text{ an integer}), \qquad (h)$$

and restrict ourselves to terms having the form of those in the last line of (e). From exercise 4, §109, we have

$$mx(L - x) = \frac{8L^2 m}{\pi^3}\left(\sin \frac{\pi x}{L} + \frac{1}{3^3}\sin \frac{3\pi x}{L} + \frac{1}{5^3}\sin \frac{5\pi x}{L} + \cdots\right). \qquad (i)$$

Hence conditions (18), (f), and (g) are satisfied by]

$$y = \frac{8L^2 m}{\pi^3}\left[\frac{1}{1^3}\cos \frac{a\pi t}{L}\sin \frac{\pi x}{L} + \frac{1}{3^3}\cos \frac{3\pi a t}{L}\sin \frac{3\pi x}{L} + \cdots\right]. \qquad (j)$$

PROBLEMS

1. If the string of the illustrative example is 3 ft. long and weighs $\frac{1}{30}$ lb., if $T = 10$ lb., and if $m = 0.01$, find the equation of the moving string. Find the time frequency of the first harmonic, that is, of the first term.

2. If, when $t = 0$, $y = A \sin (2\pi x/L)$ for the string of the illustrative example, find y in terms of x and t.

3. If, when $t = 0$, the particles of the string of the illustrative example have velocities defined by $(\partial y/\partial t)_{t=0} = A \sin (n\pi x/L)$, find the displacement $y(x,t)$ of the string.

4. If, when $t = 0$, the particles of the string of the illustrative example have velocities defined by $(\partial y/\partial t)_{t=0} = mx(L - x)$, find the corresponding displacement function $y(x,t)$.

111. Vibrations of a rod

Figure 5 represents a straight, elastic, homogeneous rod of density ρ, modulus of elasticity E, length L, and cross-sectional area A. It is fixed at Q and R, but the particles of the rod between Q and R move along the line QR. It is assumed that the pressure on any cross section is uniformly distributed and that all particles on any cross section have the same velocity. Let y be the displacement at time t of a particle that is distant x from Q when the rod is at rest. Then Δy is the change in length of the part of the rod marked Δx in Fig. 5. Now, by Hooke's law,

$$E = \frac{P}{A(l_1/L)}, \quad \text{or} \quad l_1 = \frac{PL}{AE}, \tag{19}$$

where l_1 is the amount that a rod of length L and cross-sectional area A is stretched by force P. Applying this equation to the piece MN

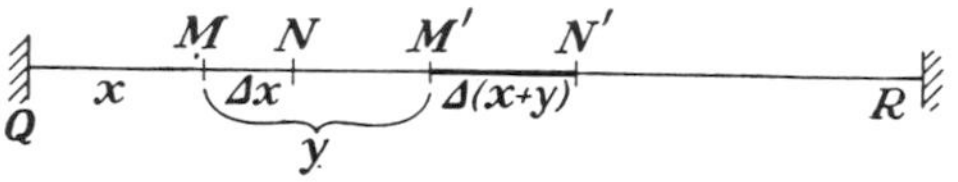

FIG. 5

in Fig. 5, we obtain

$$\Delta y = \frac{P(x_1,t)}{AE}\,\Delta x, \tag{20}$$

where x_1 satisfies $x < x_1 < x + \Delta x$. Dividing by Δx and equating the limits of the two members, we get

$$\frac{\partial y(x,t)}{\partial x} = \frac{P(x,t)}{AE}. \tag{21}$$

Now apply Newton's law of motion to the part $M'N'$ of the rod. This gives

$$P(x + \Delta x, t) - P(x,t) = \frac{A\rho\,\Delta x}{g}\,\frac{\partial^2 y_1}{\partial t^2},$$

where y_1 satisfies $y < y_1 < y + \Delta y$. Now divide by Δx and equate limits to get

$$\frac{\partial P}{\partial x} = \frac{A\rho}{g}\,\frac{\partial^2 y}{\partial t^2}, \tag{22}$$

and eliminate P between (21) and (22) to obtain

$$\mathbf{a}^2\,\frac{\partial^2 \mathbf{y(x,t)}}{\partial \mathbf{x}^2} = \frac{\partial^2 \mathbf{y(x,t)}}{\partial \mathbf{t}^2}, \quad \mathbf{a}^2 = \frac{\mathbf{Eg}}{\rho}. \tag{23}$$

Note that this equation has the same form as (18) in §110 and therefore has the solutions marked (e) in §110.

EXERCISES

1. For each of the following sets of conditions find the corresponding solution of (23):

(a) $y(0,t) = 0$, $y(L,t) = 0$, $y(x,0) = A \sin \dfrac{2\pi x}{L}$

(b) $y(0,t) = 0$, $y(L,t) = 0$, $y(x,0) = A \sin \dfrac{m\pi x}{L} + B \sin \dfrac{n\pi x}{L}$

(c) $y(0,t) = 0$, $y(L,t) = 0$, $y(x,0) = Ax(L - x)$

In solving part (c) use the result in exercise 4 of §109.

2. For a steel rod $\rho = 490$ lb./ft.³, $E = 4.3 \times 10^9$ lb./ft.², $g = 32$ ft./sec.² Using the initial conditions $y(0,t) = 0$, $y(3,t) = 0$, $y(x,0) = 0.0001x(3 - x)$, find the corresponding solution of (23) and give the frequency of the harmonic represented by the first term.

112. Flow of heat

Let $\theta(x,y,z,t)$ represent the temperature at any point in space at time t and assume that *the heat flows in the direction of decreasing temperature* and that *the rate across any small square is proportional to the area of the square and to $\partial\theta/\partial s$, where s is measured normal to the square.* Also assume that *the quantity of heat in a small body is proportional to its mass and to its temperature θ.*

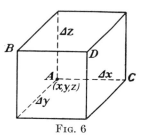

FIG. 6

To get the partial differential equation of heat flow, express in mathematical symbols the relation that *rate at which heat enters the small block of Fig. 6 minus the rate at which it leaves is equal to the rate of increase of heat in the block.* The rate at which heat leaves through face AB is $k[\partial\theta(x,y_1,z_1,t)/\partial x]\,\Delta y\,\Delta z$, where k is a constant and point (x,y_1,z_1) is a certain point in face AB. Similarly, the rate at which heat enters through face CD is approximately $k[\partial\theta(x + \Delta x,y_1,z_1,t)/\partial x]\,\Delta y\,\Delta z$. Hence the rate at which heat enters through the faces of the block perpendicular to the X-axis is

$$k\left[\frac{\partial\theta(x + \Delta x,\, y_1,\, z_1,\, t)}{\partial x} - \frac{\partial\theta(x,y_1,z_1,t)}{\partial x}\right]\Delta y\,\Delta z. \qquad (24)$$

Similarly, the rate at which heat enters the block through faces perpendicular to the Y-axis is

$$k\left[\frac{\partial\theta(x_2,\, y + \Delta y,\, z_2,\, t)}{\partial y} - \frac{\partial\theta(x_2,y,z_2,t)}{\partial y}\right]\Delta x\,\Delta z, \qquad (25)$$

and the rate for the faces perpendicular to the Z-axis is

$$k\left[\frac{\partial\theta(x_3,\, y_3,\, z + \Delta z,\, t)}{\partial z} - \frac{\partial\theta(x_3,y_3,z,t)}{\partial z}\right]\Delta y\,\Delta x. \qquad (26)$$

The rate of increase of heat in the block is

$$c\rho\,\Delta x\,\Delta y\,\Delta z\,\frac{\partial\theta(x_4,y_4,z_4,t)}{\partial t},\qquad(27)$$

where ρ is the density and (x_4,y_4,z_4) is a certain point in the block. Equating the sum of expressions (24) to (26) to expression (27), dividing the result through by $\Delta x\,\Delta y\,\Delta z$, and equating the limits of the two members as Δx, Δy, and Δz approach zero, we get

$$\mathbf{k}\left(\frac{\partial^2\theta}{\partial \mathbf{x}^2}+\frac{\partial^2\theta}{\partial \mathbf{y}^2}+\frac{\partial^2\theta}{\partial \mathbf{z}^2}\right)=c\rho\,\frac{\partial\theta}{\partial t}.\qquad(\mathbf{28})$$

To get the equation of heat flow in a plate with insulated surfaces, omit $\partial^2\theta/\partial z^2$ from (28) to obtain

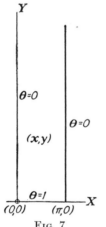

FIG. 7

$$k\left(\frac{\partial^2\theta}{\partial x^2}+\frac{\partial^2\theta}{\partial y^2}\right)=c\rho\,\frac{\partial\theta}{\partial t},\qquad(29)$$

and to get the equation for the flow in an insulated rod, leave $\partial^2\theta/\partial y^2$ from (29) to get

$$k\,\frac{\partial^2\theta}{\partial x^2}=c\rho\,\frac{\partial\theta}{\partial t}.\qquad(30)$$

After heat has flowed until the temperature at any point is constant, the steady state is reached. *To obtain the equations for flow of heat in the steady state, replace $\partial\theta/\partial t$ by zero in (28) to (30).* Thus for steady-state flow we get from (28)

$$\frac{\partial^2\theta}{\partial \mathbf{x}^2}+\frac{\partial^2\theta}{\partial \mathbf{y}^2}+\frac{\partial^2\theta}{\partial \mathbf{z}^2}=\mathbf{0}.\qquad(\mathbf{31})$$

Example. Fourier's problem is to find the temperature θ at any point (x,y) of a thin plate (see Fig. 7), π units wide and infinitely long, assuming (1) the steady state so that

$$\frac{\partial^2\theta}{\partial x^2}+\frac{\partial^2\theta}{\partial y^2}=0,\qquad(a)$$

from (29) with $\partial\theta/\partial t=0$; (2) perfectly insulated surfaces; (3) the short edge constantly at temperature unity; (4) the long edges at temperature zero.

Solution. Taking the Y-axis along an infinite edge and the X-axis along the short edge, we have the boundary conditions: (α) temperature $\theta=0$, when $x=0$; (β)$\theta=0$, when $x=\pi$; (γ)$\theta=0$, when $y=\infty$; (δ)$\theta=1$, when $y=0$.

To solve (a), substitute $\theta = X(x)Y(y)$ in it and divide by XY to obtain

$$\frac{d^2X/dx^2}{X} + \frac{d^2Y/dy^2}{Y} = 0.$$

Equating the first term to $-\omega^2$ and the second to ω^2, solving the resulting equations for X and Y, and forming $\theta = XY$, obtain

$$\theta = (c_1e^{\omega y} + c_2e^{-\omega y})(c_3 \sin \omega x + c_4 \cos \omega x). \tag{b}$$

Hence any one of the terms

$$A e^{\omega y} \sin \omega x, \qquad B e^{\omega y} \cos \omega x, \qquad C e^{-\omega y} \sin \omega x, \qquad G e^{-\omega y} \cos \omega x \quad (c)$$

is a solution of (a), and any sum of such terms is a solution. It remains to choose such a sum that the initial conditions will be satisfied by it. Conditions (α) and (β) will be satisfied by

$$\theta = \sum_{\omega=1}^{\infty} (c_{1\omega}e^{\omega y} + c_{2\omega}e^{-\omega y}) \sin \omega x, \tag{d}$$

and condition (γ) will also be satisfied by (d) if $c_{1\omega} = 0$. The expansion of unity in a Fourier series is

$$1 = \frac{4}{\pi}\left(\sin x + \frac{1}{3}\sin 3x + \frac{1}{5}\sin 5x + \cdots\right). \tag{e}$$

Hence conditions (α), (β), (γ), and (δ) are satisfied by

$$\theta = \frac{4}{\pi}\left(\frac{1}{1}\, e^{-y}\sin x + \frac{1}{3}\, e^{-3y} \sin 3x + \frac{1}{5}\, e^{-5y} \sin 5x + \cdots\right).$$

EXERCISES

1. Solve the problems obtained from the illustrative example by replacing condition (3) by (a) the short edge has temperature $\theta(x,0) = A \sin 3x$; (b) $\theta(x,0) = Ax$.

2. Find the temperature $\theta(x,y)$ for the plate of Fig. 7, assuming the steady state and $\theta(0,y) = m$, $\theta(\pi,y) = m$, $\theta(x, \infty) = m$, and $\theta(x,0) = m \sin 3x + m$. *Hint:* Use a solution having the form $\theta = A + Be^{-3y} \sin 3x$.

3. Find the temperature in the plate of Fig. 7, assuming the steady state and $\theta(0,y) = m$, $\theta(\pi,y) = m$, $\theta(x, \infty) = m$, and $\theta(x,0) = 1$. *Hint:* Use a solution having the form $\theta = B + C\varphi(x,y)$, where $\varphi(x,y)$ is the solution of the illustrative example.

4. Find the solution of $\partial^2 y/\partial t^2 = a^2\, \partial^2 y/\partial x^2$ satisfying the conditions $y = 0$ when $x = 0$, $y = 0$ when $x = c$, $y = gx$ for $0 < x < c/2$ and $t = 0$, and $y = g(c - x)$ for $c/2 < x < c$ and $t = 0$.

5. Find the temperature $\theta(x,y)$ at any point of the plate of Fig. 7 under the conditions $\theta(0,y) = 10$, $\theta(\pi,y) = 100$, $\theta(x,0) = 40$, $\theta(x, \infty) = 10 + 90x/\pi$, and the steady state.

Suggestion: Observe that $\theta = A + Bx$ satisfies equation (*a*) of the example. Hence, let

$$\theta(x,y) = A + Bx + \varphi(x,y),$$

where $\varphi(0,y) = 0$, $\varphi(\pi,y) = 0$. Then from the initial conditions we have

$$10 = A + \varphi(0,y) = A,$$
$$100 = A + \pi B + \varphi(\pi,y) = A + \pi B,$$
$$40 = A + Bx + \varphi(x,0).$$

Hence $A = 10$, $B = 90/\pi$, $\varphi(x,0) = 30 - 90x/\pi$.

113. One-dimensional heat flow

The temperature θ in an insulated rod through which heat is flowing parallel to the axis of the rod satisfies equation (30) in §112, namely,

$$\mathbf{a}^2 \frac{\partial^2 \theta(\mathbf{x},t)}{\partial \mathbf{x}^2} = \frac{\partial \theta(\mathbf{x},t)}{\partial t}, \qquad \mathbf{a}^2 = \frac{\mathbf{k}}{c\rho}. \tag{32}$$

To find solutions of (32), substitute in it

$$\theta = X(x)T(t) \tag{33}$$

and divide by XT to obtain

$$\frac{a^2 \, d^2X/dx^2}{X} = \frac{dT/dt}{T}.$$

Equate each member to $-a^2\omega^2$, solve the resulting equations for X and T, substitute the solutions in (33), and conclude that solutions of (32) may consist of sums of terms having the forms

$$Ae^{-a^2\omega^2 t} \sin \omega x, \qquad Be^{-a^2\omega^2 t} \cos \omega x. \tag{34}$$

The following example will illustrate a method of solving simple problems relating to the flow of heat.

Example. A rod L cm. long with insulated lateral surface is initially at temperature 20°C. throughout. If one end is kept at 10°C. and the other at 100°C., find the temperature θ as a function of time t and distance x from the end at 10°C.

Solution. The boundary conditions are

$$\theta(0,t) = 10, \qquad \theta(L,t) = 100, \qquad \theta(x,0) = 20. \tag{a}$$

A sum $\varphi(x,t)$ of terms having the first form of (34) will satisfy the condition $\varphi(0,t) = 0$, $\varphi(k\pi/\omega,t) = 0$, k an integer. Also $\theta = A + Bx$ satisfies (32). Now let the required solution be

$$\theta(x,t) = A + Bx + \varphi(x,t), \tag{b}$$

where

$$\varphi(x,t) = \sum_{k=1}^{\infty} A_k e^{-a^2 k^2 \pi^2 t / L^2} \sin \frac{k\pi}{L} x. \qquad (c)$$

Using the conditions (a) with (b) and (c), we obtain

$$10 = A + \varphi(0,t) = A, \qquad 100 = A + BL + \varphi(L,t)$$
$$= A + BL, \qquad 20 = A + Bx + \varphi(x,0). \qquad (d)$$

Solve (d) for A, B, and $\varphi(x,0)$ to get

$$A = 10, \qquad B = \frac{90}{L}, \qquad \varphi(x,0) = 10 - \frac{90}{L} x. \qquad (e)$$

Next expand $\varphi(x,0)$ in a Fourier series for the interval $0 < x < L$, to obtain

$$\varphi(x,0) = 10 - \frac{90x}{L} = -\frac{4}{\pi} \left(\frac{35}{1} \sin \frac{\pi x}{L} - \frac{45}{2} \sin \frac{2\pi x}{L} \right.$$
$$\left. + \frac{35}{3} \sin \frac{3\pi x}{L} - \frac{45}{4} \sin \frac{4\pi x}{L} + \cdots \right). \qquad (f)$$

To form $\varphi(x,t)$, write in front of the first, second, . . . , terms in (f) the respective results of setting $k = 1, 2, \ldots$, in $e^{-k^2 a^2 \pi^2 t / L^2}$. Then $\theta(x,t)$ from (b) is given by

$$\theta(\mathbf{x},t) = 10 + \frac{90\mathbf{x}}{L} - \frac{4}{\pi} \left(\frac{35}{1} e^{-a^2 \pi^2 t / L^2} \sin \frac{\pi \mathbf{x}}{L} \right.$$
$$\left. - \frac{45}{2} e^{-4a^2 \pi^2 t / L^2} \sin \frac{2\pi \mathbf{x}}{L} + \cdots \right). \qquad (g)$$

EXERCISES

1. What is the steady-state equation for the flow of heat in the rod of the illustrative example?

2. Find the expression $\theta(x,t)$ for temperature in the rod of the illustrative example if $\theta(0,t) = 0$, $\theta(L,t) = 100$, $\theta(x,0) = 0$.

114. Telephone, telegraph, and radio equations

Figure 8 represents a long line carrying electricity. The current goes out through AB and returns through the ground from C to D. Let L (henrys/mi.) be the inductance of the line AB, let R(ohms/mi.) be its resistance, let C(farads/mi.) be its capacitance to ground, and let G(mhos/mi.) be the leakage of current or conductance to ground. Let $e(x,t)$ and $i(x,t)$ represent the voltage and current at a point in the line AB x miles from A, and derive relations between e and i by considering the flow of electricity in a small portion PQ of the cable having length Δx.   The drop Δe in potential along PQ will be approximately

$$\Delta e = -R\,\Delta xi(x_1,t) - L\,\Delta x\,\frac{\partial i(x_1,t)}{\partial t}, \tag{35}$$

where $x < x_1 < x + \Delta x$.   Dividing this equation through by Δx and

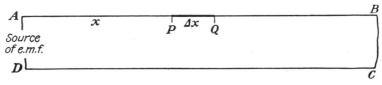

FIG. 8

equating the limits approached by its members as Δx approaches zero, we get

$$\frac{\partial e}{\partial x} = -Ri(x,t) - L\,\frac{\partial i(x,t)}{\partial t}. \tag{36}$$

Here changes in e due to leakage and capacitance to ground are of second order and therefore have nothing to do with equation (36).

Similarly, the drop in current along PQ is approximately

$$\Delta i = -G\,\Delta xe(x_1,t) - C\,\Delta x\,\frac{\partial e(x_1,t)}{\partial t}.$$

Dividing this through by Δx and equating the limits approached by its members as Δx approaches zero, we obtain

$$\frac{\partial i}{\partial x} = -Ge - C\,\frac{\partial e}{\partial t}. \tag{37}$$

Equations (36) and (37) are basic equations.   Three important sets will be derived from them.

Eliminate i between (36) and (37) by equating the partial derivatives with respect to x of the two members of (36), replacing $\partial i/\partial x$ in the result by its value from (37) and $\partial^2 i/(\partial x\,\partial t)$ by its value obtained from (37) by partial differentiation with respect to t, and simplifying; the result is

$$\frac{\partial^2 e}{\partial x^2} = RGe + (RC + LG)\,\frac{\partial e}{\partial t} + LC\,\frac{\partial^2 e}{\partial t^2}. \tag{38}$$

Similarly, eliminate e between (36) and (37) to get

$$\frac{\partial^2 i}{\partial x^2} = RGi + (RC + LG)\frac{\partial i}{\partial t} + LC\frac{\partial^2 i}{\partial t^2}. \tag{39}$$

The equations (36) to (39) are known as the *telephone equations*.

In many applications to telegraph signaling, G and L are negligible. Replacing G and L by 0 in equations (36) to (39), we obtain the telegraph equations which follow:

$$
\begin{aligned}
\frac{\partial e}{\partial x} &= -Ri, \\[4pt]
\frac{\partial i}{\partial x} &= -C\frac{\partial e}{\partial t}, \\[4pt]
\frac{\partial^2 e}{\partial x^2} &= RC\frac{\partial e}{\partial t}, \\[4pt]
\frac{\partial^2 i}{\partial x^2} &= RC\frac{\partial i}{\partial t}.
\end{aligned}
\tag{40}
$$

For high frequencies we may place $G = R = 0$ in (36) to (39) to obtain the radio equations which follow:

$$
\begin{aligned}
\frac{\partial e}{\partial x} &= -L\frac{\partial i}{\partial t}, \\[4pt]
\frac{\partial i}{\partial x} &= -C\frac{\partial e}{\partial t}, \\[4pt]
\frac{\partial^2 e}{\partial x^2} &= LC\frac{\partial^2 e}{\partial t^2}, \\[4pt]
\frac{\partial^2 i}{\partial x^2} &= LC\frac{\partial^2 i}{\partial t^2}.
\end{aligned}
\tag{41}
$$

EXERCISES

1. Substitute $e = X(x)T(t)$ in the third of the radio equations (41) and, by the usual procedure, deduce that it is satisfied by the expressions for e

$$
\begin{array}{ll}
\cos(\omega \sqrt{LC}\, x) \cos \omega t, & \cos(\omega \sqrt{LC}\, x) \sin \omega t, \\
\sin(\omega \sqrt{LC}\, x) \sin \omega t, & \sin(\omega \sqrt{LC}\, x) \cos \omega t.
\end{array}
\tag{42}
$$

If i and e are to satisfy the four radio equations (41) and $e = A \sin(\omega \sqrt{LC}\, x) \cos \omega t$, show that i must have the form $i = -A \sqrt{C/L} \cos(\omega \sqrt{LC}\, x) \sin \omega t + B$, where B is a constant.

2. If $i = A \cos(\omega \sqrt{LC}\, x) \sin \omega t$, find e so that i and e satisfy the radio equations (41).

3. Substitute $e = X(x)T(t)$ in the third equation of (40) and, by the regular procedure, deduce that some solutions of (40) have the form*

$$
A\epsilon^{-(\omega^2/RC)t} \cos \omega x, \qquad B\epsilon^{-(\omega^2/RC)t} \sin \omega x. \tag{43}
$$

* In this section $\epsilon = 2.7183$ approximately.

4. (*a*) If $e = A\epsilon^{-(\omega^2/RC)t} \cos \omega x$, find a corresponding function $i(x,t)$ such that e and i satisfy (40).   (*b*) If $i = A\epsilon^{-(\omega^2/RC)t} \sin \omega x$, find $e(x,t)$ such that i and e will satisfy (40).

5. In a steady-state condition for which i and e are functions of x only, solve (40).   Since i and e depend on x only, $\partial i/\partial t$ and $\partial e/\partial t$ are zero.

6. In Fig. 8 take L miles as the length of AB and solve the corresponding telegraph equations (40).   Use as initial conditions $e(0,t) = 0$, $e(L,t) = 0$, $e(x,0) = 2 + 3x/L$.   Results in exercise 2 of this article and in exercise 6 of §109 may be used to shorten the work.

7. Solve the third radio equation (41) by the method of §99 to obtain

$$e = \varphi_1 \left(x + \frac{1}{\sqrt{LC}}\, t \right) + \varphi_2 \left(x - \frac{1}{\sqrt{LC}}\, t \right).^*$$

Substitute this in the second of equations (41) and integrate to obtain

$$i = -\sqrt{\frac{C}{L}} \left[\varphi_1 \left(x + \frac{1}{\sqrt{LC}}\, t \right) - \varphi_2 \left(x - \frac{1}{\sqrt{LC}}\, t \right) \right] + \psi(t).$$

Now substitute these values of e and i in the first equation of (41) and deduce that $\psi(t)$ is a constant.

8. A line is called distortionless if $LG = RC$, or $G/C = R/L$.   Make the substitution

$$e = E(x,t)\epsilon^{-Gt/C}, \qquad i = I(x,t)\epsilon^{-Gt/C}$$

in (36) to (39) to obtain equations having the form (41) of the radio equations for a distortionless line.   Also check directly that (38) is satisfied by

$$e = A\epsilon^{-Gt/C} \sin (\omega \sqrt{LC}\, x) \cos \omega t,$$

when $G/C = R/L$, and find the corresponding $i(x,t)$ to satisfy (36) and (37).

115. Fluid motion

Because of the importance of fluid motion, as exemplified by the flow of air over airplane wings and the flow of water near ships, and because the solution of fluid-motion problems involves partial differential equations, a brief introduction to the subject will be given.

Consider the motion of a homogeneous fluid with continuous structure and no viscosity.†   In this case all forces exerted by the fluid on a surface will be normal to the surface.   For simplicity, think of a fluid moving between two parallel planes and assume that any particle

---

* An equation of the form $e = \varphi(x - \omega t)$ represents a wave motion, because the value of e associated with any point in the line at any instant is taken on at each point as the time t increases.   If $e = m$ at point x_1 and time t_1, then e will equal m provided $x - \omega t = x_1 - \omega t_1$, that is, as x varies with the time, the condition $e = m$ moves along the line like the crest of a wave.   Observe that $e = \varphi(x + \omega t)$ represent waves moving in a direction opposite to that of the motion represented by $e = \varphi(x - \omega t)$.

† All fluids are viscous, but many, water for example, are only slightly viscous.

remains in a plane parallel to the bounding planes and that the motions in all such planes are the same.   The flow will then be two dimensional.

The motion of the fluid will be due to pressure in the fluid and a force proportional to the mass like the pull of gravity.   Thus the pressure p in the fluid will be a function of x, y, and t, and the force per unit mass will have components $X(x,y,t)$ and $Y(x,y,t)$ parallel to the coordinate axes.   Also let $u(x,y,t)$ and $v(x,y,t)$ be the x and y components of the velocity at time t.

From calculus, we have for the x and y components of acceleration

$$a_x = \frac{du}{dt} = \frac{\partial u}{\partial x} u + \frac{\partial u}{\partial y} v + \frac{\partial u}{\partial t},$$

$$a_y = \frac{dv}{dt} = \frac{\partial v}{\partial x} u + \frac{\partial v}{\partial y} v + \frac{\partial v}{\partial t}. \tag{44}$$

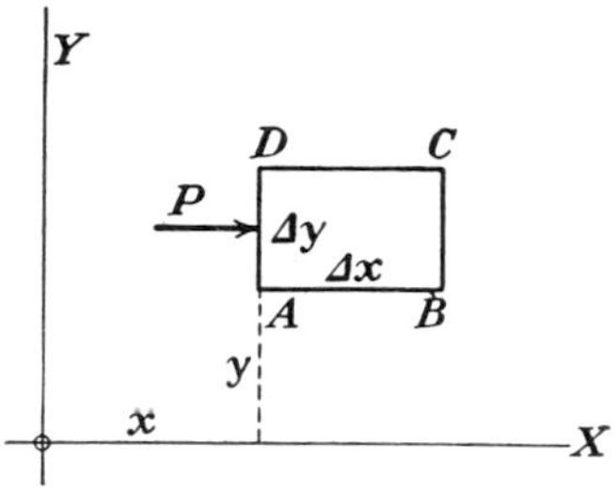

Fig. 9

Now apply Newton's law of motion to the element of fluid represented by $ABCD$ in Fig. 9.   The forces at time t on the faces represented by AD and BC may be expressed as an average pressure multiplied by the area $h \, \Delta y$, where h is the distance between the bounding planes. Accordingly we write as the total force due to pressure on the surfaces represented by AD and BC,

$$h \, \Delta y \, p(x,y_1,t) - h \, \Delta y \, p(x + \Delta x, y_1, t), \tag{45}$$

where $y < y_1 < y + \Delta y$.   Also the force proportional to mass acting on the element in the x-direction may be expressed by

$$\frac{h}{g} \, \Delta y \, \Delta x \, \bar{\rho} X \, (x_2,y_2,t), \tag{46}$$

where $\bar{\rho}$ is the average density of the fluid in the element and (x_2,y_2) is a point properly chosen in the element.   Hence we have

$$h \, \Delta y \, p(x,y_1,t) - h \, \Delta y \, p(x + \Delta x, y_1, t) + \frac{h}{g} \, \Delta y \, \Delta x \, \bar{\rho} X(x_2,y_2,t)$$
$$= \frac{\bar{\rho} h \, \Delta y \, \Delta x}{g} \frac{du(x_3,y_3,t)}{dt}, \tag{47}$$

where (x_3,y_3) is a properly chosen point in the element.   Dividing through by $\Delta x \, \Delta y$, equating the limits of the two members as Δx and Δy approach zero, and simplifying slightly we get

$$\frac{du}{dt} = X - \frac{g}{\rho} \frac{\partial p}{\partial x}. \tag{48}$$

Applying Newton's law parallel to the Y-axis, we obtain in a like manner

$$\frac{dv}{dt} = Y - \frac{g}{\rho}\frac{\partial p}{\partial y}.\qquad(49)$$

Finally express the condition that the rate of change of amount of fluid in the element is the rate at which fluid enters minus the rate at which it leaves. The rate of change of the quantity is

$$\frac{\partial}{\partial t}\,[h\,\Delta x\,\Delta y\,\rho(x_1,y_1,t)] = h\,\Delta x\,\Delta y\,\frac{\partial \bar{\rho}}{\partial t}.\qquad(50)$$

The rate of entering minus the rate of leaving is approximately

$$h\,\Delta y[\overline{\rho u}(x,y_1,t) - \overline{\rho u}(x+\Delta x,y_1,t)] + h\,\Delta x[\overline{\rho v}(x_1,y,t) - \overline{\rho v}(x_1,y+\Delta y,t)].\qquad(51)$$

Equating the limit of (51) divided by $\Delta x\,\Delta y$ as Δx and Δy approach zero to the limit of (50) divided by $\Delta x\,\Delta y$, we get

$$-\frac{\partial(\rho u)}{\partial x} - \frac{\partial(\rho v)}{\partial y} = \frac{\partial\rho}{\partial t}.\qquad(52)$$

Equations (48), (49), and (52) are the differential equations of fluid flow for the special case considered.

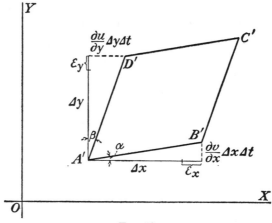

Fig. 10

To understand the simplest case, the idea of *rotation* will be required. Figure 10 shows positions $A'B'C'D'$, after Δt units of time, of four fluid particles originally at points A, B, C, and D of Fig. 9. ϵ_x and ϵ_y represent infinitesimals of higher order than Δx, Δy, and Δt. Disregarding infinitesimals of higher order than the first, we get for the angular velocity ω_x of $A'B'$

$$\omega_x = \frac{(\partial v/\partial x)\,\Delta x\,\Delta t}{\Delta t\,\Delta x} = \frac{\partial v}{\partial x}, \tag{53}$$

and for the angular velocity ω_y of $A'D'$

$$\omega_y = \frac{-(\partial u/\partial y)\,\Delta y\,\Delta t}{\Delta t\,\Delta y} = \frac{-\partial u}{\partial y}. \tag{54}$$

One-half the sum of the velocities ω_x and ω_y is called the *rotation* of the fluid, that is,

$$\text{Rotation} = \frac{1}{2}\left(\frac{\partial v}{\partial x} - \frac{\partial u}{\partial y}\right). \tag{55}$$

Now consider the motion of a fluid for which the rotation is zero, that is,

$$\frac{\partial v}{\partial x} = \frac{\partial u}{\partial y}; \tag{56}$$

the fluid is incompressible, that is,

$$\rho = \text{constant}; \tag{57}$$

the fluid is in the steady state, that is, u and v are functions of x and y only; and the force is conservative, that is, there exists a force function $U(x,y)$ such that

$$\frac{\partial U}{\partial x} = X, \qquad \frac{\partial U}{\partial y} = Y. \tag{58}$$

From (44), (56), and the fact that the steady state exists,

$$\frac{du}{dt} = \frac{\partial u}{\partial x}u + \frac{\partial u}{\partial y}v = \frac{\partial u}{\partial x}u + \frac{\partial v}{\partial x}v. \tag{59}$$

Hence, taking account of (56) to (59), we may write (48) in the form

$$u\frac{\partial u}{\partial x} + v\frac{\partial v}{\partial x} = \frac{\partial U}{\partial x} - \frac{g}{\rho}\frac{\partial p}{\partial x}. \tag{60}$$

The integral of (60) is

$$\frac{u^2 + v^2}{2} = U - \frac{g}{\rho}p + C. \tag{61}$$

EXERCISES

1. From (56) deduce that in steady-state irrotational fluid motion there is a *velocity potential* $\varphi(x,y)$ such that

$$\frac{\partial \varphi}{\partial x} = u, \qquad \frac{\partial \varphi}{\partial y} = v.$$

The curves $\varphi(x,y) = c$ are called *curves of constant velocity potential.*

2. A streamline of a fluid in motion is a curve at each of whose points the direction of the velocity is the same as that of the curve. Hence along streamlines, $dy/dx = v/u$ or

$$v\,dx - u\,dy = 0.$$

Show that, for steady-state irrotational motion of an incompressible fluid, this equation is exact because of (52), which, for the case in question, simplifies to $\partial u/\partial x + \partial v/\partial y = 0$. Hence show that there are streamlines represented by

$$\psi(x,y) = C, \qquad \frac{\partial \psi}{\partial x} = v, \qquad \frac{\partial \psi}{\partial y} = -u.$$

Also show that the streamlines $\psi(x,y) = C$ are the orthogonal trajectories of the velocity potential curves considered in exercise 1.

3. If $f(z) = v(x,y) + iu(x,y)$, where u and v are real functions of x and y, is analytic, then

$$\frac{\partial v}{\partial x} = \frac{\partial u}{\partial y}, \qquad \frac{\partial u}{\partial x} = -\frac{\partial v}{\partial y}.$$

These are equivalent to (56) and (52) for steady-state irrotational motion of an incompressible fluid.

(*a*) Using $f(z) = (x + iy)^2 = x^2 - y^2 + 2ixy$, take $v = x^2 - y^2$, $u = 2xy$, and find the corresponding equations of the streamlines and curves of constant velocity potential. Also assuming that $X = 0$, $Y = -g$, find p in terms of x and y. (*b*) Carry out the same process for $f(z) = 1/z$, assuming $X = 0$, $Y = -g$.

ANSWERS

§2, page 3

1. 1, 1. **2.** 2, 1. **3.** 1, 2. **4.** 2, 2. **5.** 2, 2. **6.** 3, 1. **7.** 1, 3. **8.** 1, 2. **9.** 2, 2.
10. 2, 2.

§4, page 7

1. $\dfrac{dy}{dx} = 2x$. **2.** $x\dfrac{dy}{dx} = 2y$. **3.** $y = x\dfrac{dy}{dx} + 3$. **4.** $y = (x+1)\dfrac{dy}{dx}$. **5.** $\dfrac{dy}{dx} = y$.

6. $x + y\dfrac{dy}{dx} = 0$. **7.** $x\dfrac{d^2y}{dx^2} = \dfrac{dy}{dx}$. **8.** $x^2\dfrac{d^2y}{dx^2} - 2x\dfrac{dy}{dx} + 2y = 0$. **9.** $y = x\dfrac{dy}{dx} +$

$\left(\dfrac{dy}{dx}\right)^2 - 2\dfrac{dy}{dx}$. **10.** $\dfrac{d^2y}{dx^2} + 4y = 0$. **11.** $\dfrac{d^2y}{dx^2} - 3\dfrac{dy}{dx} + 2y = 0$. **12.** $\dfrac{d^2y}{dx^2} + y =$

x^2. **13.** $\dfrac{d^2y}{dx^2} - 5\dfrac{dy}{dx} + 6y = 6x^2 - 10x + 2$. **14.** $\dfrac{d^2y}{dx^2} - 2\dfrac{dy}{dx} + y = 0$. **15.** $y^2 =$

$2xy\dfrac{dy}{dx} + 4y^2\left(\dfrac{dy}{dx}\right)^2 + 3$. **16.** $\left(y - x\dfrac{dy}{dx}\right)^2 + x^2y^2 = x^4$. **17.** $y^2(1 + y'^2) = 25$.

18. $\left[1 + \left(\dfrac{dy}{dx}\right)^2\right]^3 = 25\left(\dfrac{d^2y}{dx^2}\right)^2$. **19.** $x\dfrac{dy}{dx} = y$. **20.** $x\,dx + y\,dy = 0$. **21.** $\dfrac{d^2y}{dx^2}$

$= 0$. **22.** $\left(x + y\dfrac{dy}{dx}\right)\left(x\dfrac{dy}{dx} - y\right) = 4\dfrac{dy}{dx}$. **23.** $y = x\dfrac{dy}{dx} - \left(\dfrac{dy}{dx}\right)^2$. **24.** $y = x\dfrac{dy}{dx}$

$- \dfrac{1}{2}\dfrac{dy}{dx} - \dfrac{1}{4}\left(\dfrac{dy}{dx}\right)^3$. **25.** $(2x - 2)y + (y^2 - x^2 + 2x)\dfrac{dy}{dx} = 0$. **26.** $(y - x)^2\left[1 +\right.$

$\left.\left(\dfrac{dy}{dx}\right)^2\right] = \left(1 + \dfrac{dy}{dx}\right)^2$.

§5, page 10

$\dfrac{\partial f}{y}$ does not exist at $(x_0, 0)$.

§6, page 12

1. $x^2 - y^2 = c$. **2.** $x^3 + y^3 = c$. **3.** $(x - 1)^2 + 2(y + 1)^2 = c$. **4.** $-\dfrac{1}{y} + \dfrac{1}{x} = c$,

or $y - x = cxy$. **5.** $1 + 2x^2 = c(1 + y^2)$. **6.** $y = cx$. **7.** $xy^3 = c$. **8.** $\rho\theta = c$.
9. $\rho = ce^\theta$. **10.** $i = ce^{-Rt/L}$. **11.** $xy + 1 = cy - y^2$. **12.** $x(y + \sqrt{1 + y^2}) = c$.
13. $s = t^3 + t^2 - 5t + c$. **14.** $e^{3y} + 3e^{-x} = c$. **15.** $cxy + x = 1$. **16.** $y = (y +$
$1)ce^x$. **17.** $y = c(x + a)(1 - ay)$. **18.** $\sin^{-1} x = \sin^{-1} y + c$. **19.** $x^3 + y^2 = 17$.
20. $y^2 - x^2 = 15$. **21.** $xy^2 = 3$. **22.** $(1 + y^2) = 17x^2$. **23.** $(x + 1)(y - 1) = 2$.
24. $\rho = 2\sin\theta$. **25.** $y^2 = 4(1 + x^2)$. **26.** $2x = 1 + 5e^{-2y}$. **27.** $2y + 1 = 2e^{2/x}$.
28. $y^4(2 + x) = 3(x - 2)$. **29.** $xy = 2(x - 1)e^{2/x}$. **30.** $(1 + e^x)^3 \tan y = 27$.

§7, page 15

1. (a) $y = x^2 - 2x + 1$. (b) $y^2 = 2x + 10$. (c) $3y = 4x$. (d) $16y^2 - 9x^2 = 175$. (e) $(x + 1)^2 + (y - 1)^2 = 25$. (f) $4(y - 1) = 3(x + 1)$. **3.** $y = c_1 x$. **4.** $xy = c$. **5.** $y^2 + 2x^2 = c$. **6.** $x^2 + 5y^2 = c$. **7.** $x^3 + 3y = c$. **8.** $y^2 = \log(cx)$. **9.** $2x^2 + 3y^2 = c$. **10.** Because the orthogonality must apply for curves crossing at any point and therefore must be independent of c. **11.** $x^2 + y^2 = c$. **12.** $y^2 + 2x^2 = c$. **13.** $xy = c$. **14.** $y^2 = \pm x^2 + c$. **15.** $y^2 = 2mx + c$. **16.** $y = ce^{-x/m}$. **17.** $y(c - x) = 2k$. **18.** $y = ce^{x/k}$. **19.** $(c - \pi x)y = k$. **20.** $y = x - \log|2x + 1| + c$, or $y = -x - \log|2x - 1| + c$.

§8, page 18

1. $\rho = c \cos \theta$. **2.** $\rho^2 = c \cos \theta$. **3.** $\rho = c(\sin \theta - \cos \theta)$. **4.** $\rho^n = c \cos \theta$. **5.** $\rho = \dfrac{c}{1 + \cos \theta}$. **6.** $\rho = c(1 - \sin \theta)$. **7.** $\rho = c(1 + \cos \theta)$. **8.** $\rho^4 = c \cos 2\theta$. **9.** $\rho^2 = c \cos 2\theta$. **10.** $\rho = ae^{\theta \cot \alpha}$. **11.** (a) $\rho = c \sin \theta$. (b) $\rho = c \sin^2 \frac{1}{2}\theta$, $\rho = c \csc^4(135° - \frac{1}{4}\theta)$. **12.** (a) $\rho = a\theta + c$. (b) $\rho(\theta + c) + a = 0$. **14.** Set (b) are not the orthogonal trajectories of set (a).

§11, page 21

1. $\theta = 100(0.9)^{t/20}$; 22.4 min.; 62.2°C. **2.** $\theta = 20 + 80(\frac{7}{8})^{t/20}$; 23.0 min.; 63.8°C. **3.** (a) \$1.062. (b) \$1.822. **4.** (a) 11.55 years. (b) 18.31 years. **5.** \$42,511. **6.** $i = 30(\frac{11}{30})^{100t}$. **7.** 0.0208 sec. **8.** $p = 14.7e^{-0.0000375h}$; 8.37 lb./in.^{2}

§12, page 23

3. $v = \dfrac{20}{1 + 6t}, \dfrac{20}{61}$ ft./sec.; $v = 20e^{-0.3s}$. **4.** (a) $v = 7.5(1 - e^{-0.161t})$. (b) 6 ft./sec. (c) 7.5 ft./sec. **5.** (a) $v = \frac{1}{2}(15 + 29e^{-0.161t})$. (b) 10.4 ft./sec. (c) 7.5 ft./sec. **6.** (a) $v = \frac{15}{4}(1 - e^{-0.322t})$. (b) 3.6 ft./sec. (c) 3.75 ft./sec. **7.** (a) $v = 20(1 - e^{-0.00322t})$. (b) 20 ft./sec. (c) 11 min. 55 sec. **8.** 32,000 ft./sec. or about 6 mi./sec.; limiting speed about 7 mi./sec. **9.** $\dfrac{2000wm^n}{pg} \displaystyle\int_{\frac{1}{2}m}^{\frac{3}{4}m} \dfrac{dv}{m^n - v^n}$. **10.** $v = 3t^2$; $s = t^3$.

§13, page 26

1. (a) 172.9 lb. (b) 200 lb. (c) 34.7 min. **2.** 54.4 lb. **3.** 30.5 min. **4.** $a = -0.02$, $b = 4$. **5.** 0.531 gal.

§14, page 26

1. $Q = 150 - 100e^{-0.02t}$. **2.** $v = 20 - 160e^{-5t}$. **3.** $i = \dfrac{E}{R}(1 - e^{-Rt/L})$. **4.** $(4 \log x - 13)(y - 1) + 5 = 0$. **5.** $pv^k = c$. **6.** $x^2 + (y - c)^2 = 2k$. **7.** $\rho = c \sin \theta$, $\rho = c \csc \theta$. **8.** $\rho = a \sec(\theta + c)$. **9.** $\rho = \dfrac{c}{1 + \cos \theta} = \dfrac{1}{2}c \sec^2 \dfrac{1}{2}\theta$. **10.** $\rho \cos \theta = c$, $\rho \sec \theta = c$. **11.** $\rho = ce^{\frac{1}{2}\theta/k} \csc \theta$. **13.** $v = 173(1 - e^{-gt/173})$; 151 ft./sec. **14.** (a) 1.37×10^8 cal. (b) 1.66×10^6 cal. **15.** 9.33×10^5 cal.; 7.21×10^4 cal.; 1.17×10^5 cal. **16.** (a) 1 min. 44 sec. (b) 1 min. 48 sec. **17.** 26 min. 28 sec. **18.** 7 min. 59 sec.

§15, page 30

1. $2x - \log(2x - 2y + 1) = c$. **2.** $\log(2x + 3y - 3) + y = c$. **3.** $(x + y)^2 - 4y = c$. **4.** $x + y + 6 \log(6 - 2x - y) = c$. **5.** $(x - 2y)^2 + 10(x - 2y) + 2y = c$. **6.** $x + y + 3 \log(2x + y + 3) = c$. **7.** $x - \tan^{-1}(x + \frac{1}{2}y) = c$. **8.** $y = \log\left(\dfrac{4x - y - 2}{4x - y + 2}\right) + c$. **9.** $x^2y^2 = 3y^4 + 1$. **10.** $(x^2 + y^2)(10 - 9x) = 5x$. **11.** $(st - 2)^3 t = cs$. **12.** $x^3 + 3xy^2 = 14$. **13.** $x^4 + 4xy^3 = 5$. **14.** $x^2 + xy - y^2 = c$. **15.** $5x^2 - 2xy + y^2 = c$. **16.** $\rho^3\theta^3(c - e^\theta) = 1$. **17.** $x^3y = x^8 + 2$. **18.** $(x + y)^2 + (3x - y)^2 = c$. **19.** $(2y + cx)(x + y)^2 + x = 0$. **20.** $x^2y^2 = c(x^2 + y^2)$.

§16, page 33

2. $x^2 - xy - y^2 = c$. **3.** $3x^2 + 2xy = c$. **4.** $2x^2 + 3xy - y^2 = c$. **5.** $x(5x^2 - 21y^2) = c$. **6.** $\theta^2 + 4\rho\theta - 6\rho^2 = c$. **7.** $y^3 = 3x^3 \log x$. **8.** $2x + y \log x = 3y$. **9.** $x \log y + 4y = 5x$. **10.** $4y^2 + x^2 = cy$. **11.** $y \log xy = x + cy$. **12.** $2x^2 \log(xy^2) - y^2 = cx^2$. **13.** $y^5 = cx^2(y - x)$. **14.** $2y^2 \log\left(\dfrac{y^3}{x^2}\right) + 2xy + x^2 = c$. **15.** $y(x + y)^2 = ce^{-x/y}$. **16.** $y + \sqrt{x^2 + y^2} = cx^2$. **17.** $\sin\left(\dfrac{y}{x}\right) + \log cx = 0$. **18.** $\sin\left(\dfrac{y}{x}\right) = \log cx$. **20.** $x^2 + y^2 = cy$. **21.** $\log(x^2 + y^2) = \pm 2 \tan^{-1}\left(\dfrac{y}{x}\right) + c$.

§17, page 34

1. $(x + y - 1)^3 = c(x - y + 3)$. **2.** $(y - 2x - 3)^4 = c(x + 1)^3$. **3.** $(y + 2x - 4)^2 = c(x + y - 1)$. **4.** $5x - 10y + \log(10x + 5y - 2) = c$. **5.** $x + 2y + \log(2x - y) = c$. **6.** $4(x - 1)^2 + 6y(x - 1) - 7y^2 = c$. **7.** $\log[(y - x)^2 + (x - 1)^2] + 2 \tan^{-1}\dfrac{y - x}{x - 1} = c$.

§18, page 35

1. (a) $(3x^3 - y^2 - 8xy) dx - (2xy + 4x^2) dy$. (b) $\dfrac{5}{xy}(x\,dy + y\,dx)$. (c) $(4x^3y^4 + \cos x) dx + 4x^4y^3 dy$. **2.** (a) $3x^2y\,dx + (x^3 - 2y)\,dy = 0$. (b) $2x\,dx - \left(2y + \dfrac{3}{y}\right)dy = 0$. (c) $(2ax + by)\,dx + bx\,dy = 0$. **4.** (a) $x^2 + xy - y^2 + c$. (b) $x^2 + xy - y^3 - 3y + c$. (c) $x^3 - x^2y + y^4 + 3y + c$. (d) $x^2 + x \tan y - y^3 + c$.

§20, page 38

1. $x^2 + y^2 - xy + 5x = c$. **2.** $2x^3 + 3x^2y^2 - 2y^3 + 4y = c$. **3.** $2x^3 + 6xy^2 + 9y^2 - 6y = c$. **4.** $y^3 + 3xy^2 + 3x^2y - 3a^2x = c$. **5.** $ax^2 + bxy + cy^2 + gx + ey = c$. **6.** $\rho^2(\sec 2\theta + 2) = c$. **7.** $\rho \sin 2\theta - \rho^2 \cos 2\theta = c$. **8.** $x = cy$. **9.** $y = cx$. **10.** $x^m y^n = c$. **11.** $x^m = cy^n$. **12.** $x^2 - 3y^2 + 2x \tan y = c$. **13.** $\sec x + \sec y - xy + 2y = c$. **14.** $x^2y + xy^2 + \log y = c$. **15.** $y(x^4 + c) + 4x = 0$. **16.** $x + \sqrt{x^2 + y^2} = c$. **17.** $x^2y^2(x^2 - y^2) = c$. **18.** $\cos x \cos y = c$.

§21, page 40

1. $3 \log (xy) = x^3 + c.$ **2.** $3 \log (x^2 + y^2) = 2y^3 + c.$ **3.** $3 \log \dfrac{y}{x} = x^3 + c.$ **4.**

$y = x^2 + 3 + cx.$ **5.** $4 \tan^{-1} \dfrac{y}{x} = y^4 + c.$ **6.** $(m - n + 1)(xy)^{1-n} = (1 - n)x^{m-n+1}$

$+ c.$ **7.** $4x^3 y = x^4 + c.$ **8.** $3x^3 \log x = y^3 + cx^3.$ **9.** $2 \tan^{-1} \dfrac{y}{x} = \log (x^2 + y^2) +$

$c.$ **10.** $(x^2 + y^2)^2 = 4 \tan^{-1} \left(\dfrac{y}{x} \right) + c.$ **11.** (a) $x = ce^{x/y}.$ (b) $y^3 + 3x^3 \log cx = 0.$

(c) $2x^2 \log cx + 2xy - y^2 = 0.$ **12.** (a) $x^3 y^2 = Re^x.$ (b) $x^3 y^4 + 2 = cx^3 y^2.$ (c) $x^4 y^6 + cx^{10} y^6 = 3.$ (d) $x^3 = y^{11} + cy^4.$ **13.** (a) $(7y^4 + x^3)x^{\frac{1}{2}} = c.$ (b) $x^5 + x^3 y + x^2 y^2 = c.$ **14.** (a) $2x^3 y^3 + 2y^3 + 9y^2 = c.$ (b) $x^3 + 3xy^2 + 3y = cy^3.$ (c) $x^3 + 3 = ce^{y^3}.$ **15.** $e^{\int f(x)dx}; \; x^2 y^2 + 3 = ce^{-2x}.$ **16.** (a) $\log \left(\dfrac{y^2}{x^2} \right) + x^2 y^2 = c.$ (b)

$x^2 y^2 - 2 \log y = c.$ (c) $cxy + 1 = xy \log \dfrac{x^2}{y}.$

§22, page 43

1. $10xy = 2x^5 - 15x^2 + c.$ **2.** $15x^2 y = 3x^5 + 10x^3 + c.$ **3.** $y = x^2 \log x + 2x^2 - x.$ **4.** $y \cos x + 3e^{-\sin x} = 7.$ **5.** $4x^3 y + 2x \cos 2x = c + \sin 2x.$ **6.** $(n - m)y = ae^{nx} + ce^{mx}.$ **7.** $y = (ax + c)e^{mx}.$ **8.** $2x = 7y^4 + y^6.$ **9.** $x = \sin^2 y \; (c - \cot y).$ **10.** $2s = (t^3 + ct)e^{3t}.$ **11.** $y = 4e^{\frac{1}{2}x^2} + e^{x^2}.$ **12.** $2x + 4y = 1 - 5e^{-2x}.$ **13.** $y = ax + 2a \sqrt{1 + x^2}.$ **14.** $(3xy + ax^2 + 2a) \sqrt{1 - x^2} = c.$ **15.** $\rho = \sin \theta - 1 + ce^{-\sin \theta}.$ **16.** $y = x^2(1 + ce^{1/x}).$ **17.** $y(1 + x) = ce^x - a.$ **18.** $(y - 1)f(x) = c.$ **19.** $6y = [f(x)]^3 + c[f(x)]^{-3}.$

§23, page 44

1. $xy^{-2} + x^5 = c.$ **2.** $x^{-3} y^{-3} + x^2 = c.$ **3.** $y^{-1} + 12e^{2x} = ce^x.$ **4.** $y^3(x + 1) = (x + 1)^3 + c.$ **5.** $y^{\frac{1}{2}} = 2e^{3x^2} + ce^{x^2}.$ **6.** $y(x^2 + 1) = 2x.$ **7.** $xy(1 - \log^2 x) = 2.$ **8.** $y(2 \sin x + 1) = 2 \sec x + 2 \tan x.$ **9.** $x^{-1} = 2 - y^2 - e^{-\frac{1}{2}y^2}.$ **10.** $2x^{-2} = m(1 - 2y) + ce^{-2y}.$

§24, page 46

1. $x = t^2 + c_1, \; y = c_1 t + c_2.$ **2.** $x = c_1 e^{-t} + c_2, \; y = (t + c_1)e^{-t}.$ **3.** $x = 1000t + c_1, \; y = 500t - 8t^2 + c_2.$ **4.** $\rho = \frac{1}{2}e^t + c_1 e^{-t}, \; \theta = \frac{1}{2}e^t - c_1 e^{-t} + c_2.$ **5.** $x = 6t^2 + 2c_1 t, \; y = -2t^3 + (6 - c_1)t^2 + 2c_1 t + c_2.$ **6.** $x = t + c_1 t^{-1}, \; y = c_1 \log t - t - c_1 t^{-1} + c_2.$ **7.** $x^2 = t^2(2 \log t + c_1), \; 2y = t^3(2 \log t + c_1 - 1) + c_2 t.$ **8.** $x = 4e^t(t - 1) + 2e^{2t} + c_1, \; y = 4e^t - e^{2t}(2t - 1) + c_2.$ **9.** $\rho = c_1 t, \; \theta = (c_1 + 1)t \log t + c_2 t.$ **10.** $x = c_1 \cos (at + c_2), \; y = c_1 \sin (at + c_2).$

§25, page 48

1. $xy \log \dfrac{cx}{y} = x + y.$ **2.** $3y(x^2 + 3) + 5x^3 = c.$ **3.** $\log x + \tan^{-1} \dfrac{y + x}{2x} = c.$ **4.**

$4x - 2y = \log \dfrac{c(x + y - 1)}{x + y + 1}.$ **5.** $y \sec^3 x = 2 \tan x + c.$ **6.** $2x = y(c - x^2).$ **7.**

$x^3 + x^2 y + \sin y = 1.$ **8.** $y = x(1 + \log y).$ **9.** $x + y = \log (cxy).$ **10.** $y \log cx$

$= \pm 1$. **11.** $y = cx$, $y^2 - 2x^2 = c$. **12.** $2x^3 + xy^2 = 2x \log y + 5x - 2$. **13.** $xy + 1 = 4.946e^{-x/y}$. **14.** $5y^2 = 8 \cos x + 4 \sin x - 4e^{\pi - 2x}$. **15.** $x^3y = 8xy - 16$. **16.** $x + y + c = 4 \log (2x + 3y + 7)$. **17.** $5xy^2 = 18(y^2 - x^2)$. **18.** $xy = 3(x^2 - 1)^3 - 21(x^2 - 1)$. **19.** $6x^2y + 6xy^2 + a^2y + b^2x = c$. **20.** $\log xy + y \log \dfrac{x-1}{x+1} = c$. **21.** $(x + y + 5)^2 = 16x + 20$. **22.** $(2x + y - 5)^2 = (3x + 2y - 2)^2 + c$. **23.** $(x^2 - y)^4 = 3\sqrt{x^2 - y^2} + c$. **24.** (a) $(x^2 - xy)e^{\frac{1}{2}y^2} = c$. (b) $6x^2y + 2x - 1 = ce^{-2x}$. (c) $x(xy + 1)e^y = c$. (d) $e^{6x}(2x^2y + y^2) = c$. **25.** $xy(y - x) = c(y + x)$. **26.** $4y = \log \dfrac{c(4x - 3y - 3)}{4x - 3y + 1}$. **27.** $25y^3 + 8(1 + 2y)^2(1 - y)e^{\frac{3}{2}x^2} = 0$. **28.** $x^2 + y^2 + c = \log (3x^2 + 4y^2 - 2)$. **29.** $y(\sec x + \tan x) = x + c$. **30.** $xy(x^2 + y^2 - 1) + 1 = 0$. **31.** $y^2 + x(\log x - 4) = 0$. **32.** $y = x + x \log \dfrac{x + y}{4}$. **33.** $(x + y - 3)^3 = 125(x - y - 1)$. **34.** $3x^2 + 2xy - y^2 = c$. **35.** $6\rho\theta - 2\rho^3 + 3 \sin^2 \theta = c$. **36.** $x(x + y)^3 = 3my + cx$. **37.** $(y - x^2 - xy)(x + y)^3 = c(y + 2x^2 + 2xy)$. **38.** $(3x + 2x^2 + 2y^2)\sqrt{x^2 + y^2} = c$. **39.** $xy(x^2 - xy + y^2) = c$. **40.** (a) $\log cx^2y + xy = 0$. (b) $x^n \sin xy = c$. **41.** $x^2\sqrt{y} + \log cx = 0$. **42.** $x^{\frac{3}{2}}(x^2 + y^2) + y^{\frac{3}{2}} = c$. **43.** $x[c - (y - 2x)^2] = 2y - 10x \tan^{-1} \dfrac{y}{x}$. **44.** $x = (t + 3c_1)e^{3t}$, $9y = (12t + 36c_1 - 1)e^{3t} + c_2$. **45.** $x - y = t - c_1$, $x \log x - y = c_2x$. **46.** $xy = t^2 + c_1$, $x + y = \log (2t^2 + c_1) + c_2$. **47.** $y^2 = 2x + c_1$, $y\sqrt{y^2 + 1} + \log (y + \sqrt{y^2 + 1}) \pm 10t = c_2$.

§26, page 50

1. $4x^3 + 12xy^2 - 3y^4 = 204$. **2.** $2nk\rho^{n-2} = (n - 2)\theta + c$, $0 \leq \theta \leq 2\pi$. **3.** $y = x \tan (ky + c)$. **4.** The part above the X-axis, or the part below the X-axis, of any straight line. **5.** (a) $T(1 + \mu^2) = \rho a[(1 - \mu^2) \sin \varphi - 2\mu \cos \varphi] + ce^{\mu\varphi}$. **7.** $x^2 + y^2 = cx$. **8.** $t \log 0.75 = 300 \log \dfrac{6 - 15x}{6 - 10x}$. **9.** $x = ka(a - x)t$. **11.** A parabola. **12.** $\rho \sin \theta - 3 = c\rho^2$. **13.** $x^2 + y^2 = cx$. **14.** $a\rho^{-1} = \sin \theta + ce^{\theta \cot \alpha}$. **15.** $c\rho^2 = a - \rho \sin \theta$. **16.** $\sqrt{l^2 - y^2} + l \log \dfrac{l - \sqrt{l^2 - y^2}}{y} = c \pm x$.

§27, page 54

1. $x = (t + 1)^2$, $y = 2(t + 1)$. **4.** $x = 50{,}000(1 - e^{-0.032t})$, $y = 81{,}250 (1 - e^{-0.032t}) - 1000t$. **5.** $66\frac{2}{3}$ lb. **6.** 256 lb. **7.** 222 lb. **8.** $2x = t + \dfrac{25}{t}$, $2y = t - \dfrac{25}{t}$. **9.** $x = y = ce^{4t}$.

§28, page 56

1. $q_\infty = 0$, $q_{t=RC} = 0.368q_0$, $q_{t=2RC} = 0.135q_0$, $i_{q=0.01q_0} = 1.61RC$. **2.** $0.368I_0$, $0.135I_0$, 0. **3.** (a) $i = \dfrac{E}{R} [1 - e^{-(R/L)t}]$, starting from 0, rapidly approaches E/R.

(b) $i = \dfrac{E}{R^2 + L^2\omega^2} (R \sin \omega t - \omega L \cos \omega t + \omega Le^{-Rt/L})$ starting from zero, rapidly approaches $\dfrac{E}{R^2 + L^2\omega^2}$ $(R \sin \omega t - \omega L \cos \omega t)$. **7.** $q = q_0 \cos \dfrac{t}{\sqrt{LC}}$, $i = -\dfrac{q_0}{\sqrt{LC}}$ $\sin \dfrac{t}{\sqrt{LC}}$.

§29, page 57

1. 1.05 lb./in.^{2} **2.** $(p_0^{\frac{2}{7}} - \frac{2}{7}k^{-\frac{5}{7}}h)^{3.5}$, $\frac{7}{2}p_0^{\frac{2}{7}}k^{\frac{5}{7}}$. **3.** 98,000 ft.

§30, page 61

1. $x^2 + y^2 = c$, $y = cx$. **2.** $x^2 + 3y^2 = c$, $y = cx^3$. **3.** $xy = c$, $y^2 - x^2 = c$. **4.** $3x^2y - y^3 = c$, $3xy^2 - x^3 = c$. **5.** $\tan^{-1}\dfrac{y}{x} = c - 2y$, $\log(x^2 + y^2) = c - 4x$. **6.** $x^3 + 3xy^2 = c$, $y^2 - x^2 = cy$. **7.** $10x - 32y = c$, $32x + 10y = c$. **8.** $x^2 + y^2 = c$, $y = cx$. **9.** $x^2 + y^2 = c$, $y = cx$. **10.** $x^2 + y^2 + 9 = cx$, $x^2 + y^2 = cy + 9$. All circles through $(\pm 3,0)$. **12.** (b) $3x^2y - y^3 = c$, $x^3 - 3xy^2 = c$; $x^3y - y^3x = c$, $x^4 - 6x^2y^2 + y^4 = c$. **13.** (a) $y = cx$, $x^2 + y^2 = c$. (b) $3 \tan^{-1}\dfrac{y}{x} = c - 2y$, $3\log(x^2 + y^2) = c - 4x$. (c) $x^2 + y^2 = cy$, $x^2 + y^2 = cx$. **14.** $r_1 - r_2 = cr_1r_2$, $\cos\theta_1 - \cos\theta_2 = c$.

§32, page 65

1. $(2y - x^2 - c)(\log y - x - c) = 0$. **2.** $(3y - x^3 - c)(2\log y - x^2 - c)(xy + cy + 1) = 0$. **3.** $(y + c)^2 = x^3$. **4.** $(x + \log y - c)(x - \log y - c) = 0$. **5.** $(x - c)^2 + y^2 = 1$, $y = \pm 1$. **6.** $ay^2 = (x - c)^3$, $y = 0$. **7.** $(x^2y - c)(xy - c) = 0$. **8.** $(2y - x^2 - c)(x + y - 1 - ce^{-x}) = 0$. **9.** $2cy = c^2x^2 - 1$. **10.** $(y - c)(x + y - c)(x^2 + xy + y^2 - c) = 0$. **11.** $(2y + bx^2 - c)[x - a \sin(y + c)] = 0$. **12.** Each family of the new system will be the orthogonal trajectories of one family of the old system. **13.** $\sqrt{l^2 - y^2} - l\log\dfrac{l + \sqrt{l^2 - y^2}}{y} = \pm x + c$.

§34, page 68

3. No. **4.** $y^2 - x^2 = 0$. Yes.

§35, page 70

1. (a) $2cy = c^2x^2 + 3$, $y^2 = 3x^2$. (b) $xy = c^2x + c$, $4x^2y + 1 = 0$. **2.** (a) $x = 2p + cp^{-2}$, $y = p^2 + 2cp^{-1}$. (b) $x = 3p + 2cp^{-\frac{1}{3}}$, $y = \frac{3}{2}p^2 - cp^{\frac{2}{3}}$. **3.** $y^2 = cx^2 + c^2$. **4.** $6y(4cx + 1)^2 = 4x(6cy + x)(4cx + 1) - (6cy + x)^2$, $y = 0$. **5.** $x(y - c)^2 = 4c$, $xy = -1$. **6.** $(y + c)^2 = 4cx$, $y = x$, $x = 0$.* **7.** $(y - 4c)^2 = 4cx$, $4y + x = 0$, $x = 0$.*

§36, page 71

1. (a) $x = y + \log(1 + ce^{-y})$. (b) $y^2 = 2cx + c^2$. (c) $(x + c)^2 = 2cy - c^2$, $x^2 + 2xy - y^2 = 0$. **2.** (a) $x = c - 2p - 2\log(p - 1)$, $y = c - p^2 - 2p - 2\log(p - 1)$. (b) $x = \dfrac{c(1 + a^2p^2)}{4p\sqrt[3]{p(3 - a^2p^2)}}$, $y = \dfrac{c}{\sqrt[3]{p(3 - a^2p^2)}}$. **3.** (a) $y = c(c - x)^2$, $27y = 4x^3$, $y = 0$. (b) $y = cx + c^{-1}$, $y^2 = 4x$. (c) $c^3y = cxy + 1$, $4y^2x^3 = 27$. **4.** (a) $2cx = y^2 + a^2c^2$, $x = \pm ay$. (b) $x^2c^2 = 1 + cy^2$. **5.** $x^2c^2 = 1 + 2cy$. **6.** $y = c(x - c)^2$, $27y = -4x^3$.

*If p is replaced by $1/q$, where $q = dx/dy$, $x = 0$ satisfies the resulting equation.

§37, page 73

1. $y = cx + c^2$, $x^2 + 4y = 0$. **2.** $y = cx + c^3$, $27y^2 + 4x^3 = 0$. **3.** $y = cx \pm a\sqrt{1 + c^2}$, $x^2 + y^2 = a^2$. **4.** $e^y = cx - 3c^2$, $x^2 = 12e^y$. **5.** $y^2 = 2cx + c^3$, $27y^4 = -32x^3$. **6.** $y^{10} = cx + 0.001c^3$, $27y^{20} = -4000x^3$. **7.** (a) $(y + x - k)^2 + 4kx = 0$. (b) $2xy = a^2$. (c) $x^2 = 4(1 - y)$. **8.** (a) $y^2 = 2kx + k^2$. (b) $(k - a^2)(k - y^2) = kx^2$. (c) $4(x^2 + y^2) = k^2$. (d) $(k + a^2)(k - y^2) = kx^2$. **9.** (a) $y = px + \dfrac{1}{4p}$. (b) $y = px \pm r\sqrt{1 + p^2}$. (c) $y = px \pm \sqrt{4mp}$. (d) $y = px \pm \frac{2}{3}p^{\frac{3}{2}}$.

(e) $y = px - 3\left(\dfrac{p}{4}\right)^{\frac{4}{3}}$. (f) $y = px + \frac{3}{8}p^{-\frac{1}{3}}$. **10.** (a) $27y^2 = 4(x - 2)^3$. (b) $8y^3 = 27x^2$. (c) $3x = p^{-\frac{5}{3}}(1 + 4p^2)$, $6y = p^{-\frac{2}{3}}(5 + 2p^2)$.

§38, page 76

1. (a) $2x$. (b) $6x^2 + 12x$. (c) 0. **2.** (a) $9e^{3x}$. (b) 0. (c) $-2a^2 \sin ax$. (d) $4a^4 \cos ax$. (e) 0. (f) $2x \sin x - 2 \cos x - 2 \sin x$. **3.** (a) e^{-3x}. (b) $-64 \cos 2x$. (c) 0. (d) $-64 \cos 2x$. **4.** (a) $x^2 + c$. (b) $x^3 + c_1x + c_2$. (c) $-\sin x + c_1x^2 + c_2x + c_3$. (d) $\frac{1}{8} \cos 2x + c_1x^2 + c_2x + c_3$. **5.** (a) $(x + c)e^y$. (b) $\frac{1}{8}e^{3x} + ce^{-3x}$. (c) $(\frac{1}{6}x^2 + c)e^{4x/3}$. **6.** $-xe^{-x} + c_1e^{-x} + c_2$. **7.** (a) $(\frac{1}{2}x^2 + c_1x + c_2)e^x$. (b) $xe^x + c_1e^x + c_2$. **8.** No. No. Yes.

§39, page 77

1. (a) $-e^{2x}$. (b) $-a^5e^{ax}$. (c) $32a^5e^{ax}$. (d) $-3e^{-2x}$. (e) 0. (f) $-120e^{-3x}$. **2.** (a) 0. (b) $24xe^{2x}$. (c) $e^{-x} \sin x$. (d) $e^{-2x} \cos x$. (e) $-192e^{-3x}$. (f) $n!e^{-x}$. **5.** (a) $e^{-x}(12x^3 - 36x^2 + 24x)$. (b) $e^x(\sin x - 6 \cos x)$. (c) $2e^{3x} \tan^3 x$, (d) $e^x(4x^2 + 2x)$.

§41, page 79

1. $y = c_1e^x + c_2e^{2x}$. **2.** $y = c_1e^x + c_2e^{-5x}$. **3.** $y = c_1e^{-3x} + c_2c^{-x}$. **4.** $y = e^{\frac{3}{2}x}(c_1e^{\frac{1}{2}\sqrt{13x}} + c_2e^{-\frac{1}{2}\sqrt{13x}})$. **5.** $y = c_0 + c_2e^{\frac{1}{2}\sqrt{5}x} + c_3e^{-\frac{1}{2}\sqrt{5}x}$. **6.** $y = c_1 + c_2e^{-x} + c_3e^x$. **7.** $y = c_1e^{kx} + c_2e^{-kx}$. **8.** $y = c_1e^x + c_2e^{-x} + c_3e^{3x}$. **9.** $y = c_1e^x + c_2e^{2x} + c_3e^{-3x}$. **10.** $y = c_1 + c_2e^{3x} + e^{-x}(c_3e^{\sqrt{2}x} + c_4e^{-\sqrt{2}x})$.

§43, page 81

1. $y = e^{3x}(c_1 + c_2x)$. **2.** $y = e^{-2x}(c_1 + c_2x)$. **3.** $y = c_1 + c_2x + c_3e^x$. **4.** $y = c_1 + c_2x + c_3x^2 + c_4r^{2x} + c_5e^{-2x}$. **5.** $y = c_0 + e^x(c_1 + c_2x)$. **6.** $y = c_1 + c_2x + c_3x^2$. **7.** $y = e^x(c_1 + c_2x) + c_3e^{-x}$. **8.** $y = e^x(c_1 + c_2x + c_3x^2)$. **9.** $y = c_1 + c_2x + e^{2x}(c_3 + c_4x) + e^{-2x}(c_5 + c_6x)$. **10.** $y = c_1 + c_2x + e^{2x}(c_3 + c_4x) + c_5e^{-4x}$. **11.** $y = (5 - 14x)e^x$. **12.** $y = e^{-x}$. **13.** $y = x + 2e^x$. **14.** $y = 2x + 4e^{-x}$. **15.** $y = 1 + 2xe^{2x}$. **16.** $y = e^{-x} + (2x - 1)e^x$.

§44, page 83

1. $y = e^x(c_1 \sin x + c_2 \cos x)$. **2.** $y = c_0 + e^{2x}(c_1 \sin x + c_2 \cos x)$. **3.** $y = c_1e^{2x} + e^{-x}(c_2 \sin 3x + c_3 \cos 3x)$. **4.** $y = c_1 \sin 2x + c_2 \cos 2x$. **5.** $y = c_1 \sin kx + c_2 \cos kx$. **6.** $y = c_1e^{ax} + c_2e^{-ax} + c_3 \sin ax + c_4 \cos ax$. **7.** $y = (c_1 + c_2x) \sin 2x + (c_3 + c_4x) \cos 2x$. **8.** $y = c_1 + c_2x + c_3 \sin x + c_4 \cos x$. **9.** $y = c_1 + c_2x + (c_3 + c_4x) \sin \sqrt{3}x + (c_5 + c_6x) \cos \sqrt{3}x$. **10.** $y = c_0e^{-ax} + e^{\frac{1}{2}ax}[c_1 \sin (\frac{1}{2}\sqrt{3}ax) + c_2 \cos (\frac{1}{2}\sqrt{3}ax)]$. **11.** $y = c_1e^{-x} + c_2e^{3x} + e^{-x}(c_3 \sin \sqrt{5}x + c_4 \cos \sqrt{5}x)$. **12.**

$y = \sin x - \cos x$. **13.** $y = 2 \sin 3x$. **14.** $y = e^{-x} \sin x$. **15.** $y = 1 + e^x \sin x$.
16. $y = 4e^x \sin x - 2e^{-2x}$. **17.** $y = 4 \cos 2(x - 1)$.

§45, page 85

1. $y = c_1 \sin 2x + c_2 \cos 2x + 2x + 1$. **2.** $y = c_1 e^{-2x} + c_2 e^x + 3x$. **3.** $y = c_1 e^{-4x}$
$+ c_2 e^{2x} - 2x + 1$. **4.** $y = c_1 e^{2x} + c_2 e^{-x} - 3e^x$. **5.** $y = c_1 \sin x + c_2 \cos x + 3$
$+ 3e^x$. **6.** $y = e^{-2x}(c_1 + c_2 x) + \frac{1}{4}(x - 1 + 2e^{2x})$. **7.** $y = c_1 + c_2 e^{-x} - 1.2 \sin 2x$
$- 0.6 \cos 2x$. **8.** $y = c_1 + c_2 x + c_3 e^x + \cos x - \sin x$. **9.** $y = c_1 \sin x + c_2 \cos x$
$+ e^x(2 \sin x - 4 \cos x)$. **10.** $y = c_1 e^x + c_2 e^{-x} - 2x^2 - 4$. **11.** $y = e^{3x} - 1 -$
$\cos 3x$. **12.** $y = 3e^{-3x} + 2x$. **13.** $y = 1 + 2e^{-x} + \frac{1}{2}e^x$. **14.** $y = xe^x - \frac{3}{4}e^x - 2$.
15. $y = e^{2x} + e^x + 2e^{-x}$.

§46, page 86

1. $y = c_1 + c_2 e^{-x} + 2x^2 - 4x$. **2.** $y = c_1 e^x + c_2 e^{-x} + \frac{5}{2}xe^x$. **3.** $y = -xe^x$. **4.**
$y = -2x^2 - 2x$. **5.** $y = -\frac{1}{2}x \cos x$. **6.** $y = -\frac{1}{2}xe^{-x}$. **7.** $y = x - \frac{4}{3} + \frac{1}{2}xe^{-x}$.
8. $y = 3 + \frac{1}{2}x^2 e^x$. **9.** $y = x(-2e^{-3x} - e^{-x})$. **10.** $y = \frac{1}{4}x \sin 2x$. **11.** $y = 2x^2$
$- 2x - \frac{1}{2}xe^{-2x}$. **12.** $y = -2x \sin 2x$. **13.** $y = x - x \cos 2x$. **14.** $y = 2x +$
$\frac{1}{34}(15 \sin 2x + 60 \cos 2x)$. **15.** $y = x^3 e^x$. **16.** $y = -\frac{1}{2}xe^x \cos x$.

§47, page 90

1. (a) $\frac{1}{24}x^4 e^x$. (b) $-e^{-3x} \sin x$. (c) $e^{2x}(2 \sin x - 2 \cos x)$. **2.** (a) $\frac{1}{25} \sin 3x$.
(b) $\frac{1}{5}(2 \cos 2x + \sin 2x)$. (c) $\frac{1}{2} \sin x$. **3.** (a) $-x^2 - 2x - 2$. (b) $\frac{1}{32}(8x^2 - 4x$
$+ 1)$. (c) $\frac{1}{54}(9x^2 - 6x + 2)$. **4.** $y = 8x^3 e^{3x}$. **5.** $y = \dfrac{x^7 e^x}{42}$. **6.** $y = e^{-x} \log (2x$
$+ 3)$. **7.** $y = (8x^2 - 4x + 1)e^{2x}$. **8.** $y = (8x^2 - 4x + 1)e^{3x}$. **9.** $y = \frac{1}{9} \sin 2x$.
10. $y = -\frac{1}{3} \sin 2x - \frac{1}{8} \cos 3x$. **11.** $y = \frac{1}{2} \sin 3x - 2 \cos 2x$. **12.** $y = -e^x \sin x$.
13. $y = -3e^x \sin 3x$. **14.** $y = \frac{9}{17}e^x(\sin 2x - 4 \cos 2x)$. **15.** $y = e^x(-7 \cos 3x +$
$3 \sin 3x)$. **16.** $y = \frac{1}{2} \sin x(e^{2x} - 2e^x)$. **17.** $y = \frac{1}{6}e^x(x^3 - 3x^2 + 6x - 6)$. **18.** y
$= e^x \cos x$. **19.** $y = \frac{1}{17}e^x(\sin 2x - 4 \cos 2x)$. **20.** $y = -2e^x(\sin x + \cos x)$.
21. $y = \frac{1}{4}e^{3x}(2x^2 - 6x + 7)$. **22.** $y = \frac{9}{32}e^{2x}(8x^3 - 6x^2 + 3x)$. **23.** $y = e^{3x}(2x^2 -$
$x + \frac{1}{4})$. **24.** $y = x^2 e^{2x}$. **25.** $y = x^2 e^{-3x}$. **27.** $y = \cos x + 2x \sin x$. **28.** $y = \sin 3x$
$- 6x \cos 3x$. **29.** $y = (4x^2 - 2) \sin x + 4x \cos x$. **30.** $y = 12x \sin 2x + (3 -$
$8x^2) \cos 2x$.

§48, page 92

1. $y = c_1 \sin x + c_2 \cos x - \cos x \log (\sec x + \tan x)$. **2.** $y = (c_1 + x) \sin x +$
$(c_2 + \log \cos x) \cos x$. **3.** $y = c_1 \sin 2x + c_2 \cos 2x + \sin 2x \log (\csc 2x - \cot 2x)$.
4. $y = e^{-x}[(c_1 + x) \sin x + (c_2 + \log \cos x) \cos x]$
5. $y = e^{2x}\left[c_1 + c_2 x + \dfrac{x^{n+2}}{(n + 1)(n + 2)} \right]$, $n \neq -1$, $n \neq -2$; $y = e^{2x}(c_1 + c_2 x +$
$x \log x)$, $n = -1$; $y = e^{2x}(c_1 + c_2 x - \log x)$, $n = -2$. **6.** $y = e^{-2x}(c_1 + c_2 x -$
$\log x)$. **7.** $y = e^{-x}[c_1 + c_2 x - \log x - \frac{1}{2}(\log x)^2]$. **8.** $y = e^x[c_1 \sin x + c_2 \cos x$
$+ \sin x \log (\csc x - \cot x) - \cos x \log (\sec x + \tan x)]$. **9.** $y = e^x[c_1 + c_2 \cos x$
$+ c_3 \sin x - x \cos x + \sin x \log \cos x + \log (\sec x + \tan x)]$. **10.** $y = e^x[c_1 +$
$c_2 x + c_3 x^2 - 3x^{-1} \log x - \frac{11}{2}x^{-1}]$.

§49, page 93

1. $y = 3c^{2x}$. **2.** $y = -x^2 + x + 1$. **3.** $y = x^2 + x + xe^x$. **4.** $y = e^{-x} - \frac{1}{2} \sin x$.
5. $y = -5e^{2x} + 5e^{3x}$. **6.** $y = 1 + \cos x + \sin 2x$. **7.** $y = e^x(1 - 2 \sin x -$

$\cos x$). **8.** $y = e^{-x} + e^x(2x - 5)$. **9.** $y = e^{-x} - 6x - \sin 5x$. **10.** $y = e^x \cos 2x - e^{-x} \cos x$. **11.*** $y = 12xe^{2x}$. **12.** $y = e^{2x}(8x^2 - 4x)$. **13.** $y = 1 + xe^{-x}$. **14.** $y = (\frac{1}{3}x^3 + 2x^2 + 6x)e^{-x}$. **15.** $y = 3xe^x - 4xe^{-\frac{3}{2}x}$. **16.** $y = -\sin 2x - \cos 3x$. **17.** $y = -10 \cos 4x - 5 \sin 4x$. **18.** $y = 2 \cos 4x - 2 \sin 4x$. **19.** $y = 2x \sin 3x$. **20.** $y = 2x \cos 3x + 6x^2 \sin 3x$. **21.** $y = -2xe^x \cos x$. **22.** $y = 6xe^{-2x} \sin x$. **23.** $y = \sin x \log x$. **24.** $y = \sin x \tan x$. **25.** $y = 2 \sin 2x \log (\sec 2x + \tan 2x) - 4$. **26.** $y = e^{2x} \log x$.

§50, page 95

1. $x = 2 - (c_1 + c_2 + c_2t)e^t$, $y = (c_1 + c_2t)e^t - 2t - 4$. **2.** $x = e^{2t}(c_1 - 4t)$, $2y = (4t - c_1 + 2)e^{2t} + c_2$. **3.** $x = c_1e^{4t} - c_2e^{8t}$, $y = 3c_1e^{4t} + c_2e^{8t}$. **4.** $x = c_1e^{3t} + c_2e^{-t} + 0.4 \sin t - 0.2 \cos t$, $y = -2c_1e^{3t} + 2c_2e^{-t} + 0.2 \sin t + 0.4 \cos t$. **5.** $x = c_1e^t + c_2e^{-t} + c_3 \sin t + c_4 \cos t - 1$, $y = c_1e^t + c_2e^{-t} - c_3 \sin t - c_4 \cos t$. **6.** $x = (2c_1 + 2c_2t)e^t + (2c_3 + 2c_4t)e^{-t}$, $y = (c_2 - c_1 - c_2t)e^t - (c_3 + c_4 + c_4t)e^{-t}$. **7.** $x = (6c_2 - 2c_1 - 2c_2t)e^t - \frac{1}{3}(c_3e^{-\frac{3}{2}t} + 2)$, $y = (c_1 + c_2t)e^t + c_3e^{-\frac{3}{2}t} - t$. **8.** $x = c_1e^{\frac{3}{2}t} - 2t^2 - 8t - 16$, $y = c_1e^{\frac{3}{2}t} + c_2 - 4t$. **9.** $y = c_1e^{\sqrt{3}t} + c_2e^{-\sqrt{3}t} + c_3 \sin\left(\frac{t}{\sqrt{3}}\right) + c_4 \cos\left(\frac{t}{\sqrt{3}}\right) + 2e^t$, $x = -16e^t + (5D - 3D^3)y$. **10.** $2x = (23 - 13t)e^t + (23 + 13t)e^{-t} - 46$, $4y = (-36 + 13t)e^t - (36 + 13t)e^{-t} + 72$. **11.** $x = c_1 - 3c_2e^{2t} - 3c_3e^{-2t}$, $y = -2c_2e^{2t} + 2c_3e^{-2t}$, $z = c_2e^{2t} + c_3e^{-2t} + c_1$. **12.** $x = c_1e^{2t} + c_2e^{-t} + \frac{1}{2}$, $y = c_1e^{2t} - 2c_2e^{-t} + t - \frac{1}{2}$, $z = -2c_1e^{2t} + c_2e^{-t}$. **13.** $x = e^t(1 - c_2 - 2t) + c_3$, $y = e^t(4t + 2c_2 - 1) - c_3$, $z = e^t(1 - c_2 - 2t) + c_1$. **14.** $x = c_1e^t + c_2e^{-t} + \frac{1}{4}te^t$, $2y = -c_1e^t + (c_3 - c_2)e^{-t} - \frac{1}{4}te^t$, $z = c_1e^t - (c_2 + c_3)e^{-t} + \frac{1}{4}te^t + \frac{1}{4}e^t$.

§51, page 98

1. 5 ft., $\frac{1}{6}$ sec., 6 cycles/sec., $\frac{5}{72}$ sec., $\frac{11}{72}$ sec. **2.** $\frac{\pi}{16}$ sec., $\frac{16}{\pi}$ cycles/sec., 13 ft.

3. $y = 5 \sin 10t + 10 \cos 10t$, $\frac{5}{\pi}$ cycles/sec., $\frac{\pi}{5}$ sec., $\sqrt{125}$ ft. **4.** 2π sec., $\frac{1}{2\pi}$ cycle/sec., 5 ft. **5.** $\frac{1}{60}$ sec., 60 cycles/sec. **6.** $k^2 < 120$. **7.** 1.99 sec., $e^{-0.05t}$, 13.9 sec. **8.** $x = 2e^{-t/2} \sin 3t$, 2.09 sec., 0.223. **9.** $a = 2$, $x = 2e^{-t/3} \sin 3t$, 2.09 sec. **10.** $b = \frac{1}{5}$, $c = (120\pi)^2$ nearly. **11.** $b = 0.046$, $c = 400\pi^2$ nearly.

§54, page 104

2. $s = 0.4 \cos 10t + 0.32$, 0.4 ft., $\frac{\pi}{5}$ sec., $f = \frac{5}{\pi}$ cycles/sec. **3.** $x = e^{-0.01t}(0.0004 \sin 10t + 0.4 \cos 10t) + 0.32$, $\frac{\pi}{5}$ sec., $\frac{5}{\pi}$ cycles/sec., $e^{-0.01t}$, 69.3 sec. **4.** (a) $x = -0.6 \sin 10t + 0.4 \cos 10t + \sin 6t + 0.32$. (b) $\frac{\pi}{5}$ sec., $\frac{\pi}{3}$ cycles/sec., π. (c) 0.210 ft.

6. $x = a \cos \sqrt{\frac{y}{h}}\, t$. **7.** $x = 4 \sin (\sqrt{3g}\, t) - 3.46 \sin (2 \sqrt{g}\, t)$, 3.80 ft. **8.** $x =$

* Different answers to exercises 11 to 26 are obtained by different methods. Two answers to the same problem may differ by a solution of the right member equated to zero.

$\frac{1}{2}\sin(2\sqrt{g}\,t) - \sqrt{g}\,t\cos(2\sqrt{g}\,t)$, 157 ft. below initial position.   No.   **9.** $2\pi\frac{\sqrt{I}}{k}$.

10. $I = \dfrac{g}{16\pi^2}$ lb.-ft.^{2} **11.** $\theta = e^{-0.693t}(c_1 \sin 12.5t + c_2 \cos 12.5t)$, 0.501 sec.

12. 656 lb.   **13.** 0.886 sec., 0.886$\rho^{-\frac{1}{2}}$ sec.   **14.** $2\pi\sqrt{\dfrac{l}{g}}$.   **15.** $x = e^{-1.08t}(0.111$

$\sin 9.77t + \cos 9.77t)$, 0.643 sec.   **16.** 21.1 min.   **17.** $\dfrac{w}{20}$, 93.7 ft.   **18.** Rises 2.02

sec., then falls.   Speed approaches 80.5 ft./sec. downward.   **19.** $x + y = 36 \sin 10t$ $- 6\sqrt{6}\sin 10\sqrt{6}\,t$, $x = 24 \sin 10t + 6\sqrt{6}\sin 10\sqrt{6}\,t$.   **20.** (a) 5.4×10^7 ton-ft.^{2} (b) 9.9 sec.   **22.** (a) Small.   (b) Decrease.   (c) -99.   (d) Violent.

§55, page 110

1. $x = v_0 \cos\varphi \cdot t$, $y = v_0 \sin\varphi \cdot t - \frac{1}{2}gt^2$.   **2.** $x = 130,000(1 - e^{-0.02t})$, $y = 155,$-$500(1 - e^{-0.02t}) - 1610t$,   maximum $y = 22,000$ ft.   **3.** $x = 49,800(1 - e^{-0.04t})$, $y = 174.3t - 16.1t^2$.   **4.** $x = 347t$, $y = 118,000(1 - e^{-0.0268t}) - 1200t$, 30,000 ft., 27,000 ft.   **5.** $x = a\cos\left(\sqrt{\dfrac{k}{m}}\,t\right)$, $y = v_0\sqrt{\dfrac{m}{k}}\sin\left(\sqrt{\dfrac{k}{m}}\,t\right)$.   **6.** (a) $x = 3\sin t$, $y = 2\cos t - 2$.   (b) $x = 2.12 \sin t$, $y = 2.12\sin t + 2\cos t - 2$.   **7.** 2120 ft. **8.** 300 ft./sec., 10,600 ft.

§57, page 114

2. $q = CE\left[1 - \cos\left(\dfrac{t}{\sqrt{LC}}\right)\right]$, $i = \dfrac{CE}{\sqrt{LC}}\sin\left(\dfrac{t}{\sqrt{LC}}\right)$, $2\pi\sqrt{LC}$, CE, $2\pi\sqrt{LC}$, $E\sqrt{\dfrac{C}{L}}$.   **5.** $q = q_0\cos\left(\dfrac{t}{\sqrt{LC}}\right)$, $i = -\dfrac{q_0}{\sqrt{LC}}\sin\left(\dfrac{t}{\sqrt{LC}}\right)$.   **6.** $q = \dfrac{\epsilon^{-5t}}{1600}(-\sin 200t - 40\cos 200\,t) + \dfrac{1}{40}$, $i = 5.00\epsilon^{-5t}\sin 200\,t$, 0.460 sec., $\dfrac{1}{40}$, 0.   **7.** $q = 200\epsilon^{-\frac{1}{2}t}(-2 - t) + 400$, $i = 100t\epsilon^{-\frac{1}{2}t}$.   **8.** $q = 0.05\epsilon^{-5t}\cos 200t$, $i = \epsilon^{-5t}(-10$ $\sin 200t - 0.25\cos 200t)$, $\dfrac{\pi}{100}$, 0, 0.   **9.** $q = q_0\cos\dfrac{t}{\sqrt{LC}}$, $i = \dfrac{dq}{dt}$.   **10.** $q = -CE$ $\cos\left(\dfrac{t}{\sqrt{LC}}\right) + CE$, $i = E\sqrt{\dfrac{C}{L}}\sin\dfrac{t}{\sqrt{LC}}$.   **11.** $q = \dfrac{q_0}{\omega_1}\epsilon^{-at}(\omega_1\cos\omega_1 t + a\sin\omega_1 t)$, $i = \dfrac{dq}{dt}$.

§59, page 116

2. $i = -\dfrac{E}{Z^2}(X\cos\omega t - R\sin\omega t)$.   **3.** $q = -0.00275(3\sin 400t + \cos 400t)$, $i = 1.10(\sin 400t - 3\cos 400t)$; 0.0087 coulomb, 3.48 amperes.   **4.** (a) $i = -\dfrac{E}{L\omega}\cos\omega t$.

(b) $i = \dfrac{E}{R}\sin \omega t$.   (c) $q = CE\sin\omega t$.   (d) $q = \dfrac{EC}{1 + R^2C^2\omega^2}(\sin\omega t - RC\omega$

$\cos \omega t$), $i = \dfrac{EC\omega}{1 + R^2C^2\omega^2}$ $(\cos \omega t + RC\omega \sin \omega t)$. (e) $i = \dfrac{E}{R^2 + L^2\omega^2}$ $(R \sin \omega t -$

$L\omega \cos \omega t)$. (f) $q = \dfrac{CE}{1 - LC\omega^2} \sin \omega t$, $i = \dfrac{CE\omega}{1 - LC\omega^2} \cos \omega t$. **5.** $i = 10 \sin 500t(1$

$- \epsilon^{-5t})$, 0.0067 sec. **6.** 4.2×10^{-7} farad, 1.000018.

§60, page 121

1. $i_2 = \dfrac{E}{R} \sin \omega t$, $i_1 = \dfrac{E}{L\omega} (1 - \cos \omega t)$, $i = i_1 + i_2$. **2.** $i_1 = \dfrac{E}{-R} \sin \omega t$, $q = CE \sin \omega t$,

$i_2 = CE\omega \cos \omega t$, $i = i_1 + i_2$. **4.** $i_2 = 2 \sin 400t$. $160,100q = 40\epsilon^{-10t} + \sin 400t$
$- 40 \cos 400t$, $i_1 = dq/dt$. **6.** $q = 1 - \frac{1}{2}\epsilon^{-\frac{1}{2}t}(2 - t)$. **7.** $i = \epsilon^{-50t}(3.04 \sin 312t$
$- \cos 312t) + 1$. **8.** $i = \frac{1}{12}(1 - \cos 300t) + 10t \sin 300t$.

9. $i = \left[\dfrac{(C_1E_1 + C_2E_2)\omega}{1 - L(C_1 + C_2)\omega^2}\right]\left(\cos \omega t - \cos \dfrac{t}{\sqrt{L(C_1 + C_2)}}\right)$. **11.** (a) 100 per cent

nearly. (b) 100 per cent nearly. (c) 89 per cent. (d) Less than 20 per cent.

§62, page 125

1. $y = 2x^3 + c_1x + c_2$. **2.** $y = 6 \log x + c_1x^2 + c_2x + c_3$. **3.** $y = c_1 \log x + c_2$.
4. $y = c_1x + c_1^2 \log (x - c_1) + c_2$. **5.** $y = x^4 + c_1 \log x + c_2$. **6.** $y = c_1xe^x + c_2$.
7. $y = -4x^3 + 2x - 26$. **8.** $4y = 5 \log \left(3 \tan \dfrac{x}{2} + 1\right) - \log \left(\tan \dfrac{x}{2} + 3\right)$. **9.**
$5y = 3x^5 - 5x^4 + 10x - 8$. **10.** $ay = ae^{x/a} - x$. **11.** $y = 1$, $3y + x^3 = 3$. **12.**
$y = a^2 \sinh \dfrac{x}{a} - 2ax$. **13.** $\dfrac{v - v_1}{v - v_0} = r_0 \dfrac{r - r_1}{r_1(r - r_0)}$.

§63, page 127

1. $y^2 = c_1x + c_2$. **2.** $x = c_1y - \log y + c_2$. **3.** $y^3 = c_1x + c_2$, $y = c$. **4.** $e^y(y -$
$1) = Rx + c$. **5.** $\sqrt{cs^2 - 1} = \pm ct + c_1$. **6.** $\log (8e^s + \sqrt{8e^{2s} - c}) = \pm 8t +$
c_1. **7.** $y = 1 + \sin \sqrt{8} x$. **8.** $10e^s + \sqrt{576 + 100e^{2s}} = 36e^{10t}$. **9.** $e^s = 2.6$
$\sin (10t + \sin^{-1} \frac{5}{13})$. **10.** $e^{-\frac{1}{2}y} = \cos \dfrac{x}{2}$. **11.** $y = 1 - e^{-x}$. **12.** $2y^3 + 3y^2 = 6x + 5$.

§64, page 130

4. $(D + x + 1)(D - x)$. **5.** $(D - x)(D + 2x - 1)$. **6.** $(D + 2 - 2x)(D + x)$.
7. $(xD - 2)(xD + x + 1)$. **8.** $(xD + 1)(D + x)$. **9.** $(D - 1)(xD - 2)$. **10.**
$(D + 2x)(D + 2x + 1)$. Yes. **11.** $xy = c_1(x^2 - 2x + 2) + c_2e^{-x}$. **12.** $y + 12x$
$= c_1x^2 + c_2$. **13.** $y = 12x^2 + c_1x \log x + c_2x$. **14.** $y = (x + c_1)e^{x^2} + ce^{x^2-x}$. **15.**
$xy = (x + c_1)e^x + c_2$. **16.** $x^2y = (x^2 + c)e^{x^2} + c_1$.

§65, page 131

1. $y = c_1x^{-1} + c_2x^{-2} + c_3x^3$. **2.** $y = c_1x^3 + c_2x^{-3} + \dfrac{1}{n^2 - 9} x^n$. **3.** $y = c_1(x - 1)$
$+ c_2(x - 1)^2 + c_3(x - 1)^{-2} + \log [e(x - 1)]$. **4.** $y = c_1 + c_2x + c_3 \log x$.

§66, page 133

1. $y = c_1 x + c_2 \sqrt{x^2 - 1}$. **2.** $xy = c_1 e^{-x}(x^2 + 2x + 2) + c_2$. **3.** $y = c_1(x^2 - 1) + c_2 x + 3x^2 + x^4$. **4.** $y = (x^4 + c_2)e^x + c_1(x^3 + 3x^2 + 6x + 6)$. **5.** $y = \sin x$ log $[c_1 \sin x(\csc x - \cot x)^c]$.

§67, page 134

1. $p_2 - p_1' + p_0'' = 0$, $p_2\mu - (p_1\mu)' + (p_0\mu)'' = 0$. **2.** $p_n - (p_{n-1})' + (p_{n-2})'' - \cdots + (-1)^n p_0^{(n)} = 0$, $p_n\mu - (p_{n-1}\mu)' + (p_{n-2}\mu)'' + \cdots + (-1)^n(p_0\mu)^{(n)} = 0$.
5. $y = x^2 + c_1 x + \dfrac{c_2}{x^2}$. **7.** $y(x^2 + x - 3) = c_1 x^2 + c_2 x + c_3$. **8.** $(x^2 + 1)y = c_1(x$ log $x - x) + c_2 x + c_3$.

§68, page 137

1. (a) $(x - c_1)^2 + y^2 = c_2^2$. (b) $y = c_1 \cosh\left(\dfrac{x}{c_1} + c_2\right)$. (c) $(c_1 x + c_2)^2 = k(c_1 y^2 - 1)$. (d) $c_1 x = \cosh(c_1 y + c_2)$. (e) $x^2 + (y - c_1)^2 = c_2^2$. (f) $(y - c_1)^2 = 4c_2(x - c_2)$. **2.** $(x - c_1)^2 + (y - c_2)^2 = a^2$. **3.** $e^{x/a} = c_1 \sin\left(\dfrac{y}{a} + c_2\right)$. **4.** (a) Same as 1(a) and 1(b). (b) $c_1 - x = \sqrt{c_2^2 - y^{\frac{2}{3}}}\,(2c_2^2 + y^{\frac{2}{3}})$.

§69, page 138

1. $2Hy = wx^2$. **2.** $H\dfrac{d^2y}{dx^2} = w_1 + w_2\sqrt{1 + \left(\dfrac{dy}{dx}\right)^2}$. **3.** $y = c \cosh\sqrt{\dfrac{w}{H}}\,x$. **4.** $2Hy = wlx^2$. **6.** $y = a \cosh\sqrt{\dfrac{w}{H}}\,x$. **7.** $*y = (c + kt)\cosh\left(\sqrt{\dfrac{w}{H}}\,x\right) - kt$. **8.** $*x = w\displaystyle\int^y \dfrac{(c^2 + 2H/w - y^2)\,dy}{\sqrt{4H^2 - w^2(c^2 + 2H/w - y^2)^2}}$. **9.** $*$Like Ans. (8) with y replaced by $y + kt$. **10.** $x_0 = a \tanh^{-1}\dfrac{b}{l}$, $y_0 = l \coth\dfrac{c}{a} - a$, where a satisfies $l^2 - b^2 = a^2 \sinh^2\dfrac{c}{a}$.

§70, page 142

1. $y = \dfrac{w}{24EI}(2lx^3 - x^4 - l^3 x)$; maximum deflection $= \dfrac{5wl^4}{384EI}$. **2.** $y = \dfrac{P}{EI}\left(\dfrac{1}{12}x^3 - \dfrac{1}{16}l^2 x\right)$; maximum deflection $= \dfrac{Pl^3}{48EI}$. **3.** $\dfrac{5wl^4}{384EI} + \dfrac{1}{48}\dfrac{Pl^3}{EI}$. **4.** (a) 0.889 in. (b) 1.067 in. (c) 1.956 in. **5.** (a) $y = \dfrac{P}{6EI}(-3lx^2 + x^3)$. (b) $y = -\dfrac{w}{24EI}(x^4 - 4lx^3 + 6l^2 x^2)$. (c) y equals the sum of the y's from (a) and (b). **6.** $y =$

* c is the depth of material over the highest point of the arch, and t is the thickness of the top layer.

$$-\frac{w}{48EI}(2x^4 - 5lx^3 + 3l^2x^2);\ 0.578.$$ **7.** $y = \dfrac{P}{48EI}(4x^3 - 3lx^2).$ **8.** $y_1 = \dfrac{Px}{18EI}$

$(x^2 - 8a^2),\ y_2 = \dfrac{P}{18EI}[x^3 - 3(x - 2a)^3 - 8a^2x],\ \dfrac{16\sqrt{6}\,Pa^3}{81EI}.$ **9.** $\frac{16}{147}Pa^3.$

10. $\dfrac{kl^5}{30EI}.$ **11.** $y = \dfrac{Pb^2x^2}{6l^3EI}[(3a + b)x - 3al], x \leqq a.$

§71, page 146

2. Equation of graph $y = \dfrac{G}{P}\left(1 - \cos\dfrac{4\pi x}{l}\right)$ from $x = 0$ to $x = l$. **4.** Equation of

graph $y = -a\left(1 - \cos\dfrac{\frac{3}{2}\pi x}{l}\right),\ 0 \leqq x \leqq l.$

§72, page 149

1. $\dfrac{1}{3}a^{\frac{3}{2}}\left(2 - \dfrac{1}{\sqrt{2}}\right).$ **2.** $\dfrac{a^2}{\sqrt{k}}.$ **4.** $\rho = 2e^{2t} - e^{-2t} - \frac{1}{4},\ \theta = 2t;\ a_\theta = 16e^{2t} +$

$8e^{-2t}.$ **5.** $\rho = t + 1,\ \theta = \dfrac{2t}{t+1},\ F_\rho = \dfrac{4W}{g(t+1)^3}.$ **7.** $\rho\cosh\left(\sqrt{n-1}\,\theta\right) = b,$

$n \geqq 1,\ \rho\cos\left(\sqrt{1-n}\,\theta\right) = b,\ 0 \leqq n \leqq 1.$ **8.** $\rho = \dfrac{b}{n - (n-1)\cos\theta}.$

9. $\rho^{n+1}\cos[(n+1)\theta + c_1] = c_2.$ **11.** $(a)\ x = \dfrac{30,000}{g} \times \log\left(\dfrac{154g}{30,000}t + 1\right),$

$y = -\dfrac{30,000}{g} \times \log\cosh\dfrac{g}{\sqrt{30,000}}t.$ $(b)\ 15.3$ sec. $(c)\ 1170$ ft.

§74, page 152

1. $x^2 - y^2 = c_1,\ x + y = c_2z.$ **2.** $bx^2 - ay^2 = c_1,\ cy^2 - bz^2 = c_2.$ **3.** $y = c_1x,$
$2x - 2y = z^2 + c_2.$ **4.** $y^2 + z^2 = c_1,\ \log c_2x = \tan^{-1}\dfrac{y}{z}.$ **5.** $x - y = c_1(x - z) =$
$c_2(y - z).$ **6.** $x = c_1y,\ (3x + 2y - 2z)y = c_2.$ **7.** $x^2 - y^2 = c_1,\ (x + y)(z - 1)$
$= c_2(z + 1).$ **8.** $x^2 + y^2 + z^2 = c_1y,\ y = c_2z.$ **9.** $x + y + z = c_1,\ xyz = c_2.$ **10.**
$x - y - z = c_1,\ x^2 - y^2 = cz^2.$ **11.** $lx + my + nz = c_1,\ x^2 + y^2 + z^2 = c_2.$ **12.**
$x + y - z = c_1,\ xy - z^{-1} = c_2.$ **13.** $x^2 - y^2 = c_1,\ z^2 - w^2 = c_2,\ x + y = c_3(z + w).$ **14.** $x - y = c_1,\ x + y + z + w = c_2,\ x^2 + y^2 + z^2 + w^2 = c_3.$ **15.** $(a)\ y$
$= c_1\sin 2x + c_2\cos 2x + \frac{5}{2},\ 5z = (2c_1 + c_2)\cos 2x + (c_1 - 2c_2)\sin 2x - 10x + \frac{5}{2}.$
$(b)\ y = c_1 + c_2e^{2x} - 4e^x,\ z = -c_1 + c_2e^{2x} - 2e^x.$ $(c)\ y = c_1e^{2x} + c_2e^{-2x} - 3x, 3z$
$= 3c_1e^{2x} - c_2e^{-2x} - 3 - 3x - 6x^2.$ $(d)\ y = c_1\sin x + c_2\cos x - \frac{1}{3}a\sin 2x,\ 2z = (c_1$
$- c_2)\cos x - (c_1 + c_2)\sin x - \frac{2}{3}a(\cos 2x + \sin 2x).$

§76, page 158

1. $y = x(c + z^2).$ **2.** $x + \log(y - z) = c.$ **3.** $xy = c(z - a).$ **4.** $(x^2 + y^2)e^z +$
$z = c.$ **5.** $y(1 + zx^2y) = c.$ **6.** $xy^2 = z(c - z).$ **7.** $z = (y + c)(x + a).$ **8.** $z =$
$x^3 + y^3 + xy^2 + c.$ **9.** $x^2 + y^2 - z(x + y) = c.$ **10.** $ax - cz = c_1(ay - bz).$

11. $xy + xz + yz = cx$. **12.** (a) $\dfrac{\partial M}{\partial y} - \dfrac{\partial N}{\partial x} = M\dfrac{\partial N}{\partial z} - N\dfrac{\partial M}{\partial z}$. (b) $\dfrac{\partial M}{\partial y} = \dfrac{\partial N}{\partial z}$.

13. $ax^2 + 2(a + 2b)xy + 2by^2 - 2cx = c_1$. **14.** (a) $z = mx$, $z = ny$. (b) $xz = m$, $z^3y = n$. (c) $x^3y^2 = m$, $x^2z = n$. (d) $x^2 - y^2 = m$, $z^2 - y^2 = n$. **15.** (a) $x^2 + xy + yz = c$. (b) $z^2x - y = cx$. (c) $xy = c(z - 3)$. **16.** (a) $x^2 + y^2 - z^2 = c$. (b) $y = cx^2$.

§77, page 160

1. (a) $\dfrac{dy}{dx} = z$, $\dfrac{dz}{dx} = -x^2z - x^3y$. (b) $\dfrac{dx}{1} = \dfrac{dy}{z} = \dfrac{dz}{-Pz - Qy}$. (c) $x_1 = \dfrac{dx}{dt}$, y_1
$= \dfrac{dy}{dt}$, $y_2 = \dfrac{dy_1}{dt}$, $\dfrac{dx_1}{dt} = 3x - 3y - 2y_2$, $\dfrac{dy_2}{dt} = 3x - y_2$. **2.** $y = c_1 \sin (x + c_2)$. **3.**

(a) $y = c_1x \log x + c_2x$. (b) $y = c_1e^{-\frac{1}{2}x^2}\displaystyle\int e^{\frac{1}{2}x^2}\, dx + ce^{-\frac{1}{2}x^2}$. **4.** $\dfrac{dy}{dx} = y_1$; $\dfrac{dy_i}{dx} =$

y_{i+1}, $i = 1, 2, \ldots, (n - 2)$; $\dfrac{dy_{n-1}}{dx} + A_1y_{n-1} + A_2y_{n-2} + \cdots + A_ny = F(x)$; n.

§78, page 161

2. No. $\dfrac{dy}{dx} = \dfrac{y}{x}$ is not defined when $x = 0$. **3.** $y = 0$. **4.** $\dfrac{dy}{dx}$ undefined and

$\dfrac{\partial}{\partial y}\left(\dfrac{dy}{dx}\right)$ undefined. No, for $\dfrac{3y}{x}$ has no value at $(0,0)$. **5.** Yes. $y = 2x + 5$,

$z + 2e^x + 3x + 8 = 0$. **6.** No. **7.** Special case of exercise 8. **8.** A unique so-

lution $y = \varphi(x)$ through (x_0, y_0) exists which has $\dfrac{d^ky}{dx^k}$ at (x_0, y_0) equal to y_{k0}, $k =$

$1, 2, \ldots, n - 1$, provided the A functions are continuous and single-valued in $|x - x_0| \leqq a$, $a > 0$. **9.** $a = 0$, $a = 1$.

§80, page 166

1. $y = c_0\left(1 + x + \dfrac{x^2}{2!} + \cdots + \dfrac{x^n}{n!} + \cdots\right) = c_0\displaystyle\sum_{n=0}^{\infty}\dfrac{x^n}{n!}$. **2.** $y = c_0\displaystyle\sum_{n=0}^{\infty}\dfrac{x^{2n}}{n!}$.

3. $y = c_0\left(1 + \dfrac{x^4}{3 \cdot 4} + \dfrac{x^8}{3 \cdot 4 \cdot 7 \cdot 8} + \cdots\right) + c_1\left(x + \dfrac{x^5}{4 \cdot 5} + \dfrac{x^9}{4 \cdot 5 \cdot 8 \cdot 9} + \cdots\right)$.

4. $y = c_0\displaystyle\sum_{n=0}^{\infty}(-1)^n(2n + 1)x^{2n} + c_1\displaystyle\sum_{n=0}^{\infty}(2n + 2)x^{2n+1}$. **5.** $y = c_1(x - x^3) +$

$c_2\displaystyle\sum_{n=0}^{\infty}\dfrac{3}{(2n - 1)(2n - 3)}x^{2n}$. **6.** $y = c_0x^2 + c_1x^3$. **7.** $y = c_0\displaystyle\sum_{n=0}^{\infty}(2n + 1)(x -$

$1)^{2n} + c_1\displaystyle\sum_{n=0}^{\infty}(n + 1)(x - 1)^{2n+1}$. **8.** $y = c_0\displaystyle\sum_{n=0}^{\infty}(n + 1)(2n + 1)(x + 1)^{2n} +$

$c_1 \displaystyle\sum_{n=0}^{\infty} (n+1)(2n+3)(x+1)^{2n+1}$. **9.** $y = c_0 + c_1 x + \dfrac{c_0 x^2}{2!} + \dfrac{(c_1 + c_0)x^3}{3!} +$

$\dfrac{(3c_0 + 2c_1)x^4}{4!} + \cdots$ **10.** $y = c_0 + c_1 x - \frac{1}{6}(c_0 + c_1)x^3 - \frac{1}{12}c_1 x^4 + \frac{3}{40}(c_0 + c_1)x^5$

$+ \cdots$ **11.** $y = -x^{-3} - x^{-4} + 24 \displaystyle\sum_{n=5}^{\infty} (-1)^{n-1} \dfrac{x^{-n}}{n!}$. **12.** $c_0 e^{-x2/2}$, $c_2(1 - 2x^2)$

$e^{-x2/2}$, $c_3(x - \frac{2}{3}x^3)e^{-x2/2}$. **13.** $y = \dfrac{2}{5}x^5 \displaystyle\sum_{n=0}^{\infty} \dfrac{(-1)^n x^{2n}}{2^{n+2}(n+2)!}$.

§81, page 168

1. $y = A\left(1 + \dfrac{2x}{1!1} + \dfrac{2^2 x^2}{2!(1 \cdot 3)} + \cdots\right) + Bx^{\frac{1}{2}}\left(1 + \dfrac{2x}{1!3} + \dfrac{2^2 x^2}{2!3 \cdot 5} + \cdots\right)$.

2. $y = A(1 + 2x^2 + 3x^4 + 4x^6 + \cdots) + Bx^{-1}(1 + 3x^2 + 5x^4 + 7x^6 + \cdots)$.

3. $y = A\left(\dfrac{1}{2} + \dfrac{1 \cdot 4}{5!}x^3 + \dfrac{1 \cdot 4 \cdot 7}{8!}x^6 + \cdots\right)$

$\qquad\qquad\qquad + Bx^{-2}\left(1 + \dfrac{2x^3}{3!} + \dfrac{2 \cdot 5}{6!}x^6 + \cdots\right)$.

4. $y = Ax^2\left(1 - \dfrac{2 \cdot 2}{5}x + \dfrac{3 \cdot 2^2}{5 \cdot 6}x^2 - \cdots\right) + B\left(\dfrac{1}{x^2} - \dfrac{4}{3x} + \dfrac{2}{3}\right)$.

6. $y = Ax^{-1} + B\left(1 + \dfrac{x^2}{3} + \dfrac{x^4}{5} + \cdots\right)$.

7. $y = A(x+1) + B(x^2 + x^3 + x^4 + \cdots)$.

8. $y = A\left(1 - \dfrac{x^{-2}}{3!} - \dfrac{x^{-4}}{5!} - \dfrac{3x^{-6}}{7!} - \cdots\right) + B(x - x^{-1})$.

12. $y = A\left(1 - \dfrac{2a^3 x^3}{5!} + \dfrac{2a^6 x^6}{8!} - \cdots\right) + Bx^{-1}\left(1 - \dfrac{a^3 x^3}{4!} + \dfrac{a^6 x^6}{7!} - \cdots\right)$

$\qquad\qquad\qquad + Cx^{-2}\left(1 - \dfrac{a^3 x^3}{3!} + \dfrac{a^6 x^6}{6!} + \cdots\right)$.

13. $y = x^{\frac{3}{2}} \displaystyle\sum_{n=0}^{\infty} \dfrac{4^{n+1} x^{2n}}{[1 \cdot 5 \cdot 9 \cdots (4n+1)]^2 (4n+5)}$.

§82, page 172

1. $y = c_0 x - c_1 x \log x + c_1\left(1 + x \displaystyle\sum_{n=2}^{\infty} \dfrac{x^n}{n-1}\right)$

2. $y = (c_0 + c_1 \log x)(1 + 2x + x^2) + c_1\left[-3x - 3x^2 + \displaystyle\sum_{n=3}^{\infty} \dfrac{(-1)^n 2 x^n}{n(n-1)(n-2)}\right]$.

3.* $y = (c_0 + c_1 \log x) \sum_{n=0}^{\infty} \left(\frac{x}{2}\right)^{2n} \frac{1}{(n!)^2} - c_1 \sum_{n=1}^{\infty} \left(\frac{x}{2}\right)^{2n} \frac{1}{(n!)^2} \sum_{k=1}^{n} \frac{1}{k}.$

4. $y = (c_0 + c_1 \log x) \sum_{n=1}^{\infty} \frac{x^n}{(n-1)!n!} + c_1 \left[1 - \sum_{n=1}^{\infty} \frac{x^n}{(n-1)!n!} \left(\frac{1}{n} + \sum_{k=1}^{n-1} \frac{2}{k} \right) \right].$

5. $y = (c_0 + c_1 \log x) \sum_{n=0}^{\infty} \frac{(-1)^n x^n}{(n!)^2} - c_1 \sum_{n=1}^{\infty} \frac{(-1)^n x^n}{(n!)^2} \sum_{k=1}^{n} \frac{2}{k}.$

6. $y = (c_0 + c_1 \log x) \sum_{n=0}^{\infty} \frac{x^{3n}}{3^{2n}(n!)^2} - 2c_1 \sum_{n=1}^{\infty} \frac{x^{3n}}{3^{2n}(n!)^2} \sum_{k=1}^{n} \frac{1}{3k}.$

7. $y = \left(c_0 - \frac{1}{2} c_1 \log x \right) \sum_{n=0}^{\infty} \left(\frac{x}{2}\right)^{2n} \frac{(-1)^n}{n!(n+1)!}$

$+ c_1 x^{-2} \left[1 + \frac{1}{4} x^2 - \sum_{n=2}^{\infty} 2 \left(\frac{x}{2}\right)^{2n} \frac{(-1)^n}{n!(n-1)!} \left(\frac{1}{2n} + \sum_{k=1}^{n-1} \frac{1}{k} \right) \right].$

8. $y = (A - B \log x) \sum_{n=0}^{\infty} \frac{x^{-n}}{n!(n+1)!}$

$+ Bx \left[1 - x^{-1} \sum_{n=1}^{\infty} \frac{x^{-n}}{(n-1)!n!} \left(\frac{1}{n} + \sum_{k=1}^{n-1} \frac{2}{k} \right) \right]$

9. $y = (c_1 x + c_3 x \log x) \sum_{n=0}^{\infty} \frac{x^{2n}}{(2n+1)!(2n+2)!}$

$+ (c_2 + c_4 \log x) \sum_{n=0}^{\infty} \frac{x^{2n}}{(2n)!(2n+1)!} + c_3 x^{-1} \left[1 - \sum_{n=1}^{\infty} \frac{x^{2n}}{(2n-1)!(2n)!} \right.$

$\left. \left(\sum_{j=1}^{2n-1} \frac{2}{j} + \frac{1}{2n} \right) \right] + c_4 \left[1 - \sum_{n=1}^{\infty} \frac{x^{2n}}{(2n)!(2n+1)!} \left(\frac{1}{2n+1} + \sum_{j=2}^{2n} \frac{2}{j} \right) \right]$

§84, page 175

2. $\frac{21}{16}(11x^6 - 15x^4 + 5x^2 - \frac{5}{24})$.　**4.** $x^4 = \frac{1}{5}P_0(x) + \frac{4}{7}P_2(x) + \frac{8}{35}P_4(x)$.

5. $1.175P_0(x) + 1.104P_1(x) + 0.357P_2(x) + 0.077P_3(x) + \cdots$.

* By definition $0! = 1$.

§85, page 177

1. (a) $y = c_1 x^{\frac{1}{2}}\left(1 - \dfrac{x^2}{3!} + \dfrac{x^4}{5!} - \cdots\right) + c_2 x^{-\frac{1}{2}}\left(1 - \dfrac{x^2}{2!} + \dfrac{x^4}{4!} - \cdots\right).$

(b) $y = c_1 x^3 \displaystyle\sum_{r=0}^{\infty} \dfrac{(-1)^r (x/2)^{2r} 3!}{r!(r+3)!} + c_2 \left(x^{-3} \log x \displaystyle\sum_{r=3}^{\infty} 2\,\dfrac{(x/2)^{2r}(-1)^r}{r!(r-3)!} \right.$

$\left. + 2x^{-3} + \dfrac{x^{-1}}{4} + \dfrac{x}{32} + x^{-3} \displaystyle\sum_{r=3}^{\infty} \left\{ 2\,\dfrac{(-1)^{r+1}(x/2)^{2r}}{r!(r-3)!} \displaystyle\sum_{n=1}^{r} \left[\dfrac{1}{2n} + \dfrac{1}{2(\bar{n}-3)} \right] \right\} \right),$

where $\bar{n}$ does not take the value 3 but takes all the other values from 1 to r.

2. $y = c_1 \displaystyle\sum_{r=0}^{\infty} \dfrac{(x/2)^{2r}(-1)^r}{(r!)^2} + c_2 \left[\log x \displaystyle\sum_{r=0}^{\infty} \dfrac{(x/2)^{2r}(-1)^r}{(r!)^2} \right.$

$\left. + \displaystyle\sum_{r=1}^{\infty} \dfrac{(x/2)^{2r}(-1)^{r+1}}{(r!)^2} \displaystyle\sum_{n=1}^{r} \dfrac{1}{n} \right].$

§86, page 177

3. $H_6 = 64x^6 - 480x^4 + 720x^2 - 120.$

4. $q!\left(1 - qx + \dfrac{q(q-1)}{(2!)^2} x^2 - \dfrac{q(q-1)(q-2)}{(3!)^2} x^3 + \cdots\right).$

§88, page 180

1. $y = 1 + x + x^2 + 2\left(\dfrac{x^3}{3!} + \dfrac{x^4}{4!} + \cdots\right).$ **2.** $y = 1 + x + \dfrac{x^2}{2} + \dfrac{x^3}{3} + \dfrac{x^4}{2 \cdot 4}$

$+ \dfrac{x^5}{3 \cdot 5} + \dfrac{x^6}{2 \cdot 4 \cdot 6} + \dfrac{x^7}{3 \cdot 5 \cdot 7} + \cdots.$ **3.** $x = 1 - t + \dfrac{t^2}{2!} + \dfrac{t^4}{4!} + \dfrac{t^6}{6!} + \cdots,$

$y = -1 + t + \dfrac{t^3}{3!} + \dfrac{t^5}{5!} + \cdots.$ **4.** $y = 1 + \dfrac{1x^3}{3!} + \dfrac{1 \cdot 4x^6}{6!} + \dfrac{1 \cdot 4 \cdot 7x^9}{9!} + \cdots.$

5. $y = 1 + x + 3x^2 + \frac{1}{2}x^3 - \frac{3}{40}x^5 + \cdots.$

§89, page 182

1. $x = 0.4$, $y = 2.8918$.   **2.** $(0,1)$ $(0.1, 1.1053)$ $(0.2, 1.2229)$.   **3.** $t = 0.1$, $x = 1.1003$, $y = 1.1100$; $t = 0.2$, $x = 1.2026$, $y = 1.2401$; $t = 0.3$, $x = 1.3090$, $y = 1.3906$.

§91, page 186

1. (a) $z = px + qy$.   (b) $p = q^2$.   (c) $z = xp + yq$.   (d) $q = f(p)$.   **2.** (a) $z = px + qy$.   (b) $z = px + qy - \dfrac{pq}{p + q - pq}$.   (c) $y^2(1 + p^2 + q^2) = q^2$.   (d) $(1 + q)(x + zp) - (1 + p)(y + zq) = 0$.   (e) $py = qx$.   (f) $x^2 + y^2 + 2z(xp + yq) = z^2$.   **3.** (a) $p = q$.   (b) $x(p - q) = z$.   (c) $y(q - p) = z$.   (d) $pt = qs$.   (e) $s = 0$.   (f) $q(r - s) + p(t - s) = 0$.   (g) $2r + s - t = 0$.   (h) $x(rx + p) = y(ty + q)$.   **5.** $z = px + qy$.   **6.** $py - qx = 0$.

§92, page 188

1. $z = x^3 + xy^2 + \varphi(y)$. **2.** $yz = x^2y + \varphi(x)$. **3.** $yz = x^2y + \varphi(x) + \psi(y)$. **4.** $z = \iint f(x,y)\, dx^2 + x\varphi(y) + \psi(y)$. **5.** $2z = x^2 \log y + 2axy + \varphi(x) + \psi(y)$. **6.** $z = -ye^x + e^y[y + \varphi(x)] + \psi(x)$. **7.** $2z = x^2y - 2xy + \varphi(y) + e^{-x}\psi(y)$. **8.** $4z = x^2y + \varphi(y) \log x + \psi(y)$. **9.** $z = \log\,[e^{xy}\varphi(y) - e^{-xy}] + \psi(y)$. **10.** $2z^2 = (2x - 1)y^2 + \varphi(y)e^{-2x}$. **11.** $\pm z = \sqrt{a - \varphi(y)e^{-2x}} + \sqrt{a} \log\,[\sqrt{ae^{2x} - \varphi(y)} - \sqrt{ae^x}] + \psi(y)$. **12.** $z = 6x^2 + e^{-y}\varphi(x) + x\psi(y) + \theta(y)$. **13.** $z = x^2y^3 + y^{-1}\varphi(x) + \psi(x)$.

§93, page 192

1. $z = e^x\varphi(x - y)$. **2.** $z = x^2\varphi\left(\dfrac{y}{x}\right)$. **3.** $y + z = x\varphi[x(y - z)]$. **4.** $az = cx + \varphi(bx - ay)$. **5.** $\tan^{-1}\dfrac{y}{z} = \log x + \varphi(z^2 + y^2)$. **6.** $3xz = y^2 + \varphi(xy)$. **7.** $z(y - x) = axy \log\left(\dfrac{y}{x}\right) + (y - x)\varphi\left(\dfrac{x - y}{xy}\right)$. **8.** $x^2 - y^2 = \varphi(z^2 + 2y^2)$. **9.** $3y^2 \log z + ax = 3y^2\varphi(xy)$. **10.** $(x + y) \log z - x = \varphi(x + y)$. **11.** $y = x\varphi(z)$. **12.** $y^2 = z^2 + \varphi(x)$. **13.** $x^2 = 2xz + 2yz + \varphi(y)$. **14.** $x^2 = y^2 + 2xy + \varphi(z)$. **15.** $(x + y)(x^2 - y^2 - z) = \varphi(x^2 - y^2)$. **16.** $3z = 2x^3 + \varphi(ye^{-x}) + \psi(y)$. **17.** $2z = x^2 + xy + \varphi\left(\dfrac{y}{x}\right) + \psi(y)$. **19.** Generally ∞; for $\varphi(a^2 + b^2, c - a) = 0$ may be written $c = a + \psi(a^2 + b^2)$, and a and b may be chosen arbitrarily. **20.** $z = y^3\varphi\left(\dfrac{x^5}{y^3}\right)$. **21.** $(y - x)^2 + 2z^2 = \varphi(x + y)$. **22.** $(y + y^2)^{-2}$. **23.** (a) $e^{\int f(y)\, dy}$. (b) $e^{-\int f(x)\, dx}$. (c) $(xy)^k$. (d) $\dfrac{1}{x^2 + y^2}$. (e) $x^b y^a$. **24.** $\dfrac{e^x}{y}$.

§94, page 194

2. (a) $z(1 + xy) = 10xy$. (b) $z(x^2y^2 + z^2) = 2x^3y^3$. (c) $1 + xy = 2xyz$. **3.** (a) $x^2 + y^2 + z^2 = 25(x + y)^2$. (b) $x^2 + z^2 = 25(x - z)^2$. (c) $yz = y^2 + 2xy + 4x^2$. **4.** (a) $z = e^y \sin (x - y)$. (b) $z = (a - x + y)^2 e^{x-a}$. (c) $z^2 = [a^2 - (x - y)^2]e^{2y}$. **5.** $\varphi\left(\dfrac{x - 1}{y}, \dfrac{z}{y}\right) = 0$, $y^2 + z^2 = 25(x - 1)^2$. **6.** $z = \dfrac{1}{3}\dfrac{y^2}{x} + \dfrac{1}{6}x^2y^2 + xy + \log (xy - 1) + c$. **7.** $10z = 10x - xy^3 + 10y^2$.

§95, page 197

2. $z = ax + \psi(a)y$, $x + \psi(a) + \psi'(a)(y + a) = 0$; $2z + (x + y)^2 = 0$. **3.** $z = ax + \psi(a)y$, $x = \psi'(a)y$. **4.** $2(x - a)^2 + 2[y - \psi(a)]^2 + 2z^2 = a^2 + \psi^2(a)$, $2(x - a) + 2[y - \psi(a)]\psi'(a) + 2a + 2\psi(a)\psi'(a) = 0$. The complete solution represents spheres with centers in the XY-plane and tangent to the cone $z^2 = x^2 + y^2$. The general solution represents envelopes of families of the spheres. **5.** $4(x - a)^2 + 4[y - \psi(a)]^2 + z^2 = [\psi(a) - a]^2$, $4(x - a) + 4[y - \psi(a)]\psi'(a) + [\psi(a) - a][\psi'(a) - 1] = 0$. The complete solution represents ellipsoids having centers in the XY-plane and tangent to the cone $z^2 = 2(x - y)^2$. The general solution represents envelopes of families of these ellipsoids.

§96, page 200

2. (a) $(5a - 6) \log z = ax + y + b$. (b) $2 \sqrt{z} = ax + b + \dfrac{y}{a}$. **3.** $z = e^{x^2}(-ax + ay + b)$. **4.** $z = a \log \left(\dfrac{x}{y}\right) + b$. **5.** (a) $z(ax + y + b) + a + 1 = 0$. (b) $2 \sqrt{z} = ax + \sqrt{1 - a^2}\, y + b$. (c) $(a^2 + 1)(c^2 - z^2) = (x + ay + b)^2$. (d) $2(a^2z^n + a)^{\frac{3}{2}} = 3a^2nR(ax + y + b)$. **6.** (a) $z = ax + by + ab$. (b) $z = ax + by - na^{1/n}b^{1/n}$. (c) $z = ax + by$. (d) $f(z - ax - by, a, b) = 0$. **7.** (a) $2z = (a + y)^2 - (a - x)^2 + b$. (b) $3z = 2(a + x)^{\frac{3}{2}} + 2(a + y)^{\frac{3}{2}} + b$. (c) $3z = 2(ax)^{\frac{3}{2}} + 2(ay)^{\frac{3}{2}} + b$. (d) $z = ax + f(x) + ay - F(y) + b$. **8.** (a) $z = ax + \dfrac{y}{a} + b$. (b) $z = a(x + y) + b$, $2z = a(2x - 3y) + b$. (c) $z = e^{ax} + ay + b$. (d) $z = ay + (6 - a^2 - 5a)x + b$. **9.** (a) $z = a^2x^2 + ay + b$. (b) $z^2 = a^2x^2 + (ay + b)^2$. (c) $2 \sqrt{z} = \sqrt{ax} + (y - ay^2)^{\frac{1}{2}} + \frac{1}{2}a^{-\frac{1}{2}} \sin^{-1}(2ay - 1) + b$. (d) $z^{\frac{3}{2}} = (x + a)^{\frac{3}{2}} + (y + a)^{\frac{3}{2}} + b$. (e) $(x + a)z = y + 2(x + a) \log (x + a) + 2a + b(x + a)$. (f) $zx = a^2x^2 + ay + b$.

§101, page 207

1. $z = \varphi_1(y) + \varphi_2(y - x) + \varphi_3(y + 2x)$. **2.** $z = {}^*\varphi_1(y) + x\varphi_2(y) + x^2\varphi_3(y) + \varphi_4(y - x)$. **3.** $z = \varphi(y + 2x) + \varphi(x) + y\psi(x)$. **4.** $z = \varphi_1(y) + x\varphi_2(y) + \varphi_3(x) + y\varphi_4(x)$. **5.** $y = \displaystyle\sum^n e^{n(y+2x)}(a_n \cos 3nx + b_n \sin 3nx)$. **6.** $z = \displaystyle\sum^n e^{ny}(a_n \cos nax + b_n \sin nax)$. **7.** $z = \varphi(y - ax) + \psi(y + ax)$. **8.** $z = \varphi(y + ax) + \psi(y - ax) + \displaystyle\sum^n e^{ny}(a_n \cos anx + b_n \sin anx)$. **9.** $z = \varphi(y + 2x) + \displaystyle\sum^n e^{n(y-x)}(a_n \sin \sqrt{3}\, nx + b_n \cos \sqrt{3}\, nx)$. **10.** $z = \varphi_1(y) + x\varphi_2(y) + x^2\varphi_3(y) + \cdots + x^{n-1}\varphi_n(y)$. **11.** $z = (x + y + 1)^3 - (x - y - 1)^3 - 2$. **12.** $z = by^4 + (y + 2x)^2 + (y - 2x)^9$.

§103, page 209

2. $z = \varphi(y + x) + e^{-3x}\psi(y - x)$. **3.** $z = e^{-2x}\varphi(y) + e^{3x}\varphi(y + x)$. **4.** $z = e^{-4y}\varphi(x) + e^{3x/2}\psi(y - \frac{3}{2}x)$. **5.** $z = e^{-x}[\varphi_1(y - x) + x\varphi_2(y - x) + x^2\varphi_3(y - x)]$. **6.** $z = \varphi(y) + e^{3y}[\varphi_1(x - 2y) + x\varphi_2(x - 2y)]$. **7.** $z = e^{4y}\varphi(x) + e^{-y}\psi(x - y)$. **8.** $z = e^{4y}\varphi(x) + e^{-4y}\psi(x)$. **9.** $z = e^{-ax}\varphi(y) + e^{ay}\varphi_1(x) + e^{-ay}\varphi_2(x)$. **10.** $z = \displaystyle\sum^h e^{hx - h^3y}$. **11.** $z = \displaystyle\sum^h a_h e^{hx - h^3y} + \displaystyle\sum^h b_h e^{hy - h^2x}$. **12.** $z = e^x\varphi(y) + e^{-x}\psi(x + y)$. **13.** $z = e^{-hx}\psi(y) + e^{-ay}\psi(x)$. **14.** $z = e^{-y}\varphi(x) + e^x\psi(y - x)$. **15.** $z = e^{-y}\varphi(x + 2y) + \psi(x + y)$. **18.** $z = e^{-mx}[\varphi(y - ax) \cos nx + \psi(y - ax) \sin nx]$. **19.** $z = e^{-2x}[\varphi(y - x) + x\psi(y - x)]$. **20.** $z = \varphi(y - x) \cos x + \psi(y - x) \sin x$. **21.** $z = \displaystyle\sum^k a_k e^{ky + 2k^{\frac{3}{2}}x}$.

§104, page 211

1. $z = \sum^{k} (a_k e^{\sqrt{k}x} + b_k e^{-\sqrt{k}x})(c_k \sin \sqrt{k}y + d_k \cos \sqrt{k}y)$; same with x and y

interchanged; $z = c_1 xy + c_2 x + c_3 y + c_4$.   **2.** $z = \sum^{k} e^{ky}(a_k e^{\sqrt{k}x} + b_k e^{-\sqrt{k}x})$; z

$= \sum^{k} e^{-ky}(a_k \sin \sqrt{k}x + b_k \cos \sqrt{k}x)$; $z = c_1 + c_2 x$.   **3.** $z = \sum^{k} c_k e^{k(x-y)}$ **4.**

$z = \sum^{k} c_k e^{k(x-y)+3y}$.   **5.** $z = \sum^{k} (a_k e^{\sqrt{k-1}x} + b_k e^{-\sqrt{k-1}x})(c_k \sin \sqrt{k}y + d_k$

$\cos \sqrt{k}y)$; $k = 1$, $0 < k < 1$, $k = 0$, $k < 0$.   **6.** (a) $k < -\frac{1}{4}$.   (b) $k > 1$.   (c)

$-\frac{1}{4} \le x \le 1$.   **7.** $u = \sum^{k,l,m} (a_k e^{\sqrt{l}x} + b_k e^{-\sqrt{l}x})(c_k e^{\sqrt{m}y} + d_k e^{-\sqrt{m}y})$

$(g_k \sin \sqrt{l+mz} + f_k \cos \sqrt{l+mz})$; 13 types.   **9.** $z = \sum^{k} e^{kx - ky/2}[a_k \sin (\frac{1}{2}\sqrt{3}ky)$

$+ b_k \cos (\frac{1}{2}\sqrt{3}ky)]$.

§105,* page 213

1. $z = -e^{2x+3y}$.   **2.** $z = \frac{1}{2}x^2 y$.   **3.** $z = \frac{1}{2}x^2 y$.   **4.** $z = 2x^2 + 2xy$.   **5.** $z = 2x^5 y^2$

$- \frac{2}{21}x^7$.   **6.** $z = \frac{2}{5}\cos(2x - y) - \frac{1}{5}\sin(2x - y)$.   **7.** $z = -e^{2x-3y}\cos(x+3y)$.

8. $z = -2xy - x - y - 1$.   **9.** $z = 20x^3 y - x^5$.   **10.** $z = -e^{x+y}(3xy^2 + 2y^3)$.

11. $z = 3xy^2 - y^3 - \frac{3}{4}y^2$.   **12.** $z = e^{-2y}(x^2 - x + \frac{1}{2})$.   **13.** $z + y \log x = 0$.   **14.**

$z = \frac{1}{2}x^4$.   **15.** $z = 3x^2 y - \frac{8}{3}x^3$.   **16.** $z = x^4(5y - x)$.   **17.** $z = 7x^6 y^3 - \frac{3}{4}x^8 y$.   **18.**

$z = x^2 e^{x-y}$.   **19.** $z = \frac{1}{128}e^{4x-y}\sin(4x - y)$.   **20.** $z = \frac{13}{12}x^{12}y^2 + \frac{1}{4}x^{14}$.   **21.** $z =$

$xy - 2y - 2e^{x-2y}$.

§106, page 216

1. (a) $z = 2xy^3 + y\varphi(x) + \psi(x)$.   (b) $z = -x^2 e^{-3y} + \varphi(x) + \psi(y)$.   **2.** (a) $z =$
$\varphi_1(y)e^{-3x} + \varphi_2(y)e^{2x}$.   (b) $z = \varphi_1(x)e^{-2y} + \varphi_2(x)e^{y}$.   (c) $z = \varphi_1(x)\sin 2y + \varphi_2(x)$

$\cos 2y + \frac{1}{4}x^2$.   (d) $z = \varphi_1(y)e^{2xy} + \varphi_2(y)e^{-xy} - x + \dfrac{1}{2y}$.   **3.** (a) $yz + 2xy^2 =$

$\varphi(xy) + \psi(y)$.   (b) $z = y\varphi\left(\dfrac{x}{y}\right) + \psi(y)$.   (c) $xz - 2x^2 y = \varphi(xy) + \psi(x)$.   (d) $z +$

$3x^2 = \varphi(x)e^y + \psi(y)$.   (e) $x^2 z - 6x^3 y^2 = \varphi(xy) + \psi(x)$.   (f) $z = x\varphi(y + x^2) +$

$\psi(x)$.   **4.** (a) $\pm 2zy = xy\sqrt{x^2 y^2 + \varphi(y)} + \varphi(y)\log[xy + \sqrt{x^2 y^2 + \varphi(y)}] + \psi(y)$.

(b) $z = \varphi(ye^x) + \psi(y)$.   (c) $4z = 2x^2 \log x - x^2 + y\varphi\left(\dfrac{y}{x^2}\right) + \psi(y)$.   (d) $z =$

$\varphi(y)e^x + \psi(y)e^{-5x/2} - y(5x + 3)$.   (e) $z + xy = \varphi(x^2 y) + \psi(x)$.   (f) $2z + 3x^2 y =$

$\varphi(x)e^{2y} + \psi(x)$.   (g) $z = y\varphi\left(\dfrac{e^x}{y}\right) + \psi(y)$.   (h) $z = \varphi\left(\dfrac{e^y}{x}\right) + \psi(y)$.   (i) $2z =$

$\varphi(y)\cos(\log x) + \psi(y)\sin(\log x) + xy$.   (j) $y = \varphi(x) + \psi(z)$.

§107, page 218

1. $z = x^2\varphi(x - y) + \psi(x - y)$.   **2.** $z = \varphi\left(\dfrac{y}{x}\right) + x\psi\left(\dfrac{y}{x}\right)$.   **3.** $z = \varphi(x - y) +$

* Many answers are possible.   The student should check his results.

$\psi(ye^x)$. **4.** $z = x^2\varphi(x + y) + \psi(x + y)$. **5.** $z = \varphi(x - y) + \psi(xy)$. **6.** $z = \varphi(xy)$
$+ \psi(x + y)$. **7.** $z = \varphi\left(\dfrac{x}{y}\right) + \psi(xy)$. **8.** $z = \varphi(ye^x) + \psi(ye^{-2x})$. **9.** $z = e^{2x}\psi(ye^{2x})$
$+ \varphi(y) - ye^{2x}$. **10.** $z = xy + x^2e^{2y} + \varphi(xe^{2y}) + \psi(x)$. **11.** $y = \varphi(z) + e^{xz}\psi(z)$.
12. $y = x\varphi(z) + \psi(z)$. **13.** $z = x\varphi(y) + \psi(xy)$. **14.** $z = y^3 + y\varphi(2x + y^2) +$
$\psi(2x + y^2)$. **15.** $x = \varphi(z) + \psi(y)$. **16.** $z = \varphi(ye^x) + \psi(ye^{2x})$. **17.** $z = \varphi(ye^x) +$
$\psi(ye^{-x})$. **18.** $z = \varphi(xy) + \psi(x^2y)$.

§108, page 223

2. $x = 2\left(\dfrac{\sin x}{1} - \dfrac{\sin 2x}{2} + \dfrac{\sin 3x}{3} - \cdots\right)$. **3.** $x = \dfrac{1}{2} + \dfrac{2}{\pi}\left(\dfrac{\sin x}{1} + \dfrac{\sin 3x}{3}\right.$

$\left. + \dfrac{\sin 5x}{5} + \cdots\right)$. **4.** $x = \dfrac{1}{2} - \dfrac{2}{\pi^2}\left(\dfrac{\cos x}{1^2} + \dfrac{\cos 3x}{3^2} + \dfrac{\cos 5x}{5^2} + \cdots\right)$

$- \dfrac{1}{\pi}\left(\dfrac{\sin 2x}{2} + \dfrac{\sin 4x}{4} + \dfrac{\sin 6x}{6} + \cdots\right)$.

§109, page 225

1. (a) $x = \dfrac{2c}{\pi}\left(\sin\dfrac{\pi x}{c} - \dfrac{1}{2}\sin\dfrac{2\pi x}{c} + \dfrac{1}{3}\sin\dfrac{3\pi x}{c} - \dfrac{1}{4}\sin\dfrac{4\pi x}{c} + \cdots\right)$. (b) $x^2 = \dfrac{c^2}{3}$

$- \dfrac{4c^2}{\pi^2}\left(\dfrac{1}{1^2}\cos\dfrac{\pi x}{c} - \dfrac{1}{2^2}\cos\dfrac{2\pi x}{c} + \dfrac{1}{3^2}\cos\dfrac{3\pi x}{c} - \cdots\right)$. **2.** Same as 1(a).

3. $x = \dfrac{\pi}{2} - \dfrac{4}{\pi}\left(\dfrac{\cos x}{1^2} + \dfrac{\cos 3x}{3^2} + \dfrac{\cos 5x}{5^2} + \cdots\right)$. **5.** $x^2 = \dfrac{2c^2}{\pi^3}\left[\left(\dfrac{\pi^2}{1}\right.\right.$

$\left. - \dfrac{4}{1^3}\right)\sin\dfrac{\pi x}{c} - \dfrac{\pi^2}{2}\sin\dfrac{2\pi x}{c} + \left(\dfrac{\pi^2}{3} - \dfrac{4}{3^3}\right)\sin\dfrac{3\pi x}{c} - \dfrac{\pi^2}{4}\sin\dfrac{4\pi x}{c} + \cdots\left.\right]$.

6. $h + kx = \dfrac{2}{\pi}\left(\dfrac{2h + kc}{1}\sin\dfrac{\pi x}{c} - \dfrac{kc}{4}\sin\dfrac{2\pi x}{c} + \dfrac{2h + kc}{3}\sin\dfrac{3\pi x}{c} - \dfrac{kc}{4}\sin\dfrac{4\pi x}{c}\right.$

$\left. + \cdots\right)$.

§110, page 227

1. $y = 0.0232\left(\cos 178t \sin\dfrac{\pi x}{3} + \dfrac{1}{3^3}\cos\dfrac{3 \cdot 178t}{3}\sin\dfrac{3\pi x}{c} + \cdots\right)$; about 28 vibra-

tions per second. **2.** $y = A\cos\dfrac{2a\pi t}{L}\sin\dfrac{2\pi x}{L}$. **3.** $y = \dfrac{LA}{na\pi}\sin\dfrac{an\pi t}{L}\sin\dfrac{n\pi x}{L}$. **4.** y

$= \dfrac{8L^3m}{a\pi^4}\left(\dfrac{1}{1^4}\sin\dfrac{a\pi t}{L}\sin\dfrac{\pi x}{L} + \dfrac{1}{3^4}\sin\dfrac{3a\pi t}{L}\sin\dfrac{3\pi x}{L} + \dfrac{1}{5^4}\sin\dfrac{5a\pi t}{L}\sin\dfrac{5\pi x}{L} + \cdots\right)$.

§111, page 229

1. (a) $y(x,t) = A\sin\dfrac{2\pi x}{L}\cos\dfrac{2\pi at}{L}$. (b) $y(x,t) = A\sin\dfrac{m\pi x}{L}\cos\dfrac{m\pi at}{L}$

$+ B\sin\dfrac{n\pi x}{L}\cos\dfrac{n\pi at}{L}$. (c) $y(x,t) = \dfrac{8AL^2}{\pi^3}\left(\dfrac{1}{1^3}\cos\dfrac{\pi at}{L}\sin\dfrac{\pi x}{L} + \dfrac{1}{3^3}\cos\dfrac{3\pi at}{L}\sin\dfrac{3\pi x}{L}\right.$

$+ \dfrac{1}{5^3} \cos \dfrac{5\pi at}{L} \sin \dfrac{5\pi x}{L} + \cdots \Big)$. **2.** Same as 1(c) with $L = 3$ ft., $A = 0.001$, and $a = 17{,}000$; frequency, 2800 oscillations/sec.

§112, page 231

1. (a) $\theta(x,y) = Ae^{-3y} \sin 3x$. (b) $\theta(x,y) = 2A \displaystyle\sum_{n=1}^{\infty} (-1)^{n+1} \dfrac{e^{-ny}}{n} \sin nx$.

2. $\theta = m + me^{-3y} \sin 3x$. **3.** $\theta = m + (1-m)\dfrac{4}{\pi}\Big(e^{-y} \sin x + \dfrac{1}{3} e^{-3y} \sin 3x + \cdots \Big)$.

4. $y = \dfrac{4cg}{\pi^2} \displaystyle\sum_{m=1}^{\infty} \Big(\dfrac{1}{m^2} \sin \dfrac{m\pi}{2} \sin \dfrac{m\pi x}{c} \cos \dfrac{m\pi at}{c} \Big)$. **5.** $\theta(x,y) = 10 + \dfrac{90x}{\pi}$

$- \dfrac{20}{\pi} \Big(3e^{-y} \sin x - \dfrac{9}{2} e^{-2y} \sin 2x + \dfrac{3}{3} e^{-3y} \sin 3x - \dfrac{9}{4} e^{-4y} \sin 4x + \cdots \Big)$.

§113, page 233

1. $\theta = 10 + \dfrac{90x}{L}$. **2.** $\theta(x,t) = \dfrac{100x}{L} - \dfrac{200}{\pi} \Big(e^{-a^2\pi^2 t/L^2} \sin \dfrac{\pi x}{L} - \dfrac{1}{2} e^{-4a^2\pi^2 t/L^2} \sin \dfrac{2\pi x}{L}$

$+ \dfrac{1}{3} e^{-9a^2\pi^2 t/L^2} \sin \dfrac{3\pi x}{L} - \cdots \Big)$.

§114, page 235

2. $e = -A \sqrt{\dfrac{L}{C}} \sin (\omega \sqrt{LC}\, x) \cos \omega t + B$. **4.** (a) $i = \dfrac{A\omega}{R} e^{(-\omega^2/RC)t} \sin \omega x$.

(b) $e = \dfrac{AR}{\omega} e^{(-\omega^2/RC)t} \cos \omega x + B$. **5.** $e = Ax + B$, $i = -\dfrac{A}{R}$. **6.** $e =$

$- \dfrac{2}{\pi} \Big(7e^{-at} \sin \dfrac{\pi x}{L} - \dfrac{3}{2} e^{-4at} \sin \dfrac{2\pi x}{L} + \dfrac{7}{3} e^{-9at} \sin \dfrac{3\pi x}{L} - \dfrac{3}{4} e^{-16at} \sin \dfrac{4\pi x}{L} + \cdots \Big)$,

$i = \dfrac{2}{RL} \Big(7e^{-at} \cos \dfrac{\pi x}{L} - 3e^{-4at} \cos \dfrac{2\pi x}{L} + 7e^{-9at} \cos \dfrac{3\pi x}{L} - 3e^{-16at} \cos \dfrac{4\pi x}{L} + \cdots \Big)$,

where $a = \dfrac{\pi^2}{L^2 RC}$, $t > 0$. **8.** $i = -A \sqrt{\dfrac{C}{L}} e^{-(G/C)t} \cos (\omega \sqrt{LC}\, x) \sin \omega t$.

§115, page 240

3. (a) $x^3 - 3xy^2 = c$, $3x^2 y - y^3 = c$, $p = \dfrac{\rho}{g}\Big[c - gy - \dfrac{1}{2}(x^2 + y^2)^2 \Big]$. (b) $x^2 +$

$y^2 = c$, $y = cx$, $p = \dfrac{\rho}{g}\Big[c - gy - \dfrac{1}{2}(x^2 + y^2)^{-1} \Big]$.

INDEX

263